The New Resourceful Physics Teacher

For Liz

The New Resourceful Physics Teacher

Creative ideas and experiments for Physics teaching

Keith Gibbs

Schoolphysics Publishing
Somerset

Published by Schoolphysics Publications, Somerset, England www.schoolphysics.co.uk

ISBN 978-0-9569231-0-3

First published 2011

Cover image design by Leila Hodgkins www.lurexlounge.com
Other illustrations Keith Gibbs

Printed by Butler, Tanner and Dennis, Caxton Road, Frome, Somerset

CONTENTS

INTRODUCTION

Some years ago I was attending a conference at which a professor from one of the universities in the United States was giving a lecture about demonstration experiments in Physics. I had then been teaching for about thirty years and so thought I was fairly experienced. However, I decided to go along to see if I could pick up a new experiment or two. Two and a half hours later I emerged absolutely amazed – I had not known a single experiment!

This started me thinking. If that was true for me, how many other people were unaware of these ideas? Indeed, did I have ideas that my colleagues in other schools did not know about? I decided to start collecting these together and the result is this book.

I do not claim that all the ideas are my own; indeed, many have been suggested by relatives, friends and colleagues, not to mention many of my past and present pupils who have encouraged me over the years.

I have put in some explanation and background theory where space allows to help those teachers whose basic specialisation is not in Physics. However, if any of you want to find out more please visit the www.schoolphysics.co.uk website or consult the schoolphysics Complete Edition CD.

I have tried to make it of use to all Physics teachers both new and experienced, and although many of you who read it will come across old favourites I hope that everyone will find at least something that is new and challenging. I like analogies and I have included a number of these within the text. I also hope that the ideas will go some way to popularise the subject and make people realise that there is much of fun and interest in Physics.

One particular advantage of the collection is that many of the experiments can be carried out with very simple apparatus, not requiring a traditional laboratory. This should be particularly useful not only to those of you teaching in countries without the facilities of much of the UK but also to teachers in Britain, like me, who have had to use huts with neither gas, water or proper benches. Interactive whiteboards and computers are great and I enjoy using them but you will find that they are required by virtually none of the experiments described here.

I am especially grateful to all those teachers who have allowed me to add their ideas to this collection. If you have not been individually mentioned I apologise, but without you the collection would have been the poorer.

An alternative subtitle to the book was to be 'Fun and informative experiments in Physics' and that is what it is really all about.

I imagine that very few people read introductions to a book. If you have read this, then thank you! It might have given you an idea about what I have tried to put together and why.

Enjoy the rest of the book. I hope that the ideas in it are a help to your teaching.

Keith Gibbs
Taunton 2011

SAFETY CONSIDERATIONS

By their nature, some activities in this book may be hazardous if due care is not taken. Specific hazards are identified within the text by the use of the following general warning sign:

Particular hazards identified in boxes such as this with suggested control measures.

Every effort has been made to see that the activities suggested in this book have had hazards identified and control measures put in place. However, it is the responsibility of the experimenter to take the necessary precautions, and the author of the book does not accept any responsibility for any injuries caused as a result of carrying out any piece of practical work mentioned therein.

The hazards highlighted are not necessarily exhaustive and teachers must use caution at all times when carrying out experiments. Teachers must always follow good practice, including that given in the current ASE publication 'Safeguards in the School Laboratory'.

- Unless otherwise instructed, or if it is impossible, practical work should be conducted in a properly equipped laboratory.
- Suitable eye protection should be worn whenever there is the slightest recognised risk to the pupils' or teacher's eyes. A safety screen should be placed between the teacher and the audience if there is the remotest risk of even a tiny explosion or when objects might be projected towards those watching.
- All mains electrical equipment should be properly maintained.
- A heatproof mat should be placed on the bench if any experiments involving heating are to be performed. A large tray should be placed under any apparatus where a corrosive or staining liquid might be spilled.
- Risk assessments should always be undertaken before carrying out practical work of any kind for the first time.
- Pupils should be taught safe techniques and good laboratory practice.

The summary above is intended to provide basic guidelines for safe practical work.

Although I have taken reasonable steps to identify specific hazards you should not assume that all necessary warnings and precautionary measures are contained in this book or that other additional measures are not required. However, if a zero risk policy were to be adopted we would do no practical work at all!

Readers requiring further guidance are referred to:
- Hazcards (CLEAPSS, 1995 or 1998, 2000 updates)
- Topics in safety, 3rd edition (ASE, 2001)
- Safeguards in the school laboratory, 11th edition (ASE, 2006)

I am most grateful to Joe Jefferies (Health and Safety Consultant) for his considerable help and advice with the identification of safety issues and for suggesting suitable control measures.

Keith Gibbs
Taunton 2011

GENERAL

1. Quotations

"Physics is a subject that if you understand it you do not have to know much."
(Susan, once a member of one of my Lower Sixth classes.)

I was once at a dinner party where a lady asked me what I did. "I am a teacher," I replied.
"What age group?" "From eleven years to eighteen years old"
She looked a little concerned, a difficult age. "What subject?" "Science," I said
"What type of science?" she asked. "Physics" I said
Her final remark left me speechless and with a determination to try to alter people's attitude.
"Ah, Physics. End of conversation." And she walked away!

2. How odd are you?

This set of measurements is a useful introduction to Physics or General Science for the pupils as they arrive at a new school. It gets them to collect and present results, draw block graphs, work out averages and also to get to know the other members of the class.

Ask them to make the following measurements of the other members of the class:

(a) height
(b) hand span
(c) pulse rate (resting)
(d) eye colour

Try to present them in a form that means something! Using the heights of the class to make a block graph is best for this analytical part of the experiments. The maximum height, the most common height range and the average height of the class can then be found.

3. Simulations and spreadsheets

Spreadsheets such as Microsoft Excel can be very useful in Physics teaching to simulate SHM, damped SHM, reflection of waves, refraction of waves and longitudinal waves. They can also be used for the analysis of data such as radioactive decay.

4. Gradients

Accurate drawing of a gradient to a curve can be made simpler by using a plane mirror. This should first be placed standing on your graph and at right angles to the line. This is relatively simple to do as you adjust it until the curve and its reflection join smoothly without a kink at the reflecting surface. Now draw along the back of the mirror to give a normal (90° line) to the curve. Finally draw a line at right angles to this to get the gradient of the curve at that point.

5. Estimates of quantities

It is always important in Physics to have a rough idea of the values of quantities that you are attempting to measure. Introduce this idea by a set of intelligent guesses.

Get the pupils to guess:

(a) the temperature of hot water (at about 50°C) in a bucket by putting their hands in it

(b) the length of a time interval of twenty seconds by closing their eyes and counting while a friend measures the interval with a stop clock

(c) the mass of a lump of stone (say 10 kg) or a building block by lifting it up

(d) the length of the lab just by looking at it - no cheating by pacing it out

It's not always so easy – I remember standing above Bryce Canyon in Utah and being asked by the guide how far away I thought a mountain on the horizon was. The air was beautifully clear and I guessed thirty miles - it was actually a hundred miles away! The Apollo astronauts also had great difficulty estimating distances on the Moon. Due to the lack of atmosphere distant mountains were not blurred, leading to problems with perspective and hence navigation.

Age range: 11 – 13   Apparatus required: •Bucket of hot (50°C) water •Stop clock •Thermometer •Measuring tape •Rock (10 kg)

6. Dimensional farm animals

This demonstration is designed to show the difference between quantities with different units and also dimensions. I use a collection of toy farm animals: pigs, sheep and cows.

Take one or two pigs, a couple of sheep and a cow and ask - "How many are there?" The students should then reply with the question "How many what?"

Can you add up cows and pigs? Not really. The whole point is that it is still just a mixture of animals! In the same way you cannot add metres and kilograms! I find it an amusing way of introducing students to the higher level course. Consider balancing equations. Use the animals to show that if you have two pigs (pig squared!) on one side of an equation then you must have two pigs on the other. Is a pig on its back "$([pig]^{-1})$"!?

Age range: 16 – 18   Apparatus required: •Set of farm animals

7. Use of a closed circuit TV camera

After teaching for many years I bought a small TV camera. This made an enormous difference to some demonstration experiments. You can use either a camcorder or a security camera – this cost about £300 for a colour model. This latter type is very small, can be easily mounted on a retort stand base and gives excellent quality. I have used it:

(a) to make small scale demonstrations visible to the whole class. If you think the pupils can see everything go to the back of the room and look back at the front desk for yourself!

(b) in place of a vernier callipers as a measuring device by putting a ruler graduated in half millimetres in the field of view and then taking all measurements of both the scale and the object from the TV screen

(c) to produce a large image of a cathode ray oscilloscope screen on the TV - the waveforms can then be seen by the whole class

(d) to make recordings of tricky experiments for later use

(e) to observe infra red radiation – see radiation section

8. Romance and Physics?

Imagine a romantic evening - how could Physics explain the effects? "How beautiful your eyes are" - or - "I see that the molecules in your iris have not joined together to form longer chains and so you have blue eyes".

"That is a beautiful sparkling diamond ring" - or - "The refractive index of that transparent material in your ring is large and it has been cut to show multiple internal reflection".

"The waves on this beach are breaking gently on the sand" - or - "I see that the velocity of the circular motion of the water particles is decreasing as they move up the beach".

"What a beautiful sunset" - or - "The electromagnetic radiation of longer wavelength from the nearest star has not been scattered so much and the sky to the west is red".

"Let's estimate the depth of this wishing well by dropping a penny in and seeing how long it takes to reach the bottom".

I suppose that perhaps the suggestions are not really what you would want to say!

9. Communication

The idea of this experiment is to demonstrate communication, or the lack of it, between people in a group.

Six people with a long dowel rod should stand in two equal rows facing each other. They each support it on their two forefingers. The idea is to lower the dowel rod to the ground. It sounds simple but their fingers must remain touching the rod. It is surprisingly difficult. In their desire to keep touching it the result is that the dowel rod usually goes upwards rather than downwards. Usually nobody takes control!

(Thanks to Mark for this idea)

Age range: Any
Apparatus required: •People •A piece of dowel rod (at least 2m long with a diameter of about 1 cm)

10. Getting values for the sizes of small quantities

The sizes of small measurements (mass or length) can best be found by measuring a large number of the objects and then dividing the result by the number of objects.

For example:

The thickness of a sheet of paper is best found by measuring the thickness of a number of sheets (or use a micrometer).

The mass of a paper pellet can be found by finding the area of a sheet of paper and then finding the area of paper used to make the pellet.

The mass of a single small ball bearing can be found by measuring the mass of a known large number of them.

11. Simple measurements in Physics

As an introduction to measurement get the pupils to measure:

(a) the length of a line

(b) the distance between two dots

(c) the diagonal of a rectangle and

(d) the diameter of a circle

Prepare both large and small shapes on which to experiment.

12. Methods of teaching and style of lessons

It seems to me that the following options are available to the physics teacher at the beginning of the twenty-first century:

- Individual student practical
- Group student practical
- Demonstration practical
- Video/film
- Computer simulation
- CD/DVD
- OHT
- Work sheet
- Dialogue and discussion
- Books
- Internet
- Lecture type presentation using interactive whiteboard
- Lecture type presentation using traditional 'blackboard'
- Visit outside school
- Visiting lecturer
- Role play

All these methods should find a place in a school Physics course if school resources permit. However, it is not sensible to put these in a precise order of preference. The best way of delivering knowledge and understanding of Physics facts, ideas and methods will, and should, vary from topic to topic, from school to school and even from class to class.

A variety of methods of presentation will increase the students' interest in the course.

It is vital that computer simulations do not completely replace the student practical, whether individual or in groups. They have their place but should not be used in place of practical work that can easily be carried out by the class.

DENSITY, UPTHRUST AND ARCHIMEDES

General theory for this section:

Archimedes' principle states that:

When an object is immersed in a fluid there is an upthrust which is equal to the weight of the fluid displaced. When the object is floating, the upthrust = the weight of the object = the weight of fluid displaced = $V\rho g$, where V is the volume of the fluid displaced, ρ is the density of the fluid and g the gravitational field strength.

If the density of the fluid is low then the object floats lower in the fluid so as to displace more of it.

1. Oil and vinegar
2. Hippos
3. Archimedes and solid rubber balls
4. Cartesian divers
5. Ferries – displacement
6. Boats and Archimedes
7. Drinking straw hydrometer
8. Archimedes - Upthrust - top pan balance
9. Upthrust
10. Density and fizzy drinks cans
11. Plasticine boat
12. Helium balloon and upthrust
13. Vegetable oil and alcohol
14. Raisins and fizzy lemonade
15. Mass and weight

1. Oil and vinegar

An interesting example of flotation is the problem of different mixes of salad dressing poured from one bottle. A man and his wife go on a picnic but for their salad dressing they only take one bottle containing oil and vinegar - the oil floats on the vinegar. The problem is that they both like a different mix of oil and vinegar. How can they get this from just one bottle?

Solution - pour off some oil and then turn the bottle upside down - the oil still floats on the vinegar so if you put your thumb over the neck of the bottle as you turn it upside down removing the thumb can let the required amount of vinegar out!

Age range: 11-18 depending on treatment   Apparatus required: •Narrow necked bottle •Oil •Vinegar

2. Hippos

I like to draw three hippos floating in water of different densities to show the change in immersed volume. They sink deeper to retain the same upthrust as the density of the water gets less.

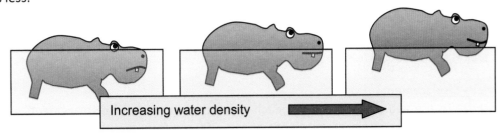

Increasing water density

Mention the change in displacement depth as a ship goes from salty water to fresh water and the ease with which a person can float in the very salty waters of the Dead Sea. You may also notice the difference between a freshwater swimming pool and the sea – I can float in the sea without difficulty but not in the lower density fresh water in a swimming pool.

Age range: 11-13

3. Archimedes and solid rubber balls

Find a rubber ball that just sinks in fresh water. Add salt to the water to show that in the salty water it will begin to rise and eventually float. Experiment with the type of ball. A way of getting one that works is to drill a hole in a table tennis ball and add water until it just sinks, closing the hole with tape or wax. This shows that when the average density of the ball is the same as that of the salty water it will float.

Age range: 11-13   Apparatus required: •Large plastic tank •Ball •Wax

4. Cartesian divers

(a) Blow a small bulb roughly 1 cm in diameter (smaller ones will work but they are not so easy to use or so impressive) on the end of a glass tube. After it has cooled cut it off leaving a short (0.5 cm) stem and then partly fill it with water. The actual amount needed will have to be done by trial and error but a little less than half full seems to work well. Then place it inside a large (2 litre) plastic drinks bottle which is filled almost full with water with the bulb at the top and put the top of the bottle on. Squeeze the bottle - the diver sinks because the increased pressure causes a decrease in the volume of air in the bulb; this reduces the upthrust by decreasing the volume of water displaced by the diver and the diver goes down. Try adding salt to the water to see the effect of an increase in the density.

(b) Another form of Cartesian diver can be made from the rubber top of a small dropping pipette. Fixing some strands of coloured plastic to the bottom will help adjust the weight and also make it look like a squid.

(c) A larger form of Cartesian diver (see experiment 4) can be made using a test tube. Take a gas jar and immerse in it a test tube with copper gauze over the mouth, adjusting the amount of water in the tube until it just floats. Now fix a rubber sheet over the top of the gas jar. Pressing this in should make the test tube sink.

Age range: 11-14
Apparatus required: •Large plastic bottle •Rubber top of dropping pipette •Plastic strips •Water •Glass tube •Large plastic bottle •Bunsen •Heat resistant mat •Glass cutting knife •Water

5. Ferries - displacement

It is helpful to use actual ferry data to teach a practical example of displacement. Ask the students to suggest the displacement depth of a 25 000 ton ferry and then calculate it in the following way.

Theory:
Upthrust of a floating object = weight of object = weight of water displaced. The one I use as an example works out to have a displacement depth (draft) of about 6 m and it agrees with the P and O shipping line data. (Length 180 m, breadth 28m, gross tonnage 28 000 tons)

Age range: 16-18

6. Boats and Archimedes

Use a toy boat containing blocks of different materials and a beaker of oil. Float the boat and its contents in a tank of water. (My sons had a plastic boat about 15 cm long that was ideal for this.)

What happens to the water level in the tank if:

(a) a wooden block is taken out of the boat and floated on the water

(b) an iron block is taken out of the boat and allowed to sink to the bottom of the tank

(c) an iron block is taken out of the boat, tied to a piece of string and allowed to hang from the boat but not touching the bottom

(d) some oil is poured from the beaker in the boat onto the water surface

Theory

A floating body displaces its own **weight** of water while one that sinks will displace its own **volume** of water. This means that there is no change of level if the blocks float when they are taken out of the boat but if they sink their density must be greater than water, they therefore displace a smaller volume of water than their own weight of water and so the level in the tank will fall.

Age range: 11-18 depending on treatment
Apparatus required: •Toy boat •Various blocks •Transparent plastic tank •TV camera if possible

7. Drinking straw hydrometer

Stick a lump of plasticine to one end of a plastic drinking straw so that it will float upright in liquids. If the depth to which it sinks in pure water is marked and used as a calibration point it can then be used to measure the density of other liquids such as brine and methylated spirits.

Age range: 11-13
Apparatus required: •Drinking straw •Plasticine •Measuring cylinder or tall beaker and liquids

8. Archimedes - Upthrust - top pan balance

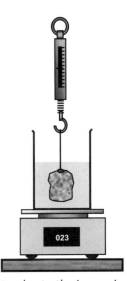

(a) Put a beaker of water on a top pan balance and lower a lump of stone into the water. The stone should be suspended by a thread from a newton meter so that readings of the tension in the thread and the top pan balance can be compared as the stone is moved from being totally in air to totally in water. Just putting your finger into the water gives a good demonstration of an increased reading on the top pan balance.

(b) Repeat the experiment using a bag of water instead of the stone. The readings on both the spring balance and the top pan balance should not change during the experiment since the weight of water displaced by the bag of water is equal to the weight of the water itself.

Theory

The reading on the spring balance decreases as the stone is lowered into the water due to the increasing upthrust as more of it is immersed. The reading on the top pan balance increases - the sum of both readings being constant and equal to the weight of the stone (if the weight of the container and water is allowed for).

Age range: 11-18 depending on treatment
Apparatus required: •Balance •Beaker •Newton meter •Water •Stone •Thread

9. Upthrust

A wonderful experiment can be carried out by dripping olive oil into alcohol. Put the olive oil into a funnel with a tap so that the outlet is below the surface of a large beaker of alcohol. Run some olive oil out slowly – the buoyancy of the alcohol "cancels" the effect of gravity and allows the surface tension of the oil to pull it into spherical bubbles. Really large bubbles can be made since the olive oil has very nearly the same density as the alcohol.

Age range: 14 – 18   Apparatus required: •Funnel with tap •Large beaker •Alcohol •Olive oil

10. Density and cans of fizzy drink

Take two cans of fizzy drink – one ordinary and one diet. Float them in water. One will float much lower in the water than the other. This can be explained by thinking about the amount of dissolved sugar in the 'non-diet' version.

Age range: 11-14
Apparatus required: •Two cans of fizzy drinks – one ordinary and one diet
•Transparent tank of water in which to float the cans

11. Plasticine boat

A ball of plasticine can be used to demonstrate why ships float. Take a ball of plasticine and drop it into a beaker of water – it will sink. The density of plasticine is greater than the density of water. Now take the SAME ball of plasticine and make a small hollow boat from it. This can now be made to float on the water.

The boat floats because the average density of the plasticine and the air within the boat is less than that of the water.

Age range: 11 – 14   Apparatus required: •Plasticine •Beaker of water

12. Helium balloon and upthrust

Take a helium balloon of the kind you can buy for parties but ask the shop not to inflate it fully. Fix a small plastic pot to the balloon string and load the pot until the balloon just sinks. Then warm the balloon gently using a hair drier on a low setting. Turn off the hair drier. The balloon expands and rises – demonstrating the concept of upthrust. The balloon has an overall lower density but a constant mass.

 Do not use a hot hair dryer such as a paint stripper

Age range: 11 – 14   Apparatus required: •Slightly deflated helium balloon •Heat source - hair dryer

13. Vegetable oil and alcohol

Half fill a measuring cylinder with water and then carefully add alcohol to form a layered liquid. Drip in some vegetable oil using a dropper or pipette. The oil will sink until it reaches a level where the density of the oil will match that of the alcohol-water liquid. It will come to rest and so large bubbles can then be formed at this point.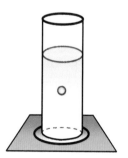

Age range: 11 – 16
Apparatus required: •Water •Alcohol •Measuring cylinder •Dropper or pipette

14. Raisins and fizzy lemonade

This is a really delightful demonstration. Fill a tall beaker (at least 1 litre) with fizzy lemonade. Take a raisin and ask the pupils if the raisin will sink or float if it is dropped into the lemonade.

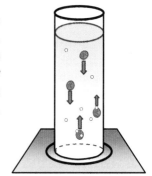

Now drop the raisin in. It sinks, but as it falls through the lemonade it collects tiny bubbles of carbon dioxide in its wrinkly surface. Eventually there is enough gas to support the raisin and so it stops falling. As more bubbles collect, the raisin has a positive buoyancy and so it floats up to the surface. Reaching the surface, the bubbles of gas burst and the raisin sinks again. The process repeats itself. Putting ten or so raisins in at once is very impressive.

If you try the same experiment with smooth beads or smooth fruit it won't work as there are no wrinkles to trap the bubbles of gas. It won't work in pure water either since there is no dissolved gas to form bubbles to collect in the wrinkles of the raisins.

Age range: 11-14
Apparatus required: •Large beaker •Raisins •Fizzy lemonade

15. Mass of air

This is a simple experiment to show that air has weight. An extension would actually enable you to measure the mass of the air and possibly its density.

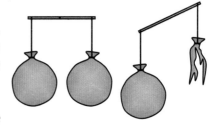

Blow up two balloons, preferably about the same size, and tie them to the two ends of a straw. Put a needle through the centre of the straw and adjust the distance of the balloons from the pivot so that they balance.

Now carefully pop one of the balloons using a pin. Make sure that none of the rubber flies off as you do this.

The balloon that still contains air will be heavier than the empty one and so the straw will tilt, showing that the air in the blown up balloon has weight.

The use of a small rider would enable you to make an estimate of the mass of the air in the balloon. The effects of upthrust should be considered and it must be remembered that the air in the balloon is above atmospheric pressure.

Theory
The mass of an object is a measure of the 'quantity of matter' in the object. The weight of an object is the gravitational pull on that object. The mass is constant but the weight can vary at different points on, or above, the surface of the Earth. The density of an object is its mass divided by its volume.

Age range: 11-13 or younger
Apparatus required: •Two similar balloons •Straw •Needle or pin for pivot
•Cork and retort stand to hold the needle

PRESSURE

General theory for this section:
Pressure = Force/Area   Units for pressure are Pascal (Pa). 1 Pa = 1 N/m^2.
The greater the area of contact the less the pressure between two solid surfaces.

1. Pressure - bed of nails
2. Penny and hook - pressure
3. Scrubbing brush
4. Cheese and wire, rucksacks and shoulders
5. Elephant and girl - pressure
6. Pupil pressure
7. Pencil
8. Standing on gravel and sand
9. More pressure examples
10. Pressure and stick slip motion

1. Pressure - bed of nails

Why can people lie on a bed of nails without excruciating pain? It is all to do with the area of contact. Although each nail has a sharp point the total area of the ends of the nails makes the pressure on any one part of the body bearable. A demonstration of this is to use a bed of nails with a loaded balloon to represent the body. Further experiments can be carried out with a weight resting on the balloon to show how much it can stand without bursting. A very careful demonstration using a compression Newton meter and a drawing pin could be used to find out the pressure exerted on a thumb before it hurts!

Theory:
Pressure = Force/Area of contact

 | **I do not recommend getting pupils, or staff, to lie on beds of nails. I have seen it done with plenty of nails put in close together. The demonstrator got on and off carefully!**

Age range: 11-13
Apparatus required: •Board with nails facing upwards •Board without nails •Balloons •Kilogram masses

2. Penny and hook - pressure

This is a very simple example of the dependence of pressure on the area of contact. Put an S hook on the end of your finger and suspend a 1 kg mass from it - it hurts. Now do the same thing but have a small coin between the S hook and your finger - it hurts much less. The pressure on your finger is much lower since although the force is the same (or very nearly if you disregard the weight of the penny) the area is much greater.

Age range: 11-13
Apparatus required: •S hook •One kilogram mass •Small coin such as a 1 p piece

3. Scrubbing brush with stiff bristles

Hold a scrubbing brush between the palms of your hands and press. The side with the bristles hurts a lot more. There is a much smaller area of contact but the same force as the flat side.

Age range: 11-18   Apparatus required: •Scrubbing brush with stiff bristles

4. Cheese and wire, rucksacks and shoulders - pressure

These two demonstrations are both good practical example of solid pressure.

(a) Cut through a piece of cheese with a cheese wire and actually measure the pressure on the cheese. You simply need to pull the wire down with a Newton meter and use a micrometer to measure the diameter of the wire.

(b) Get one of the pupils to put a rucksack on their shoulders and then load it with weights – the straps begin to press in and it hurts. Increase the area of contact between the straps and their shoulders by putting some large pieces of foam rubber in between. It hurts less!

Age range: 11-13
Apparatus required: •Cheese •Thin wire •Micrometer •Newton meter •Rucksack
•Large masses as a load

5. Elephant and girl - pressure

In order to emphasise the dependence of pressure on the area of contact compare the pressure between a girl in stiletto heels and an elephant standing on one foot. We usually estimate the elephant to have a mass of two or three tons (3000 kg) and a foot of area about 300 cm^2. Try and get one member of the class to bring in a stiletto heeled shoe to measure!

Age range: 11-13
Apparatus required: •Stiletto heeled shoe •Data about elephants •Bathroom scales

6. Pupil pressure

The students can work out the pressure between their feet and the ground when they are standing by first finding their weight and then measuring the area of their own feet by standing on graph paper and drawing round their feet without their shoes on. A good estimate of the area of their feet in contact with the ground can be made by counting the squares. It is interesting to see who thinks that they are very flat-footed.

Typical results for this experiment
Weight of a twelve year old pupil ≈ 400 N   Area of contact = 200 cm^2 Pressure = 400/200 = 2 N cm^{-2}

Get them to estimate the pressure of a pet's foot for homework!

Age range: 11-13
Apparatus required: •Bathroom scales •Graph paper

7. Pencil pressure

A very simple demonstration of the effect of area on pressure is to hold a sharp pencil between your thumb and first finger. When you press, the sharp end hurts more than the flat end because although the forces on each end are the same the area of the sharp end is much smaller than that of the flat end.

Age range: 11-18   Apparatus required: •Pencil

8. Standing on gravel and sand

These two simple experiments demonstrate the effect of different areas of contact between a person and the ground.

(a) Stand on some gravel in a tray with your shoes on. Then take your shoes off and do it again. It is much more painful - the area of contact is much less.

(b) Stand on some sand in a tray with your shoes on. Now put a small block of wood on the sand and stand on that - it will sink in showing the increased pressure even though the force is unchanged. If you can get a large tray, try making some hardboard shapes to fix to the underside of their shoes to increase the size of the area of contact.

The police could also get an idea of the weight of burglars by the depths of the imprint of their feet in soft earth.

Age range: 11-13
Apparatus required: •Tray •Gravel •Sand •Ruler

9. More pressure examples

- People who wear stiletto heels are asked not to walk on soft floors
- Running spikes dig into the take off board of a long jump
- Snow shoes stop you sinking through soft snow
- The lunar landers were fitted with large foot pads
- The studs of soccer boots make indents in the turf of the pitch
- Tractors that have to work on soft ground are fitted with wide tyres
- When you use a car jack on soft tarmac put a flat board underneath it
- Some buildings on soft ground are built on concrete rafts

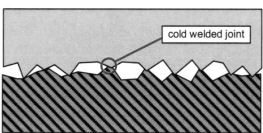

Age range: 7-13

10. Pressure and stick-slip motion

When one solid metal object is placed on top of another they do not touch over the whole of their surfaces but only at a small number of points. This is because they are not really totally smooth. This means that the whole weight of the top object will be supported on the very small area of the top of these points.

The pressure there will be large and so the two metals are "cold welded" together. If the top surface is pulled sideways it will not move until these welds are broken. When it does it will jerk forward and the welds will then reform. Pulling again will break these new welds and so on.

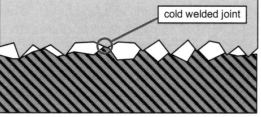

cold welded joint

A stick-slip motion results.

PRESSURE IN LIQUIDS

General theory for this section:
In a liquid the pressure at a point within it depends on two things:
(a) the density of the liquid and
(b) the vertical distance below the liquid surface
Pressure in a liquid = depth (h) x liquid density (ρ) x gravitational field strength (g)
In a liquid the pressure acts in all directions

1. Can with holes
2. Ball with rubber tube
3. Bottle with holes – the whole parabola
4. Pressure in liquids
5. Pressure and liquid flow

 | **Minimise the risk of slipping and falling over on wet floors by using large trays and mopping up any spillage.**

1. Can with holes

You can demonstrate the increase in water pressure by using a can or plastic bucket with a series of holes - both up and down (to show the increase in depth) and round the side (to show pressure acting in all directions). A 2m long 3 cm diameter plastic water pipe would show this much better - the large head of water will give some impressive jets near the bottom. To show this correctly a small tube should project at each orifice. A detailed consideration of Torricelli's theorem is needed to predict which jets will go the furthest.

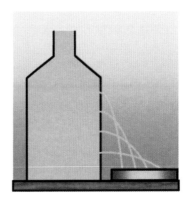

There some further considerations of this simple experiment.

First, it is better to make the holes so that they are not vertically above each other. Doing this will avoids the jets hitting each other when they curve down through the air.

Secondly, the jets at the bottom may not necessarily travel further before they hit the collecting container. This is because they have less far to fall and so have less time to move in the horizontal direction. Doing the experiment over the edge of the bench will allow the lower jets time to travel out further and the usually produced diagrams of the experiment will then be correct.

A full analysis of this fact is given in the following diagram. A series of water paths are shown (each one being a parabola). The velocity of the water emerging from each hole has been calculated using Torricelli's formula (v = √2gd where d is the depth of the water)

(Thanks to Geoff for the initial ideas)

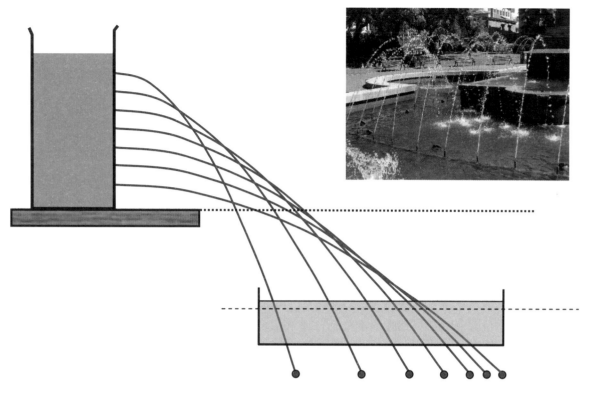

Notice that the lower jet only reaches further out than the upper ones if the water collecting tray is placed below the level shown in the diagram by the dashed line.

An example of the shape of water jets in air is shown in the accompanying photograph.

Age range: 11-13 depending on treatment
Apparatus required: •Plastic bottle or can with holes in the side •Drain pipe with holes in the side •Water •Bucket

2. Ball with rubber tube

Another way of showing that pressure at a point in a liquid acts equally in all directions is to take a tennis ball, or any hollow rubber ball of that size, and make a number of small holes (diameter two or three millimetres) in it. Then fix a long glass tube into the top of the ball. Pour water into the tube and show that since the pressure acts in all directions water comes out of all the holes round the ball with roughly equal force.

Age range: 11-13
Apparatus required: •Ball with holes with long glass tube fitted into it •Water

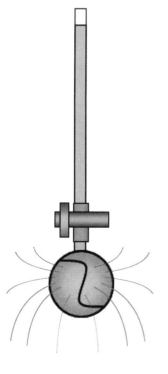

3. The bottle with holes – the whole parabola

We usually say that the path of a water jet under gravity is a parabola, but are seldom able to see the whole parabola. The following experiment is a simple way of showing all, or nearly all, of a parabolic shape when water comes out of the base of a bottle.

Now get a large plastic drinks bottle. Make two holes in either side of the neck of the bottle close to the cap of the bottle. Then put a hole in the bottom of the bottle so that the air can get in when the bottle is inverted. (Cover this hole with your finger when filling the bottle!)

Fill the bottle with water, put the cap on, put your fingers over the two holes by the cap and turn the bottle upside down. Take your fingers away and hold up the bottle.

Water will spurt out of both holes and give the two halves of a parabola. The only bit you can't see is the part occupied by the bottle itself.

Age range: 11-14
Apparatus required: •Large plastic drinks bottle •Water •Scissors or sharp craft knife •Bowl to collect water (maybe two!) •Sharp point for making the holes

4. Pressure in liquids

To show that the pressure in a liquid depends only on the depth in the liquid and its density, set up the arrangement shown. The apparatus is filled with water. The pressure at a certain depth in the water is the same at all points at that depth whatever the shape of the container.

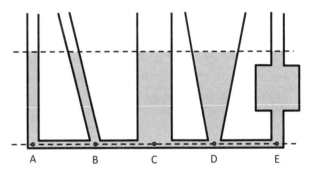

Pressure at A = Pressure at B = Pressure at C = Pressure at D = Pressure at E

Age range: 11-14   Apparatus required: •Glassware as shown •Water •Connecting rubber tubes

5. Pressure and liquid flow

Fit a short tube into the centre of the bottom of each of two transparent plastic cylinders. (CD boxes or large drinks bottles are suitable.) Now add a long rubber tube to one of these tubes (see diagram). Get someone to cover the end of the outlets from both cylinders and then add the same depth of water to each cylinder. Now uncover the ends. The cylinders do not empty at the same rate. The one with the long tube empties more rapidly.

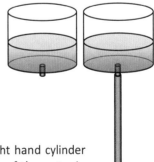

Theory: The pressure difference between the top of the water in the right hand cylinder and the bottom of the rubber tube, is greater than that between the top of the water in the left hand cylinder and the base of that cylinder.
(Thanks to the students from the Nutuurkunde Circus of Eindhoven for this idea)

Age range: 11-14   Apparatus required: •Two plastic cylinders •Two short lengths of metal tubing •One longer length of rubber tubing

ATMOSPHERIC AND GAS PRESSURE

General theory and information for this section

The pressure of the Earth's atmosphere at sea level is about 10^5 Pa and the density of the air at sea level is 1.2 kgm^{-3}. If the atmosphere were compressed to a uniform density equal to that at the Earth's surface it would form a layer 8.6 km deep round the planet.

It is important to emphasise here that, in all these experiments, the forces are **pushing** on the walls of containers or liquids rather than producing a **pulling** effect due to suction.

1. Rubber sucker
2. Party blowers and air pressure
3. The hose pipe problem
4. Lath and newspaper
5. Balloon in a bell jar
6. Pouring a can of lemonade
7. Glass and card
8. Drinking through a long straw
9. Lifting a pupil by blowing
10. Pump with reversed washer
11. Air pressure and a plastic drinks bottle
12. Lung pressure
13. Atmospheric pressure - the fountain
14. Bucket of blancmange - air pressure
15. Collapsing can, collapsing bottle
16. Test tube in a bell jar
17. Balloon in a bottle
18. A household vacuum cleaner
19. Gas pressure
20. Water barometer
21. Atmospheric pressure and a CD

1. Rubber sucker

A rubber sucker gives a simple demonstration of air pressure. Press the rubber sucker against a wall or other smooth surface. It sticks to the wall since the pressure outside the sucker is greater than that inside! Moistening the edges of the rubber helps to improve the seal between it and a solid surface and prevents air leaking in.

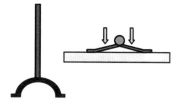

Age range: 11-13
Apparatus required: •Rubber sucker or sink plunger

2. Party blowers and air pressure

This is a self explanatory and simple model of a Bourdon gauge. The harder you blow, and therefore the greater the pressure inside the paper tube, the more it unwinds. The springy wire along the blower coils it up again when you stop blowing. Compare the party blower with an actual Bourdon gauge.

Age range: 11-13   Apparatus required: •Party blower •Bourdon gauge.

3. The hose pipe problem

Wrap a long piece of rubber tube round a can. Fit a funnel into one end and put the other end into a bucket. Hold the can horizontally in a clamp and pour some water into the funnel. You would expect water to come out of the other end and flow into the bucket but in fact the funnel overflows. No water ever emerges from the other end. The demonstration is more impressive if you can borrow a hosepipe wound round a reel. The funnel can then be a metre or two above the reel and still no water comes out of the other end. It works - or rather it doesn't work because once you have some air trapped in a loop the build up of air pressure as more water is poured in prevents the water moving round the loop.

4. Lath and newspaper

This very simple experiment demonstrates the pressure of the atmosphere. Take a thin strip of wood (known as a lath) about the size of a 30 cm ruler and lay it on the table with about a third of its length projecting over the edge. Now smooth out a large sheet of newspaper so that it covers the part of the lath on the bench. Gently lift the exposed end of the lath - the paper lifts - air has had a chance to get underneath. Now smooth the paper back and hit the exposed section of the wood smartly with the edge of your hand, or a short length of broom handle, like a karate chop - air does not have a chance to get underneath, the pressure of the atmosphere holds the paper down and the lath breaks. However, the newspaper is completely undamaged.

Theory:
Pressure of the atmosphere = 10^5 Pa so the weight of air on a sheet of newspaper opened out to an area of 1 m x 0.75 m is 7.5×10^4 N

Age range: 11-13
Apparatus required: •Thin wooden lath (20 mm x 300 mm x 2.5 mm). (The thickness is quite critical - too thick and it won't break and too thin it becomes too whippy and still won't break. I usually use a strip of hardboard.) •Sheet of newspaper

5. Balloon in a bell jar

(a) Partly inflate a balloon and put it in a bell jar connected to a vacuum pump. The partly inflated balloon will inflate if the air is pumped out of the bell jar because the air pressure inside the balloon is greater than that outside.

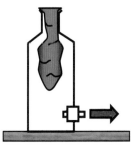

 Eye protection required. Only bell jars designed to be evacuated should be used. Ensure that there are no cracks or chips in the glass which could cause the jar to implode when evacuated.

(b) A demonstration using simpler apparatus to that just described now follows. Fix a bicycle pump valve into the side of a plastic bottle near the base. Put a balloon inside with the neck of the balloon over the neck of the bottle. Using a bicycle pump with a reversed washer pump out some air from below the balloon - it will inflate. It needs to be a strong bottle otherwise the bottle itself will begin to collapse! A further alternative is to put a balloon in the bottle in a version of experiment 15b before the water is added and use a rigid bottle such as a wine demijohn.

(c) Yet another variation is to use experiment (a) but with a marshmallow in the bell jar instead of the balloon. As the air pressure in the bell jar is reduced the air is drawn out of the marshmallow which should then theoretically collapse to about half its original volume! In fact the reduction in pressure causes the ones that I have used to expand – they shrink when air is let back in the bell jar. Chocolate covered ones exude a stream of white foam!

Age range: 11-13
Apparatus required: •Balloon •Vacuum pump •Bell jar •Bicycle pump •Marshmallow •Plastic bottle

6. Pouring a can of lemonade – one hole or two?

When you try and pour lemonade out of a can through one small hole you find that it is very difficult. It is worth demonstrating this by using two prepared tins, both with removable lids that can be filled with water. One has only one small hole but the other has two at opposite sides of the can. Pouring liquid out of one hole would leave a partial vacuum behind so resisting further pouring. The addition of the second hole allows air to get in.

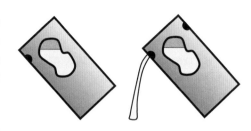

An even simpler demonstration of this is to fill a milk bottle with water and upend it over a sink - the water comes out relatively slowly in great "lumps". Tilting the bottle allows air to pass into it over the outgoing water and makes the pouring simpler and quicker. Emptying a wine demijohn is also made easier if it is spun to create a vortex through which air can enter when it is turned upside down.

Age range: 11-13
Apparatus required: •Milk bottle •Water •Bucket or sink •Wine demijohn

7. Glass and card

(a) Fill a glass to the brim with water: carefully slide a card over the top and then turn it upside down over a sink, holding the card in place with your hand. When the glass is upside down take your hand away. The card will stay there, it is being held on to the glass because the air pressure below the card is greater than the water pressure above it.

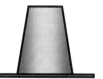

Ask the pupils the following questions:

(a) What is the longest beaker that you could invert full of water before the card comes off?
(b) What happens if a little air leaks into the glass?

(b) In a variation of the previous classic experiment you can use instead a table tennis ball in the mouth of a milk bottle. If the bottle is filled with water with the table tennis ball on the end the bottle can then be turned upside down. The pressure of the atmosphere acts up on the ball and the pressure of the water acts downwards on the ball. The pressure of the atmosphere is much bigger and so the ball stays on. In this case the water molecules cannot run past the ball – it sort of acts as an atmospheric stopper. It also works quite well with some air in the bottle - I have done it with the bottle almost empty!

The advantage of this method is that it is much more stable – the bottle can be tilted and the table tennis ball will still stay in place.

Age range: 11-13
Apparatus required:
(a) •Glass •Piece of cardboard •Water •Sink or bowl   (b) •Milk bottle •Table tennis ball

8. Drinking through a long straw

(a) Put a can of lemonade at the bottom of a flight of stairs. Get a pupil to stand at the top and then ask them to try and drink some of the lemonade using a long clear plastic tube - they can't - or at least they find that it is very difficult. Using a clear plastic tube is better since you can actually watch the progress of the liquid. This is a convincing demonstration of atmospheric pressure and its limitations. (Use disposable mouthpieces for each pupil. These can be made from plastic straws that fit tightly inside the tube.)

Theory:
The maximum height of water (or fizzy drink) that the atmosphere can support is about 10 m. Therefore even if the pressure in the straw is reduced to zero the liquid will rise no higher than this. In practice the height risen is much less! Height of water (drink) = Atmospheric pressure/g x density of water = 10 m.

(b) Another way of **not** getting any drink into your mouth when you try and suck it up a straw is to put two straws into your mouth! One has its other end in the liquid while the other has its open end in air. No matter how hard you suck no liquid will rise up the tube - you are simply not able to reduce the pressure in your mouth - it remains at atmospheric pressure because one of the straws has an end open to the air.

Age range: 11-13
Apparatus required: •Can of drink •Long clear plastic tube (makes the rise of the liquid visible)

9. Lifting a pupil by blowing

Stand a pupil on a wooden board which is resting on top of a plastic bag to which a rubber tube has been fitted. Blow into the bag through the tube and show that you can lift the pupil up!
Pouring water down a tube into a rubber hot water bottle on which someone is sitting has the same effect.

Theory:
Force (= weight of the pupil) = Pressure x Area. If your lung pressure is say 0.1 atmospheres (10^4 Pa) above atmospheric pressure then to lift a child of weight 400 N you need a board with an area of contact of 0.04 m^2 (20 cm x 20 cm).

Age range: 11-13
Apparatus required: •Plastic bag with rubber tube sealed into the neck   •Wooden board (about 0.5 metre square)

10. Atmospheric pressure - pump with reversed washer

This is a simple experiment to demonstrate the pressure of the atmosphere and can even be used to get a very rough estimate of its value. Reverse the washer in a bicycle pump and mount the pump vertically in a clamp. Hanging weights on the handle can then be used as a way of showing the pressure of the atmosphere. The weights pull downwards on the handle but the pressure of the atmosphere acting upwards on the reversed washer prevents the piston from descending.

Theory:
If the cross-sectional area of the pump is measured then by using Pressure = Force/Area the pressure of the atmosphere can be estimated.

Age range: 11-13
Apparatus required: •Bicycle pump •Slotted masses •Retort stand and clamp

11. Atmospheric pressure, hot water and a plastic drinks bottle

Boil a kettle of water, allow it to cool a little and then pour the hot water into a large plastic drinks bottle through a plastic funnel. Swill the water round so that it heats the bottle and the air inside it before pouring the water out. Quickly screw on the lid. As the air in the bottle cools down, the bottle will be squashed by the air pressure outside it.

 Check that the bottle and funnel will not melt when the water is poured in.

Age range: 11 – 14   Apparatus required: •Kettle of boiling water •Large plastic drinks bottle

12. Lung pressure

This is a simple class experiment or demonstration of the pressure of your lungs. A large manometer filled with coloured water is all that is needed. Pupils blow into the lower end and see how far they can raise the water in the open end. Differences in levels of up to about two metres are usual with twelve-year-old pupils. To show the effect of exertion, the experiment can be done before and after some form of physical exercise.

Age range: 11-13
Apparatus required: •Large manometer - up to 2 m high filled with coloured water
•Use tubing connectors as mouthpieces, keeping them in disinfectant to sterilise them before use

13. Atmospheric pressure - the fountain

Fit a glass tube through a bung fitted in the top of a round-bottomed flask which is about a quarter full of water. To the end of the tube attach a short length of rubber tubing that can be closed with a tube clip. Mount the flask in a clamp so that it can be rotated. Heat the flask until there is steam coming from the tube showing vigorous boiling. After boiling has been going on for a few moments remove from the heat and immediately close the clip. Then upend the flask so that the end of the tube is under the water in the beaker and open the clip. As the pressure in the flask reduces water spurts up the tube.

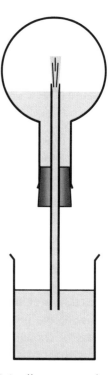

 Don't heat the flask when the clip is closed, and use only a Pyrex or similar flask so that it will not crack when the cold water rushes in.

Age range: 11-13
Apparatus required: •Retort stand and clamp •Beaker of water •Bunsen
•Round bottomed flask with a glass tube fitted through a rubber bung in its neck

14. Bucket of chocolate blancmange - air pressure

Imagine a bucket full of chocolate blancmange with a tight fitting lid with a hole in the centre. The lid can be pushed down into the bucket. As you push down on the lid the blancmange is forced up out of the hole. This was originally supposed to be an analogy for a Fortin barometer with the blancmange replacing the column of mercury.

However if the Fortin barometer is not a familiar instrument the demonstration can simply be an analogy of how liquids are forced up a tube when the pressure on the liquid outside the tube is greater than that above the liquid in the tube.

15. Collapsing can, collapsing bottle and air pressure

Both of these experiments are vivid demonstrations of the pressure of the atmosphere.

(a) Get a tin can and put a little water in it. Heat the can vigorously over a Bunsen until the water has been boiling for some time. Although there will be some liquid left, the can will be full of steam. Remove the can from the heat and quickly insert the stopper or screw on the lid.

 Do not heat a closed can. Show the pupils how to deal with minor burns using running cold water.

before   after

As the can cools, the steam inside the can condenses and therefore the pressure drops. After a few moments the pressure difference between the atmosphere outside and the small amount of residual air inside is enough to crush the can flat!

I usually stand on the top of the can first before starting the experiment to demonstrate how strong it is and then get a pupil to try and straighten out the can at the end after it has cooled.

A variation of this is to use an empty drinks can. Make a small hole in one side, put a little water in it and boil the water as before. Then pick it up with a pair of tongs and rapidly invert it in a bowl of water. The steam inside the can condenses, the small hole in the can prevents water from being sucked in too rapidly and the can collapses.

(b) This next demonstration of atmospheric pressure is very simple and direct and avoids heating cans of air! Completely fill a plastic squash bottle with water - bigger bottles are more impressive. Put a bung in it with a glass tube in the centre and attach a 2 m length of rubber tubing to the tube - more if the height of your lab will allow it. Get someone to hold the end of the tube closed while you climb on a bench and upend the bottle with the rubber tube dangling vertically downwards. Now open the lower end of the tube.

As the water runs out, the bottle will be squashed flat by the pressure of the air on the outside! The long tube gives a bigger pressure difference between the top and bottom of the water column and also prevents air leaking in.

Theory
Pressure difference between the two ends of the water column of height h = $\rho g h$ where ρ is the density of the water.

Age range: 11-13
Apparatus required:
(a) •Tin can •Bunsen •Heat proof mat •Drinks can •Tongs
(b) •Plastic bottle with rubber tube fitted to a bung in its neck •Water •Bucket

16. Test tube in a bell jar

Take a large test tube filled with water and invert it in a beaker of water, making sure that the total volume of water present is less than the volume of the beaker. Place the arrangement in a bell jar connected to a vacuum pump and slowly reduce the pressure. The water level in the test tube will begin to fall as the pressure in the bell jar decreases, the water levels inside and outside the tube eventually becoming almost equal. (You need to be able to reduce the pressure below 0.01 atmospheres (10^3 Pa) to get much effect.)

If the air is allowed to leak slowly back into the bell jar the water level in the tube will rise again – a convincing demonstration that it is the air pressure on the water in the beaker that is forcing the water up the tube.

 Eye protection required. Only bell jars designed to be evacuated should be used. Ensure that there are no cracks or chips in the glass which could cause the jar to implode when evacuated.

Age range: 11-13
Apparatus required: •Vacuum pump •Bell jar •Large test tube •Beaker of water

17. Balloon in a bottle

Put a balloon in a large plastic bottle with the neck of the balloon over the neck of the bottle. Try and blow up the balloon. You can't, because of the pressure of the air inside the bottle.

Now make a small hole in the bottom of the bottle. You will now be able to blow up the balloon.

Now cover the top of the bottle with your thumb and the hole at the bottom of the bottle with a finger so that the balloon stays inflated in the bottle. Finally remove your thumb – the air rushes out of the balloon, the balloon deflates and the bottle collapses because of the greater air pressure outside it.

Age range: 11-14
Apparatus required: •Large plastic bottle •Balloon

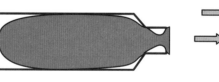

18. A vacuum cleaner

An ordinary household vacuum cleaner can make a very adequate vacuum pump. The pressure of the atmosphere can be shown by getting a pupil to stand in a large bin liner with a slot cut for their head and with it sealed around their waist. If the air is sucked out using a hose attached to a cylinder vacuum cleaner the bag will shrink to stick closely to the child showing the pressure of the atmosphere from outside the bag. You will have to find a suitable way of fixing the tube of the vacuum cleaner to the bag.

 Under no circumstances allow a pupil to put their head in a plastic bag.

Age range: 11 – 14
Apparatus required: •Large bin liner •Sticky tape •Vacuum cleaner

19. Gas pressure
Use a small water-filled manometer connected to a gas tap to measure the pressure of the gas. The difference in levels between the end of the U tube open to the atmosphere and that fixed to the gas tap gives the pressure of the gas in centimetres of water. (This is usually about 10 – 15 cm).

Age range: 11-13
Apparatus required: •U tube manometer (25 cm high) filled with water

20. A water barometer
A water barometer can theoretically support about 10 m of water. The simplest way to make one is to fill a 10.5 m length of clear plastic tube with water and then close one end with a clamp. Put the open end in a bucket of water at the bottom of a stair well 10 m deep. Take the top end up the stair well and you should see that the pressure of the air will keep the water in the tube.

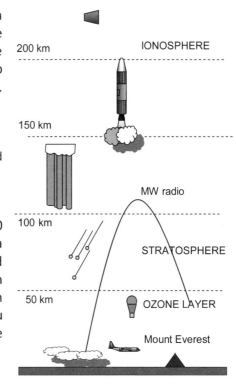

Age range: 11 – 14
Apparatus required: •10.5 m length of clear plastic tube •Tube clamp •Bucket •Water •10.5 m stair well

21. Atmospheric pressure – CD and newspaper
Fix a paper clip to a length of string, pass the string through a CD and then through a hole in the centre of a sheet of newspaper so that the CD is beneath the paper when it is placed on the desk. Smooth out the paper.

Now give the string a sharp tug vertically. It will be very difficult to move the CD upwards because of the downwards atmospheric pressure on the newspaper.

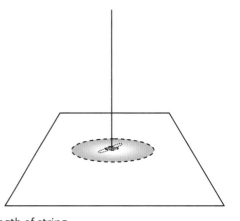

Age range: 11-14
Apparatus required: •CD •Paper clip •Sheet of newspaper •Length of string

MOTION

General theory for this section:
Speed = Distance/Time (for steady speed)
Acceleration = Change in speed/Time taken for steady acceleration
Acceleration due to gravity at the Earth's surface (g) = 9.8 m/s^2 (often simplified to 10 m/s^2)

1. Animal Olympics sheets
2. Reaction time
3. Tachographs and v-t curves
4. Velocity - it's a vector - two people walking

5. Acceleration
6. Horizontal and vertical motion
7. Table tennis ball accelerometer
8. Resource suggestions

1. Animal Olympics sheets

I have a collection of sheets of speeds and athletic performances of various animals, birds and fishes which I use at the beginning of work on speed and acceleration as a comparison with humans. They include 100m, 1500m, marathon, long jump, high jump, swimming speeds and flying speeds.

Some data:

200 m	Man 25 mph	Ostrich 37 mph	Race horse 44 mph	Cheetah 60 mph
1500 m	Man 16 mph	Gazelle 50 mph		
Marathon	Man 12 mph	Race horse 17 mph	Reindeer 25 mph	Antelope 36 mph
100 m freestyle	Man 5 mph	Salmon 20 mph	Killer whale 30 mph	Wahoo 50 mph
Flying	Wasp 12 mph	Bee 20 mph	Partridge 55 mph	Ring necked duck 66 mph

Age range: 11-14
Apparatus required: •Animal Olympics sheets

2. Reaction time

This is a simple way of demonstrating and measuring the reaction time of a pupil. Hold a ruler vertically and ask one of the pupils to put their thumb and forefinger either side of the bottom of the ruler but not touching it. Say "Now" and drop the ruler. They have to catch it by closing their thumb and finger. Their reaction time (t) is simply measured by how far the ruler falls from rest (s).
An extension of this is to fix a piece of tape to the ruler and mark it with equal time intervals (0.1 s) using the formula below.

Theory:
$s = 1/2gt^2$ to calculate t, where s is measured in metres and g = 10 ms^{-2}. Reaction time (t) = $[2s/g]^{1/2}$

Age range: 14-16   Apparatus required: •Ruler

3. Tachographs and v-t curves

It is an interesting exercise to use a tachograph (from the school minibus) to investigate real velocity-time curves. An enlarged version on an overhead projector can be used to show the change of speed with time. Who is the best driver on your staff?

Enlarged versions should be photocopied for student analysis.

Age range: 14-18   Apparatus required: •Tachograph discs

4. Velocity - it's a vector - two people walking

I use these ideas to introduce the vector nature of velocity; a vector is a quantity with both size and direction.

(a) Two pupils are placed at either side of the lab and asked to walk at say 1 m/s. In spite of having not been told to do so they invariably walk towards each other. I then get them to stand about two metres apart and ask them to repeat the procedure. It takes them a few moments to realise that the effects are quite different if one walks forwards and the other walks backwards.

(b) As a further way of emphasising the point consider the effect of a car waiting at traffic lights - if it goes into reverse instead of forwards when the lights change to green the results can be unfortunate!

5. Acceleration

Put a ball on an angled track on one of the "old fashioned" dynamics trolleys. The track angles up towards the back of the trolley at an angle with a tangent of about 0.1. (This means an angle of 5.7°). Find a rubber ball that won't move until you start pulling the truck. Now try and pull the truck along without the ball rolling off the end.

Age range: 14-18
Apparatus required: •Dynamics trolley •Ramp •Ball •String •Cardboard for the track

6. Horizontal and vertical motion

(a) Get one member of the class to sit on a wheeled chair. Push them across the lab and as they move ask them to throw a ball in the air. As far as they are concerned the ball goes straight up and comes straight down, but to the rest of the class it moves in a parabolic path. Making a large grid on the board behind the moving chair and taking a video of the motion makes this even clearer.

(b) An alternative to this experiment is to mount a dowel rod vertically on the top of a rider on a linear air track. Fix a small plastic beaker with a slot cut in one side on top of the dowel rod. Put a ball bearing in the beaker and gently push it out so that it falls vertically while the rider moves at a constant velocity. The ball bearing will always land on the rider.

Age range: 13 – 18
Apparatus required:
(a) •Wheeled chair •Ball •Large grid screen
•TV camera if possible
(b) •Linear air track •Ball bearing •Ruler •Rider

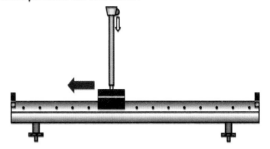

7. Table tennis ball accelerometer

(a) Fix a table tennis ball to the lid of a glass jar by a thread. Fill the jar with water, put the lid on and then turn the jar upside down. The ball floats in the water. Now accelerate the jar. This can either be done on a dynamics trolley or by placing the jar on a rotating table. The ball will swing in the direction in which the jar is accelerating - in the case of the linear motion it will move in the direction of motion - in the second case it will move towards the centre - in the direction of the centripetal acceleration. You can use a beaker as shown in the diagram but the jar with a lid stops the water from slopping out.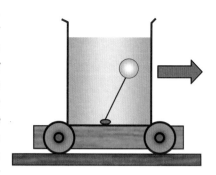

Alternative versions of this experiment are:

(b) Spirit level accelerated or spun on a turntable. The bubble goes to the forward part of the level or moves towards the end nearest the centre of the circle if it is rotated. Mount the spirit level on a truck on a linear air track and record the effects, if possible using a TV camera for later analysis.

(c) Imagine a balloon filled with helium tethered by a string to the floor of a car. If the car accelerates the balloon of helium will move forwards since it has a lower inertia than the surrounding air.

Age range: 16-18
Apparatus required: •Jar with screw top •Table tennis ball •Thread •Linear air track or rotating table •Motor

8. Resource suggestions

Use data about cars and athletes to give a real, everyday feel to the study of acceleration and motion.

100 m sprinter
Reaction time 0.109s

Distance	10m	30m	70m	100m
Time	1.84s	3.80s	7.36s	9.86s
Average speed over previous 10m	5.9ms^{-1}	10.8 ms^{-1}	11.9ms^{-1}	11.7ms^{-1}

Family saloons

	Mass (kg)	Time for 0-100kmhr^{-1} (s)	Power (kW)	Power (HP)
A	906	12.7	51	68
B	875	11.8	55	73
C	1010	16.7	48	64
D	1750	7.8	150	201

GRAVITY

General theory for this section:

When an object falls from rest and accelerates under the effect of the Earth's gravity the distance it falls (h) in a time t is given by the equation: $h = \frac{1}{2}(gt^2)$. The gravitational field strength at the surface of the Earth is approximately 9.81 Nkg^{-1} and this will give a mass of one kg an acceleration of 9.81 ms^{-2}. That means that if an object is dropped near the Earth's surface its speed increases by about 10 ms^{-1} every second if the effects of air resistance are ignored.

When a projectile is thrown it has a constant vertical acceleration (g) towards the ground but a constant horizontal velocity if we ignore air resistance. The horizontal and vertical motions are independent.

In some of the experiments a constant head apparatus is mentioned. This is simply a device for maintaining a constant head of water at an outlet.

1. Mooing carton
2. Pearls in air
3. g with a water jet
4. Diluted gravity
5. Diluted gravity - projectile paths
6. g - Gramophone turntable
7. Vertical acceleration
8. Two joined falling balls
9. Falling can and water - what happens?
10. The contracting stream
11. Diluted gravity again
12. Falling helical spring
13. Falling bar method for g
14. Monkey and hunter
15. Dropping books and paper
16. Galileo inclined planes
17. Guinea and feather tube
18. Falling can with hole at one side
19. Floating block in a falling jar
20. Two tennis balls
21. Smiley pop ups

1. Mooing milk carton

The mooing milk carton can be used as a fun problem to show the constancy of vertical acceleration in free fall and also to demonstrate g forces. Turn it upside down and drop it in "mid moo". Observe the change in the sound as it goes down. The mooing stops in free fall and starts again when the high deceleration forces occur as it is caught.

Age range: 11-18 depending on treatment
Apparatus required: •Mooing milk carton

2. Pearls in air

(a) This is a classic demonstration designed to show the parabolic path of projectiles in a gravitational field. A water jet is formed by using the glass part of a dropping pipette fixed to a thin-walled rubber tube and connected to the water tap. The rubber tube is passed through an old-style ticker timer or over a vibration generator so that the tube is alternately squeezed and released when the device is switched on.

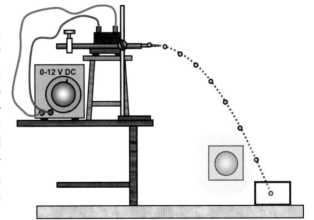

The water jet falls in a parabola from an initial horizontal direction but is also interrupted by the pulsing so that droplets of water are formed instead of a continuous stream. If the arrangement is illuminated with a stroboscope, pearl-like droplets of water can be made to stand still or move slowly through the air. The constant horizontal velocity and the increasing vertical velocity can be seen by observing the positions of successive drops. To get a permanent record you could mark the position of the shadows of the water drops on a screen behind the jet or even photograph it. A truly beautiful demonstration.

(b) An extension of the basic version is what I call the Double Pearls in Air. In this experiment two jets are used from different water taps but with tubes running under the same ticker timer bar. One is adjusted to give a parabola while water simply dribbles out from the other, falling vertically. The vertical acceleration of the drops can then be compared. Of course you can make two parabolas and compare these.

(c) I have heard of a version using a single parabola of water but TWO strobe lights, one with a red filter and one with a blue filter. Apparently, changing the flashing speed of the strobes can result in red drops moving in one direction and blue drops seemingly travelling back the other way. I have not had a chance to try this myself, but it apparently amazes people.

> **Warnings about the use of stroboscopes or flashing lights should be given for all sections of this experiment. Any pupil suffering from photo-sensitive migraine should be allowed to leave if they request it.**

Theory:
Since $h = 1/2gt^2$ and $s = vt$ the equation for the parabolic path for the water is $h = gs^2/2v^2$ where s is the horizontal distance travelled, h the vertical distance and v the horizontal velocity of the jet

Age range: 14-18
Apparatus required: •Ticker timer •Two water jets •Constant head apparatus •Bucket •Stroboscope

3. g with a water jet
The value of the acceleration due to gravity (g) can be found in a rather novel way by using a jet of water projected horizontally from a dropper attached to a constant head to give a parabolic path. The shape of the path is found by measuring pairs of values of the height fallen (h) and the distance horizontally from the orifice (s) and if the rate of flow of the water is also found the value of g can be calculated. Measure the diameter of the jet to calculate its cross sectional area (A).
The horizontal velocity (v) is obtained from the equation V = Av where V is the volume of water leaving the dropper per second (measure this by directing the jet into a measuring cylinder) and A is the cross sectional area of the jet. Using a TV camera to give an image on the screen, or shining light from a projector to make a shadow of the path on a board, are both helpful ways of making the measurements easier to take.

Theory:
$s = vt$ $h = 1/2gt^2$ $v = V/\pi r^2$

Age range: 16-18
Apparatus required: •Water jet •Constant head apparatus •Rulers •Base clamp •Measuring cylinder •Stop clock •Travelling microscope or vernier or TV camera •Bucket •Mop!

4. Diluted gravity

(a) Realising the problem of making accurate measurements of the acceleration due to gravity, Galileo diluted gravity by rolling balls down slopes. His original apparatus is in the History of Science Museum, Florence. We can recreate his experiment by rolling a marble down an inclined plastic ramp or tube and measuring the time it takes to travel a measured distance.

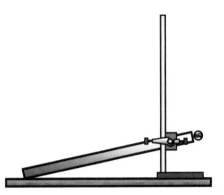

The gravitational acceleration (g) has been "diluted" to g sinA where A is the angle that the tube makes with the horizontal.

Carrying out the experiment by using a rider on a tilted linear air track (I used one 2m long) can give extremely accurate values for g.

A piece of plastic electrical trunking supported by a strip of wood makes an excellent ramp down which to roll the marbles.

(b) An alternative version of the diluted gravity experiment of Galileo can be performed on a large scale with an aerial ropeway type arrangement fixed across the lab. A wire should be fixed tightly from a high point on one side of the lab to a low point on the other. A small cup either fixed to a pulley wheel or simply tied to a loop of wire can then travel down the wire. Time, distance and angle can easily be measured.

Theory:
Acceleration down the plank or wire = g sinA $s = 1/2 \ g sinA \ t^2$
It is worth pointing out that it is much more accurate to measure the small angles by trigonometry than by fiddling around with a protractor!

Age range: 14-16
Apparatus required:
•Wooden ramp and track or plastic tube •Marble •Stop •Ruler •Wire •Cup and pulley wheel

5. Diluted gravity - projectile paths

An extension of the diluted gravity experiment (see experiment 4) is to investigate a diluted projectile path. Get a drawing board and fix a large sheet of paper to it. On top of this fix a piece of carbon paper - face downwards. Tilt the board and then roll a heavy ball bearing across the top of the paper in a horizontal direction. The path of the ball bearing will be produced on the paper. Different angles of tilt and different path directions can be used. This would be suitable for an introduction to projectiles or, at a more advanced level, where a calculation of the parameters of the paths can be made.

Age range: 16-18
Apparatus required: •Drawing board •Large ball bearing •Carbon paper •White paper

6. g - Gramophone turntable

A rather quaint experiment is the use of an old gramophone turntable to measure the acceleration due to gravity (g).

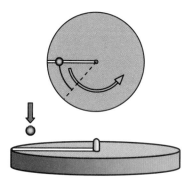

The problem with all such measurements is to find a way of determining the time of fall that will always be pretty small over the distances possible in a laboratory. In this method this small time is found by using a gramophone turntable. First, fix a piece of tape along a radius. Hold a ball bearing a height h above the rotating turntable and release it at just the moment when the tape passes beneath it. The angle through which the turntable has rotated before the ball bearing hits it is found by either covering the surface with plasticine or a piece of carbon paper over a white sheet of paper.

The period of rotation of the turntable is determined using a stopwatch and may be used to calculate the time of fall (t). The acceleration due to gravity is then worked out using the formula $g = 2h/t^2$.

Admittedly it's a very inaccurate method, but it does give you a means of getting g and then commenting on why it would be an unreliable answer.

Age range: 16-18
Apparatus required: •Gramophone turntable or an electric drill and plywood disc •Large ball bearing •Carbon paper and white paper or plasticine •Ruler

7. Vertical acceleration

The "feel" of the value of the acceleration due to gravity can be gained by putting a small object such as a ball bearing on your hand and then moving your hand downwards. If you move it with an acceleration of less than g the ball bearing stays in contact with your hand but if your hand accelerates with a greater acceleration than g the ball bearing leaves the surface. It is rather more difficult to do this with your hand on top of the object. You can compare this with the loop the loop in a roller coaster or with people in a car going over a bumpy road. You will leave your seat in a car if it travels over the bumps too rapidly.

8. Two balls falling joined by stretched elastic

An interesting problem involving gravity is to take two balls that are joined together by a piece of stretched elastic and hold one of them so that the other hangs below it, the elastic between them being stretched. Now release them so that they fall. What happens to their separation as they fall? It is worth doing the experiment, first with two balls of the same mass and then with two of different masses. With the two different masses try it with the greater mass at either the top or bottom.

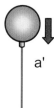

a'

Theory:
The upper ball falls with a greater acceleration than the other - the two are pulled together by the elastic and so the acceleration varies until the elastic becomes slack, when they both fall with an acceleration of g.

a"

Age range: 16-18   Apparatus required: •Two power balls •Piece of elastic

9. Falling can and water - what happens?

Take a tin can and drill a hole in the bottom. The size isn't critical but two or three millimetres in diameter will be fine. Put your finger over the hole and fill the can with water. Now drop the can - the water stays inside.

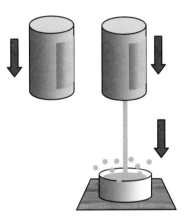

This is much as you would expect, since all objects accelerate downwards at the same rate if air resistance is ignored. Now repeat the experiment but drop the can after you have allowed some of the water to start streaming out. What happens to the water? It looks as if the can is continuing to empty itself, but this would mean that the water is falling with a greater acceleration than g.

This is impossible of course! The can and the water both accelerate at the same rate, g, and the can has the same amount of water in it when it reaches the ground as it had at the start of the drop.

Age range: 14-18
Apparatus required: •Bowl or bucket •Tin can with hole

10. The contracting stream

The speed of a jet of water falling vertically from a tap into a sink increases the further from the tap it gets. This would seem to suggest that more water reaches the sink every second than is being emitted from the tap. Clearly impossible! This can only be explained if the stream of water gets thinner with increasing depth below the tap. This can be verified by turning the tap on slightly and observing the stream.

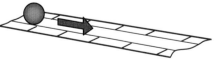

Age range: 14-18
Apparatus required: •Water tap

11. Diluted gravity again

Another variation of the diluted gravity experiment is to use a 30 cm long clear plastic ruler that has a groove down its centre, a ball bearing and an overhead projector. Put the ruler on the overhead projector with one end slightly raised (a millimetre or two). (You may need to support the ruler in the middle to stop it bowing.)

Now let the ball bearing roll down it, using the image of the ruler on a screen to show the distance reached at certain time intervals. Calculate the acceleration due to gravity as in experiment three.

Age range: 14-16
Apparatus required: •Overhead projector •Ball bearing •30 cm clear plastic ruler •Stop clock

12. Falling helical spring

A variation of experiment nine is to drop an extended helical spring and observe what happens to various parts of it as it falls. You will find that during the drop the bottom coils stay where they are while the upper coils catch up with them and then the whole spring falls together. During the whole motion the centre of mass falls with an acceleration of g. The information that the spring is falling will take a certain time to travel down the spring and so initially the bottom part of the spring "thinks" it is still being held up and so remains at rest.
(Thanks to Martin for this idea)

Using a TV camera to record the fall and looking at a slow motion replay will make the results of many experiments much easier to appreciate.

Age range: 16-18
Apparatus required: •Helical spring •TV camera if possible

13. Falling bar method for g

You can use the fact that the vertical acceleration of any point on any rigid falling object is the same, no matter whether it is dropped vertically or swung or projected at an angle, in the following experiment to find g. A metre ruler is pivoted at one end and held at an angle by a thread fixed to its lower end, the thread being looped over the pivot bar and with a sufficiently heavy pendulum bob tied to the other end. Now burn through or cut the thread. The pendulum bob begins to fall and the ruler begins to swing downwards at the same moment. The position where the ball meets the bar can be used to find g. Finding this position can be made easier by putting a piece of carbon paper over a strip of white paper that is fixed to the ruler.

Theory:
Since the pendulum bob hits the ruler vertically below the pivot, the time taken for the fall will be one quarter of the period of oscillation of the ruler. The period can be found by measuring the time for ten swings of the ruler and then working out the time for one quarter of a swing.

Age range: 16-18
Apparatus required:
•Pivoted metre ruler •Retort stand and clamp •Pendulum bob •Thread •Matches •Stop clock
•Carbon paper •White paper

14. Monkey and hunter

A monkey hangs from a tree in a jungle and is discovered by a hunter who decides to shoot it. Pointing the rifle between the eyes of the monkey he prepares to pull the trigger. The monkey, being fairly intelligent, reasons that if he waits until the moment the bullet leaves the barrel and then drops out of the tree the bullet will pass over his head. The hunter pulls the trigger, the monkey waits until the bullet is leaving the barrel and then lets go. To his dismay the bullet hits him directly between the eyes! He was intelligent but had forgotten his Physics!

The explanation for this can be demonstrated by a classic experiment that shows the constancy of acceleration for falling bodies.

Mount an electromagnet in a clamp about 0.5 m above the bench and mount a blowpipe horizontally in another clamp so that it is pointing just below the core of the electromagnet. Put a marble in the blowpipe, fix a small strip of aluminium foil across the mouth of the blowpipe and then connect up a series circuit with the electromagnet, a d.c. power source and the aluminium strip.

Switch on and hang a tin lid from the electromagnet making sure that the blowpipe is pointing at the centre of the tin. Blow sharply down the pipe and the marble will fly out, breaking the foil, and causing the tin lid to fall. The marble will fall at the same rate as the tin lid and should collide with it before hitting the bench.

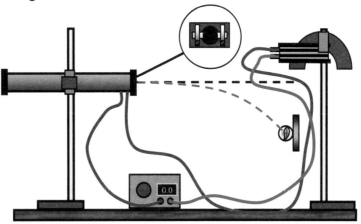

Age range: 14-18
Apparatus required: •Blow pipe •Marble •Electromagnet •Tin lid •Aluminium foil •Power supply •Leads •Two retort stands, bosses and clamps

15. Dropping books and paper - air resistance and drag
This is an interesting experiment on air friction, but it is important to stop between each part and ask the students what happens next?
(a) Drop a sheet of paper - it falls slowly due to air friction
(b) Now crumple it up - its mass is unaltered but the crumpling reduces the air friction and so it falls quicker
(c) Then use another, similar flat sheet of paper, but this time with a book on top of it; the effect of the air friction on the paper is removed
(d) Then a sheet of paper with a book underneath it - they both fall together
(e) And finally a ream of loose paper - all the sheets fall at the same rate.
An alternative to parts (c) and (d) is to use a metal disc with a similar sized paper disc placed either on top of it or below it.

These experiments remove the need for the traditional guinea and feather experiment if you don't have a vacuum pump.

Extension experiments:
(i) Make paper versions of helicopter blades, and investigate their motion when dropped
(ii) Investigate the motion of simple parachutes made in the form of paper cones

Age range: 7-18
Apparatus required: •A stack of loose paper •A book of similar area •Scissors

16. Galileo inclined planes

An interesting effect of the acceleration along inclined planes can be shown by a variation of Galileo's experiment on diluted gravity. Thread a bead onto each of a set of wires starting at one point on a vertical bicycle wheel from which the spokes have been removed and ending at different points along the circumference. When the beads are released from the top they slide down the wires keeping a circular arrangement and all reaching the end of the chord at the same time.

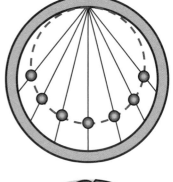

A related problem in gravitation refers to the fact that it takes 42 minutes for objects falling through holes in the Earth to reach the other side whatever chord is used. (This is of course a theoretical and ideal situation and ignores all frictional effects!) It would make an ideal and rapid transport system. You can extend the idea to SHM where the body is free to oscillate about the centre of the Earth. Students often find it difficult to accept that the acceleration is zero at the centre of the "fall".

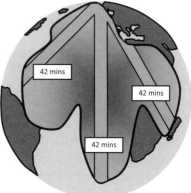

Age range: 16-18
Apparatus required: •Bicycle wheel with spokes removed and wires fitted with beads on them •Beads

17. Guinea and feather tube

This is a classic experiment to show the effect of air resistance and the constancy of the acceleration due to gravity. Take a 1 m long glass tube of diameter about 5 cm, put a small piece of feather and a penny into the tube and fit bungs tightly into both ends - one with a metal tube in the centre. Attach the tube to a vacuum pump. Upend the tube and show that the penny falls faster than the feather because it has much lower air resistance. Now pump out the air and show that they both fall at the same rate.

A video clip of astronauts dropping a falcon feather and a hammer on the Moon illustrates this as well. (It is important to realise that on the Moon there is no air, but there is still a gravitational field, about 1/6 of that at the surface of the Earth.) It is certainly not true to say that no air means no gravity.

Age range: 11- 14
Apparatus required:
•Guinea and feather tube •Vacuum pump •Coin •Feather

 Put some sticky tape around the lower few centimetres of the tube to prevent the tube shattering if the penny hits it too hard! The teacher requires eye protection and the students should view the demonstration from behind a safety screen. The glass tube should be capable of being evacuated and be undamaged.

18. Falling can with hole at one side

The can with holes (see liquid pressure) can be used to demonstrate that if there is no gravitational attraction there will be no liquid pressure. For this experiment use a can with just one hole in one side near the bottom. Fill it with water, cover the hole with your finger and then drop it. Since both can and water fall together there is no net gravitational force and so the water stays in the can.

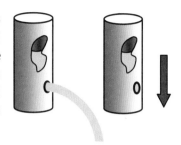

Theory:
Pressure at a point in a liquid = hρg, and since the net value of g is zero for the falling can and water there is no pressure difference between the top and bottom of the water in the can.

Age range: 16-18
Apparatus required: •Tin can with hole near the bottom •Water

19. A floating block in a falling jar

A jar about half full of water has a block of wood (or loaded straw) floating in the water and is suspended from a helical spring. Initially the jar is supported. If the jar is released, the water level stays at the same place in the jar and the block floats at the same level as it falls.

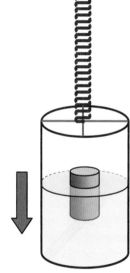

Theory:
The depth at which the block floats depends on its weight and the upthrust on it. The upthrust depends on the weight of water displaced, and so, as the acceleration of the jar and block change, BOTH the weight of the block and the upthrust change in the same way – the block floats at the same depth as it falls.

Objects in accelerated frames of reference behave in the same way as they would in gravitational fields. The falling on the spring is subject to a varying acceleration just like it would be if it were taken to the Moon where the gravitational acceleration is less. This is a very useful demonstration of one of the ideas of General Relativity! (Thanks to MartiN for this idea)

Age range: 11-18 depending on the treatment of the theory
Apparatus required: •Jar •Water •Wooden block •Helical spring

20. Two tennis balls.

Take two tennis balls and inject one with water. (Make sure that it is completely full.) The balls will still look identical and if you drop them they will both fall at the same rate.

Ask the pupils why? They will probably say that they fall at the same rate because they are the same, same size and same weight.

Then ask them to hold the balls to show that although they are of different mass they still accelerate at the same rate in a gravitational field.
(N.B The injected ball will re-seal itself when the needle is withdrawn)

Age range: 11-16   Apparatus required: •Two tennis balls •Water •Syringe

21. Smiley pop ups and projectile motion

In his book 'Experiments in Physics' Colin Siddons (*) suggested using these small 'pop-up' toys to study projectile motion. This is a really good idea and can form the basis of an investigation for students aged 14-18. The toys, called Smiley Pop Ups, are very cheap and introduce a bit of fun into the experiment.

You squash the toy on to the bench and then, as the rubber sucker slowly comes off, the toy launches itself into the air. Since the same spring is used each time the launching force should be the same. This means that both vertical motion and motion at an angle to the vertical can be investigated. For the angled motion use tilted runways or even tilt the lab tables where this is possible. Fixing a pin through a piece of sellotape stuck to the ramp or putting a piece of rough paper on the slope will stop the toys slipping down the slope.

Theory:
The range of an object projected at an angle A to the horizontal can be found as follows.
The object will hit the ground again when h = 0, i.e. when $ut \sin A = \frac{1}{2} gt^2$.
Therefore it will hit the ground after a time t, where $t = 2u \sin A/g$.

Therefore the range R is given by:
R = horizontal velocity x time = $[u\cos A \times 2u \sin A]/g = [u^2 \, 2 \sin A \cos A]/g = u^2 \sin 2A/g$

This range is of course the horizontal range from the point of launch.

Age range: 14-19
Apparatus required: •Smiley pop up (or similar) •Ruler •Ramp •Rough paper or pin •Sellotape

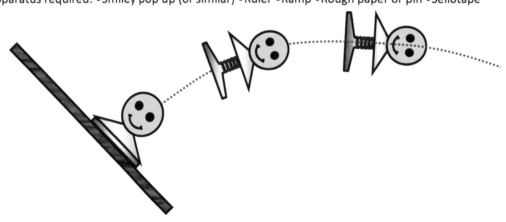

* I am very grateful to the late Colin Siddons. It was his book that helped inspire me to write the present one. I still have the letter that he wrote to me a few months before he died in which he encouraged me to complete the original version of 'The Resourceful Physics Teacher'.

FORCES and NEWTON'S LAWS

General theory for this section
To change the way an object is moving you need a force.

This force can either:
(a) **speed up** the object, like a sprinter at the start of a race
(b) **slow down** the object, like a motorbike slowing down as it approaches a red traffic signal
(c) **change the direction** in which the object is moving, like a car turning a corner

Newton's three laws of motion may be summarised as follows:
1. A body remains at rest or in a state of uniform motion unless acted on by a force. What is still stays still and what is moving stays moving at a steady speed in a straight line unless a force acts on it.
2. The resultant force on a body causes an acceleration which depends on both the size of the force and the mass of the body, i.e. Force = Mass x Acceleration
3. If a force acts on one body an equal and opposite force acts on another body.

1. Newton's Laws
2. Sling shot theory
3. Pushing and Newton's Third Law
4. Newton's Third Law
5. Knees bend on bathroom scales

6. The lift problem
7. Simple experiments with forces
8. Newton meters and a tug of war
9. Linear air track and two pulleys
10. Shopping bag and old lady

1. Newton's Laws
A simple experiment for the verification of Newton's Second Law uses a small trolley which is accelerated along a friction-compensated track by a number of washers tied to a thread which is fixed to the trolley after passing over a pulley. A way of ensuring the constancy of mass when studying Newton's Laws is to transfer the washers from the trolley to the accelerating mass or vice versa. This is a useful tip when plotting graphs of acceleration against force. (The total mass of all objects accelerating is thus kept constant.)

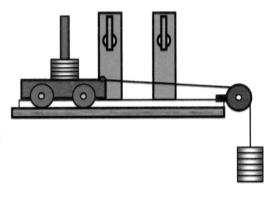

Notice that there is a degree of circularity in this 'proof' as we take the accelerating force as mg which is using the law that we are trying to verify.

Theory:
Equation of motion: Accelerating force (F) = mg = Total mass x acceleration = (M+m)a where m is the mass of the washers accelerating the trolley and M is the total mass of the trolley and all the washers.

Age range: 14-16
Apparatus required: •Trolley •Runway •Bench pulley •Washers •Ruler and stop clock or light gate assembly and timer •Leads

2. Slingshot theory

When a spacecraft approaches a planet that is moving through space the spacecraft experiences a sling shot effect due to the motion of the planet. As the spacecraft approaches the planet the gravitational attraction between them will increase the velocity of the spacecraft so that when it passes the planet it is moving with a greater velocity relative to the planet. Since the planet itself is also moving through space the absolute velocity of the spacecraft is also increased. The mass of the planet is enormous compared with that of the spacecraft and so the effect on the planet's motion is infinitesimal.

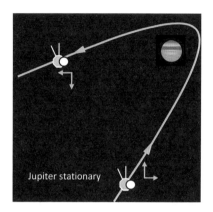 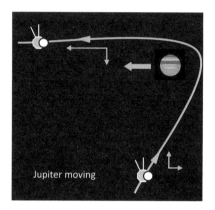

3. Pushing and Newton's Third Law

This is a very simple example of Newton's Third Law. Get two pupils of similar size to stand facing each other. Tell them to raise their hands so that the pairs of hands are touching. Then tell one pupil to push the other over. They will **both** be pushed backwards. This example of Newton's Third Law confirms that when a force acts on one body an equal and opposite force acts on another body. Trying the same thing with both pupils on skateboards may be even more impressive.

Age range: 14-16
Apparatus required: •Two pupils •Maybe two skateboards as well

4. Newton's Third Law

Mount a small bow on a dynamics trolley and fire a rubber tipped arrow from it. As the arrow goes forward the bow and frame accelerate backwards. This is an interesting and useful model with which to demonstrate both Newton's Third Law and the transfer of energy from that stored in the stretched bow string to the kinetic energy of the trolley and the arrow.

Age range: 14-18
Apparatus required: •Dynamics trolley •Toy bow •Rubber tipped arrow

5. Knees bend on bathroom scales

You can observe some very interesting effects by standing on a set of bathroom scales and then watching the reading as you bend your knees. The reading goes down as you bend your knees but increases as you straighten your legs to accelerate yourself upwards to a standing position. An alternative version is to stand on the scales holding a pair of dumbbells in your hands and watch the reading as you raise and lower them.

Age range: 14-18
Apparatus required: •Bathroom scales •Two dumbbells or weights on a bar

6. The lift problem

Make a table to discuss what happens to your mass, weight and reaction when you are in a lift that stays still, moves with constant velocity up or down, accelerates up or down or falls freely. Remember that as long as the gravitational field does not change, your weight does not alter - it is only the reaction of the floor that may change if you accelerate up or down.

Think about people travelling in a lift in a high-rise building. They would like to get to their destination floor as quickly as possible, but there clearly has to be a limit put on the lift's acceleration. Can you find out what this is?

7. Simple experiments with forces

Use the Newton spring balances or Newton scales to find the force in Newtons needed to:

A Open a drawer
B Turn twenty pages of your text book
C Push a drawing pin into a piece of wood
D Pull a small stool across the floor
E Pull a wheeled chair across the room
F Pull some sellotape off its reel
G Throw a shuttlecock
H Turn on a water tap
I Open a pair of scissors
J Open a pencil case
K Pull the top off a ball point pen

L Pull down the board projector screen
M Rip a piece of paper
N Pull apart two pieces of glued paper.
O Open a door (see if you can find one without a door closer fitted)
P Stretch an elastic band
Q Push two repelling magnets together
R Use one magnet to pick up some paper clips – see how far above them you can move the magnet before it cannot pick up a paper clip

(For younger children we need not measure the size of the forces at this stage – just feel them acting.)

8. Newton meters and a tug of war

This example shows some misconceptions about the sizes of forces.

Set up the two sets of apparatus as shown in the diagrams and ask the students what they think will be the readings on the Newton meters.

The point is that they are all the same and read W – the weight of ONE of the masses. (You need a lightweight Newton meter so that it does not affect the result significantly.)

Age range: 14-19
Apparatus required: •Three bench pulleys •Three Newton meters •Three masses of about 1kg each •String or cord •Mounting point on a wall

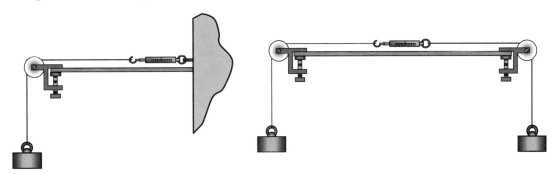

9. Linear air track and two pulleys

The effect of two unbalanced forces is very well demonstrated by having a trolley attached to two masses each hanging over the opposite ends of a linear air track. The resulting acceleration due to the resultant force can therefore be found. (To avoid the air hose, pass one thread over a pulley on an adjacent bench.)

A simplified version is to use two dissimilar masses (M and m) hanging by a thread over two pulleys fixed to retort stands with a central mass held in mid air. If this mass is not too great the string will be more or less horizontal and the applied forces will then be horizontal also.

Theory:
The resultant accelerating force (F) is given by the equation:
Accelerating force $F = Mg - mg = (M+m)a$

Age range: 16-18
Apparatus required: •Linear air track •Blower and trolley •Two pulleys •Two retort stands •Two sets of slotted masses

10. Shopping bag and old lady - acceleration

Why is it that you can lift a shopping bag full of shopping slowly without a problem but if you lift it quickly the handles break? Think about what would happen if the lady in the diagram picked up her shopping bag quickly. The handles might break because they have to produce an acceleration as well as support the weight of the bag. This can easily be demonstrated by putting a heavy weight inside a plastic shopping bag and showing that it will just support the load, but that it breaks - usually at the bottom - when accelerated briskly upwards.

Another example of this is the maximum acceleration allowed by a pilot of a rescue helicopter when lifting a stretcher from a hillside. Too great an acceleration will cause the supporting ropes to break.

Theory:
Force in handles = Weight of shopping + Force to accelerate the bag upwards. ($F = mg + ma$)

Age range: 16-18   Apparatus required: •Two 5 kg masses •Plastic shopping bag

Forces, mass and weight
The size of a force is measured in units called NEWTONS (N). You can get a rough idea of a force's size by thinking about the pull of the Earth on us.

Mass
This is the amount of stuff (matter) in an object. It is measured in kilograms (kg) and is always the same wherever the object is. The only way to change the mass of something is to chip a bit off! (Ignoring relativistic effects of course.)

Weight
The force of attraction of the Earth on us is our WEIGHT. The more massive we are the bigger is the force of attraction and the bigger is our weight. This also gives us a rough definition of the Newton.

A Newton is the pull of the Earth on about 100 g. The pull of the Earth on 1 kg is about 10 N.

WORK, ENERGY AND POWER

General theory for this section:
Work done = energy changed from one form to another = Force x displacement
Power = Energy transformed/Time taken

1. Cars and carpet
2. Crumple zones

3. Train sheets
4. Power of a pupil running upstairs

1. Cars and carpet

This experiment may be used to measure the braking force of a toy car by allowing it to run down a hardboard ramp on to a piece of carpet. Measure the stopping distance (d) and hence find the braking force. This can be done by either measuring the loss of potential energy as it runs down the ramp and on to the carpet or finding the loss of kinetic energy by measuring its speed with a light gate as it reaches the carpet.

I found braking forces of around 0.05N with the cars that I used. Compare this experiment with the use of escape lanes filled with gravel at the sides of steep hills.

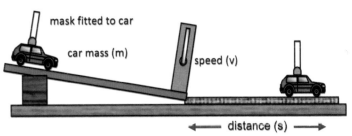

Theory:
For a car of mass m travelling down a ramp from a height h and reaching a speed v at the bottom:
Loss of kinetic energy as it brakes to a stop on the carpet = Braking force (F) x Braking distance (d)
Potential energy lost in travelling down the ramp = mgh
If we assume that this is all converted to kinetic energy then mgh = Fd
However, if we use the second method we can allow for energy lost on the ramp.
Loss of kinetic energy (measured directly with a light gate) = $\frac{1}{2} mv^2$ = Fd
A graph of velocity squared against braking distance shows the dependence of kinetic energy on v^2 and not simply v.

Age range: 11-14
Apparatus required: •Toy car •Piece of carpet (not too rough and about 0.5 m long) •Hardboard ramp (about 0.4 m long) •Ruler

2. Crumple zones

Place the block under a cardboard tube with a gap slightly longer than the length of the cylinder and crumple zone. The crumble zone under test is fitted to the lower end of the cylinder. Drop the metal cylinder down the tube on to the block. When the crumple zone hits the concrete block it will deform and the amount (length) of deformation can be measured. Test the deformation with different crumple zones, all of which should be of the same initial length.

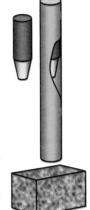

Theory: The speed (v) at which the cylinder (crumple zone) hits the floor (a solid block) can be found from $v = (2gh)^{1/2}$ where h is the high fallen and g is the acceleration due to gravity (10 m/s^2).

Age range: 14-16
Apparatus required: •Heavy concrete block •Cardboard tube about 1.5m long• Metal cylinder with a diameter just less than that of the tube •Metre ruler •Various 'crumple' zones

3. Train sheets

This is a set of sheets devised to teach the topics of work, force and energy. It introduces the idea of the energy stored in a spring, the resistive forces opposing motion and the resulting stopping distances. We have three trains with one, two and three units of stored energy and these are run on three different surfaces having one, two and three units of frictional resistance. If the train with one unit of stored energy travels 30 m on a surface with one unit of resistive force before stopping, then the pupils are asked to work out how far all the trains would travel on all the surfaces.

The end result is hopefully an understanding of the formula:

Work done = Energy transferred = Resistive Force (F) x Distance travelled (d).

Having a clockwork train for an actual demonstration helps!

Age range: 11-13
Apparatus required: •Train sheets sample (Thanks to Pete and Phil for the idea)

Energy	Force (F)	Distance travelled (d)	Force x Distance
1	1	30	30
2	1	60	60
3	1	90	90
1	2	15	30
1	3	10	30

4. Power of a pupil running upstairs

(a) This is a simple experiment to measure a pupil's power - they carry their own mass (themselves) up a known height. The pupils run up a flight of stairs of known height and measure the time that they take to do it. They then measure their own weight and so calculate the work done and the power that they developed. Carrying a rucksack loaded with books will increase their weight.

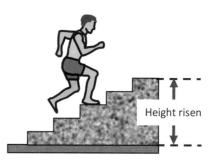
Height risen

(b) The power of their arms can be found by lifting a weight such as a bucket of sand.

Experiment (a): Only allow one pupil at a time to run up the stairs. Sensible footwear should be worn. Discourage over competitiveness which can lead to falls and injuries. Any student excused from P.E lesson is unlikely to be able to take part.

Experiment (b): No pupil should lift a weight higher than their own shoulders. Warn of back damage here.

Age range: 13-16
Apparatus required: •Bathroom scales •Flight of stairs •Stop watch •Measuring tape or ruler
•Heavy mass such as a bucket of sand

MOMENTUM, COLLISIONS & EXPLOSIONS

General theory for this section:

Momentum = mass x velocity

Momentum is conserved in all collisions whether they are elastic or not.

e.g. $m_1u_1 + m_2u_2 = m_1v_1 + m_2v_2$

If an impulse (Force x time) is given to an object the object suffers a change of momentum e.g.

$Ft = mv - mu$

1. Elastic collisions
2. Newton's cradle
3. Snooker and Newton's cradle
4. Momentum in collisions
5. Momentum and snooker/football game
6. Colliding power balls
7. Pendulum on a trolley
8. Smacking hands
9. Kicking a football
10. Toy gun on linear air track
11. The air rifle and momentum
12. Helicopter details
13. Momentum with suspended ball
14. Stopping an escalator
15. Crumpling zones in cars
16. Collisions with marbles
17. Sand falling on to a top pan balance
18. Collisions
19. Momentum in catching
20. Throwing and jumping - momentum
21. Angular momentum and the rotating table
22. Speed of a cricket ball
23. Force in a take-off or a bounce
24. Eggs and a sheet
25. Throwing nothing
26. Contracting rubber band

1. Elastic collisions

In an elastic collision no kinetic energy is lost, and this is very difficult to show in practice since elimination of friction is a problem. The ideal case can be approached by using two bar magnets. One magnet should be mounted horizontally in a block or held in a clamp. The second magnet is then suspended on four threads so that it is restricted to swing in one vertical plane and hangs with one pole facing the similar pole of the fixed magnet. It is then pulled out and released. It swings in towards the fixed magnet, is repelled and so swings back and forward and keeps going for ages. It is worth referring to the collisions between gas molecules in kinetic theory as being virtually perfect elastic collisions.

Age range: 15-18
Apparatus required:
•Two strong bar magnets •Thread •Wooden retort stand with two clamps and bosses

2. Newton's cradle

A beautiful example of collisions - try pulling out a different number of balls each time and letting them swing back inwards. You will find that however many balls you pull back, up to four out of five, the same number will always swing out at the opposite end. Pulling one ball out from each end will give a ball bouncing in and out at either end.

Theory:
At collision the impact is very nearly elastic and the momentum and energy of the swinging ball are transferred to the adjacent ball. This process is repeated along the line until the free ball at the end swings away.

Age range: 13-18   Apparatus required: •Newton's cradle •TV camera and video if possible

3. Snooker and Newton's cradle

A simple way of explaining Newton's cradle is to use snooker balls. Extend from just the two ball example where one ball stops and the other moves off (see experiment 5) to more and more balls. Each time it is only the end one that moves off (allowing for spin and friction, of course).

Age range: 15-18   Apparatus required: •Snooker balls •Snooker table if possible

4. Momentum in elastic and inelastic collisions

Set up a block on the bench and hang a power ball from a thread so that it just touches the block. Pull it up and allow it to swing back. The rebound involves a direction change and hence a large change of momentum. This means a large force and so the block topples. Repeat with a ball of soft plasticine loaded to give the same mass. The block stays upright. This time the change of momentum is only half that of the rebounding ball.

Theory
Change of momentum = Ft, and so if the momentum change is large (for a given stopping time) the force is also large.

Age range: 14 – 18   Apparatus required: •Power ball •Wooden block •Plasticine •Thread •Retort stand

5. Momentum and snooker/football game

Use a snooker or billiards table to demonstrate momentum conservation. You don't need a real snooker table for this - just the balls and some simple form of cue on the lab bench. In some ways the sliding of the balls on the smooth bench surface may improve the result. Show that if a stationary ball is hit by a moving ball the first one moves off while the second one comes to rest. Also measure the angle between directions of travel of the two balls after an oblique collision - it really does come out to be about 90° with balls of equal mass. This should be related to the collision between particles of equal mass in nuclear interactions. Mention the problem of spin. It works reasonably well if you undercut the strokes.
Trick shots: it is possible to pot the last of a line of balls as long as the last two are set up in line with the pocket.

Age range: 16-18
Apparatus required: •Snooker balls and snooker table if possible

6. Colliding power balls - dropped on top of each other

This can be bought as a demonstration experiment but simply using two power balls, one large and one small, will do. Hold the balls above the ground with the small one resting on top of the large one. Now drop them so that they fall and hit the ground. The small one on top will leap off. It's even better with more balls. A needle in the lower ball with a thread through a hole in the top ball keeps the whole thing vertical. (Assume they both hit the ground at speed u.)

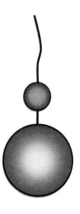

I think I was told that twelve balls stacked on top of each other would theoretically put the top one into orbit, indeed escape from the solar system! This is not only a good example of momentum conservation but also of the distribution of energy in explosions.

Theory:

In a collision or explosion the momentum before collision or explosion = the momentum after collision or explosion.

So, as the large ball rebounds from the ground at velocity u the small ball hits it at relative velocity u+u. If the collision is perfectly elastic it rebounds with relative velocity u+u, but since the large ball is moving upward with a velocity u the actual vertical velocity of the small ball is u+2u = 3u. The height (h) reached is given by $h = 9u^2/g$. (Assume that the mass of the large ball is much greater than that of the small one.)

Age range: 14-18   Apparatus required: •Two power balls - one large and one small •Thread •Needle

7. Pendulum on a trolley - momentum conservation

Hang a pendulum on a dynamics trolley or on the rider of a linear air track and observe its motion as the trolley moves along.

Age range: 16-18
Apparatus required: •Linear air track •Pendulum

8. Smacking hands

This is a simple but good example of Newton's Third Law - when a force acts on a body an equal and opposite force acts on another body. I suggest that you ask a pair of pupils to do this. I once received a nasty blow by asking one of the girls to smack my hand - it really stung. Get one of them to put their hand out and hold it still while the other one smacks them. This is going to hurt me more than it hurts you! You can extend the idea further by asking the pupils what it would be like to punch the wall. The force on your knuckles would be the same as that on the wall but the resulting effects and damage would be quite different!

Age range: 11-15   Apparatus required: •Two pupils and their hands!

9. Kicking a football

This classic experiment is used to measure the momentum change of the football and hence the force used to kick it. A piece of aluminium foil is taped to the football and another piece is fixed to the shoe of the kicker. The foil on the foot is connected by a long lead to one of the start terminals of a scaler, while the other terminal is connected by another long lead to the foil on the ball. The ball is placed on the edge of the bench at a known height above the ground and kicked off horizontally, the scaler recording the time for which the foot was in contact with the ball and the connecting wires breaking as the ball moves off. The horizontal distance travelled is measured together with the time taken to hit the ground, and from this the horizontal speed of the ball is found.

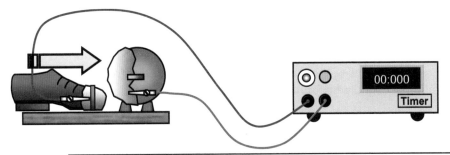

 If you are unhappy about a pupil standing on the table get one of them to hold the boot in their hand and use it to propel the ball. It also gives better control.

From the values of mass (m), velocity (v) and time (t) the force used to kick the ball can be found. I have tried it outside with a hockey ball. This works fine if the wires are allowed to separate after the ball has moved a short distance and somebody hangs on to the scaler!

Theory:

Horizontally: $s = uT$ and $Ft = mu$ Vertically: $h = 1/2(gT^2)$ where t is the time of contact between the foot and the ball and T is the time taken for the ball to reach the ground having fallen a height h and travelled horizontal distance s.

Age range: 14-18
Apparatus required: •Football •Scaler •Crocodile clips •Long leads •Aluminium foil •Tape •10m measuring tape

10. Toy gun on linear air track

The recoil of a rifle can be demonstrated by using a toy gun firing a table tennis ball fitted to a trolley on a linear air track. The toy gun moves in one direction while the table tennis ball moves in the other.

Age range: 14-18
Apparatus required: •Linear air track •Toy gun •Trolley on the air track •Table tennis balls

11. The air rifle and momentum

The rifle should be clamped to a baseboard and to the bench and means of catching the pellet should be found – a box of polystyrene backed with a wooden board is suitable for this. This experiment must only be done in a laboratory by the teacher. Use a safety screen to shield the class from possible ricochets. All present should wear eye protection and be behind the gun when it is fired. A teacher unfamiliar with this procedure should receive training before demonstrating it to a class.

(a) Fix two timing gates - simply a plastic frame with a strip of aluminium foil across the centre - a metre apart and connected to a scaler. Fire an air rifle pellet through the two gates so that it starts the timer when the first strip of aluminium foil is broken, and stops it when the second is broken. The time for the pellet to travel the one metre between the two pieces of foil is given directly and the speed of the bullet can easily be worked out.

(b) Using the same mounted air rifle, fire a pellet into a block of plasticine mounted on a model railway truck on rails. The runway should be tilted to compensate for friction and the speed of the truck (V) after impact should be found by timing its first 20 cm of movement.

Theory:
Knowing the mass of a pellet (m) and the mass of the truck and plasticine (M) the speed of the pellet can be found (mv + MV = 0)

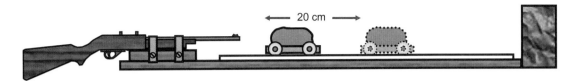

Age range: 14-18
Apparatus required: •Mounted air rifle •Truck loaded with plasticine •Scaler •Ruler •Stopwatch

12. Helicopter details

Use the actual details of a Lynx helicopter to consider momentum transfer. (Mass = 4500 kg, rotor diameter 12.8 m). Force = mg = $\rho A v^2$ where ρ is the density of air, A is the area swept out by the rotors and v is the downward speed of the air. Other examples in this topic are fire hoses, moving walkways and the water from a propeller in a boat.

13. Momentum with suspended ball

Place one ball bearing on the edge of the bench. Suspend a second one from a thread so that when it is allowed to swing it collides with the first one, knocking it off. The masses of the two ball bearings can be varied as can the height from which the second one swings. Use the horizontal distance travelled by the second ball bearing to calculate its velocity after impact and the heights of swing of the first to find its velocity before and after impact.

Theory:
If the first ball (mass m_1) falls a vertical distance h and has a horizontal velocity u_1 just before it hits the second ball and u_2 after collision, then $\frac{1}{2} m u_1^2 = mgh$. If the second ball (mass m_2) acquires a horizontal velocity V then $m_1 u_1 = m_1 u_2 + m_2 V$

Age range: 16-18
Apparatus required: •Two ball bearings •Thread •Retort stand •Ruler or measuring tape

14. Stopping an escalator

I was walking down a moving escalator outside the Pompidou centre in Paris when a little boy hit the stop button. The next step, which I had assumed would be moving away, was then dead still and I received a severe shock to my back! This painful story is a good example of why you should always bend your knees on landing after any sort of jump and why you cannot make a jump without bending your knees first - time is needed to give you the required impulse (Ft). For a given change of momentum a small stopping time (like on the escalator) means a large force.

15. Crumple zones in cars

A useful if rather unpleasant example of the energy and momentum conservation laws. The photograph is of our car! The bodywork crumples, absorbing kinetic energy and increasing both the stopping time and the stopping distance, and so reducing the forces involved. The passenger compartment was undamaged.

16. Collisions with marbles
Use marbles to investigate collisions. Give each pupil three, and ask them to investigate what happens when they are rolled together.

Age range: 11-13   Apparatus: •Marbles

17. Sand falling on to a top pan balance
The effect of the collision of a large number of particles such as gas molecules exerting a pressure or rain falling on to a roof can be simulated by using sand and a top pan balance. Put a plastic beaker on a top pan balance and pour a steady stream of sand into it from a known height. Record the reading of the balance while the sand is falling and also when no sand falls. Repeat the experiment with water falling into a beaker - both of these should show the effects of momentum change. Relate to the force and pressure on a roof in heavy rain (both flat and pitched).

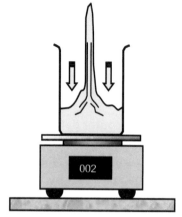

Theory
Force on balance due to stationary sand = mg
Force on the balance due to a mass of sand m' that falls on to it every second with a velocity v and is brought to rest = m'v

Age range: 16-18   Apparatus required: •Sand •Plastic beaker •Top pan balance

18. Collisions
The relative masses of the particles involved in a collision or explosion has an important bearing on what happens. Let's think of some elastic collisions.
(a) If you throw a table tennis ball at a stationary train the train hardly moves and the ball will rebound with its velocity relative to the train reversed
(b) If the train is moving, the train will move on with hardly any change to its velocity while the ball's velocity relative to the train will be reversed
(c) If one ball hits a stationary ball of the same mass (as in snooker) the first ball comes to rest while the second moves off with the original velocity of the first
(d) If one ball hits a stationary ball of rather greater mass (say ten times) the first ball will lose some of its kinetic energy, this energy being gained by the second ball
This has an important bearing on the choice of moderator for a nuclear reactor. The neutrons must be slowed down by a moderator and those chosen have nuclei which are just a few times heavier than the neutrons themselves - such as deuterium or carbon.

19. Momentum in catching
This simple demonstration emphasises the vector nature of momentum. Use a ball (soccer or netball) and throw it to a pupil. Get them first to catch it and throw it back and then to punch it backwards without catching it first. Ask them which require the biggest force - catching or punching it back. It should be clear that it is the latter, and that this gives the biggest change of momentum. This demonstration hopefully emphasises the velocity change from u to −u, and so a greater change of momentum than simply stopping the ball.

Theory:
Momentum change = mu - (-mu) = 2mu when punched back and momentum change = mu when caught
Age range: 14-16   Apparatus required: •Netball or football

20. Throwing and jumping - momentum/inertia

Give various examples of the importance of impulse when considering the time taken in kicking and catching. The longer the time during which the force can be applied, the further you can throw something, and the longer it takes you to bring the object to rest when you catch it by bringing back your hands, the smaller the force needed. The effect of the forces involved in cars crumpling in collisions should also be considered. Notice how long jumpers and high jumpers "sink" on their last stride before take-off to give time to apply an upward force.

In racket sports the same ideas apply. Also in cricket the ball can be hit further by maintaining contact between the ball and the bat by "playing down the line" of the ball

21. Angular momentum and the rotating table

(a) Get someone to stand on a rotatable table placed on the floor holding a 1 kg sandbag. Ask them to throw the sandbag to you very carefully, starting with their arm held out to the side of their body. As the mass moves forwards they will move backwards, showing the vector nature of momentum.

(b) Stand a pupil on the table with their arms outstretched and push one of their arms gently so that the table and pupil spin slowly. Then ask them to bring their arms inwards. As they do so their rate of spin increases - the distribution of mass has changed and to maintain their angular momentum their spin rate must go up.

Age range: 13-16   Apparatus required: •Rotating table •1 kg mass

22. Speed of a cricket ball

The speed of a cricket ball can be found using a variation of the rifle bullet experiment and it's much safer!

Fill a cardboard box with loosely crumpled newspaper or bubble wrap. Measure the mass of the box and its contents (M) and also that of a cricket ball (m). Put the box on a smooth flat floor and throw the ball horizontally into the box.

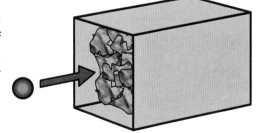

Measure the time that the box takes to recoil along the floor and the distance travelled before it comes to rest. From the distance and time work out the average speed of the box. Doubling this value will give you the speed (V) of the box and ball immediately after the ball hits it (assuming uniform deceleration on the floor).

Using the law of conservation of momentum, the speed (v) of the cricket ball before impact can be found.

Theory: $mv = (M+m)V$

Age range: 14-19
Apparatus required: •Cricket ball •Rounders ball •Baseball or hockey ball •Cardboard box •Newspaper or bubble wrap

23. Force in a long jump take off or when a ball bounces

In experiment 20 it was suggested that estimates could be made of forces involved in jumping. This can be done by fixing contacts to the jumper's feet and to the ground. Using this method try to estimate the large forces generated as the jumper "sinks" on the last stride. There is a very useful CD ROM called Multimedia Motion which enables measurements such as the time of contact between the foot and the ground to be taken from video clips. An alternative experiment is to find the force experienced by a ball when it bounces. This can be done by fixing a piece of aluminium foil to a ball and dropping it on to another piece so that it completes the circuit to a stop clock or scaler. Knowing the height from which it was dropped enables you to find the impact speed and so the momentum change and hence the force.

The contact area can be found by placing sand paper under a piece of aluminium foil so that when the ball is dropped on it an imprint is made in the foil.

Theory:
Force = change of momentum/time of contact = (mv-mu)/t

Age range: 14-18
Apparatus required: •CD ROM "Multimedia Motion" with computer

24. Eggs and a sheet

The idea of a reduced force when the stopping time and stopping distance are large can be shown by throwing raw eggs at a sheet. Some pupils hold an ordinary bed sheet vertically, and then the teacher throws an egg at the sheet. The sheet will give a little and the egg will not break (until it rolls down and hits the ground). The 'long' stopping time as the egg hits the sheet gives a small retarding force.

 Do not throw the egg too fast, and be careful not to hit the pupils. They will not 'give' as much as the sheet, and so the stopping force will be large!

Age range: 14 – 19   Apparatus required: •Sheet •Eggs (raw)

25. Throwing nothing

This seemingly odd title describes what could be a rather risky experiment, so do take care if you try it – don't be too enthusiastic or you may hurt yourself.

First of all get a heavy ball, go outside and throw it. It may be quite hard to throw it far, but your arm should feel fine. A large amount of the momentum of your arm is transferred to the ball and so the ball moves off at relatively high speed whereas your arm is left with a small amount of momentum so that it can easily be brought to rest by your arm muscles.

Now do it again but this time without the ball! You would think that this is easy but it is this part of the experiment that could damage your muscles. Your arm has no ball to which to transfer the momentum and so the arm muscles have to work much harder to bring it to rest in the same distance.

26. Contracting rubber band

This apparently simple experiment is both fascinating and thought provoking.

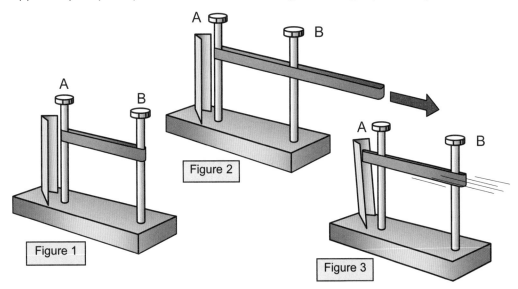

Figure 1

Figure 2

Figure 3

Set up the apparatus as shown in Figure 1 with the rubber band stretched around the two nails and the piece of light card standing in front of nail A. The band should be under tension but not too tight.

Now pull the band back from nail B (Figure 2). I have found that increasing the length of the band to almost double its length in Figure 1 works well.

Now release the band (Figure 3) while holding the wooden block in place with the other hand (Alternatively clamp the block to the bench although I have not found this necessary.)

You may not expect the result. The rubber band comes forward from nail A and the card is knocked over or even shot forwards.

Two things need to be considered. Firstly, it takes a finite, but short time before the front end of the band 'knows' that the rear end has been released. Secondly, the centre of mass of the band moves forwards and so the whole band moves forwards. The speed at which the centre of mass moves is partly dependent on the speed with which the band can contract.

A series of high speed photographs was taken of the experiment and this showed that the front end of the band only started to move forwards when the back end had collided with the rear nail.

Age range: 16-18
Apparatus required: •Two large nails hammered into a wooden block as shown •Rubber band
•Piece of card

FRICTION AND INERTIA

FRICTION

1. Glass fibre.
2. Styrocell beads
3. Polystyrene ball falling in a tube
4. Lowering friction with magnets
5. Stick-slip motion
6. Two simple hovercraft

7. Falling matchbox
8. Escalado
9. Rolling dog food and baked bean cans
10. Friction between books
11. Friction and sliding cups

1. Glass fibre
Many years ago I did a piece of research into the strength of glass fibre laminates. The problem was to measure how much friction there was between the glass fibres and the laminate itself. This could be found by measuring the friction as a piece of fibre was pulled over a section of laminate mounted on a rod. The amount of twist gave a measure of the frictional force.

2. Styrocell beads
Friction - or the lack of it - can be demonstrated when a crystallising dish is slid along over some styrocell beads that have been poured into a tray. These beads are hard plastic spheres about a millimetre in diameter and so act like ball bearings. Spinning the dish makes a good demonstration and the whole experiment can be done in the base of a small ripple tank placed on an overhead projector to make it easily visible to the whole class.

 | **Do not let the pupils take any of the beads away – they are dangerous if spread on the floor.**

Age range: 14-18   Apparatus required: •Styrocell beads •Ripple tank •Tray •Glass beaker

3. Polystyrene ball falling in a tube
Set up a vertical tube and drop a polystyrene ball into it. The diameter of the ball should be just a little smaller than the diameter of the tube. The ball falls really slowly due to air friction in the tube and it may be possible to get it to reach a terminal velocity where Weight = Drag!

Age range: 14-18
Apparatus required: •Large diameter glass tube up to two metres long •Polystyrene balls of various diameters up to almost that of the internal diameter of the glass tube •Stop clock •Ruler

4. Lowering friction with magnets
Take a bar magnet and mount it in a clamp with the poles vertically above each other. Take one or two clean ball bearings and attach them to the magnet so that they hang in a line from the lower end.   Then attach a steel disc about 3 cm in diameter to the lower ball bearing. It should just be held on but not too tightly - if the attraction is too strong add another ball bearing. Blow on the side of the disc to set it rotating. Adjusting the number and size of the ball bearings and the mass of the disc will give a situation where the disc is only just supported and the friction between it and the lower ball bearing is then very low. An old account of this experiment suggests that the disc could be made to rotate for over fifteen minutes.

Age range: 11-13
Apparatus required: •Retort stand and clamp •Two or three ball bearings (diameter about 0.8 mm depending on magnet strength) •Strong bar magnet •Steel disc

5. Stick-slip motion

The stick-slip motion in friction is beautifully illustrated by the sliding woodpecker. This is a small wooden bird fixed to a bead by a short spring. The bead fits loosely over a vertical metal rod. When the bird is still it does not slide down but as soon as it is twanged it slips jerkily down the rod.

Theory/Explanation:
The hole in the wooden bead is slightly bigger than the diameter of the metal rod. When the hole is vertical the bead slips down but as soon as it tilts, the bead "grips" the rod. The oscillatory motion of the bird on the spring alternately puts the hole upright and at an angle.

Age range: 11-14
Apparatus required: •Woodpecker toy (available from toy suppliers in England)

6. Two simple hovercraft

(a) Balloon hovercraft
Drill a hole through the centre of a circular disc of hardboard (disc diameter about 10 cm). Stick a rubber bung over the centre of the disc so that the hole in the bung coincides with the hole in the disc. Blow up a balloon and then fit it over the open end of the bung. Air rushes through the hole, and out the other side of the disc and this acts like a small hovercraft.
(b) Tile hovercraft
A simple hovercraft can be made really cheaply by using a computer-cooling fan fixed above a hole in a ceiling tile.

Age range: 11-13
Apparatus required: •Balloon •Hardboard disc with a hole and tube •Ceiling tile •Computer cooling fan

7. Falling matchbox

This fascinating short experiment shows you how energy is absorbed by friction. Take a match box – a big one is more impressive and you can leave the matches in it.

Making sure that the box is closed (Photo 1), drop in on to a hard surface from a height of about 10cm. The matchbox will bounce and fall over.

Now pull the drawer out slightly (Photo 2) and repeat the experiment. Once again the matchbox hits the table, but this time the drawer slides in a bit, absorbing some of the energy, and the matchbox should stay upright rather than bouncing.

1   2

Age range: 14-18
Apparatus required: •Hard surface
•Matchbox full of matches

8. Escalado

There was a superb horse racing game called Escalado which worked on the stick-slip principle. The horses were lead and stood on a cloth track, one end of which was securely fixed to the table by a spring while the other was attached to a rod and ratchet. As the ratchet was turned by a handle the track was pulled forward slowly and then released - the spring pulling it back rapidly – but the horses stayed where they were due to inertia. As a result they moved along the track at every rotation.

Age range: 11-18   Apparatus required: •Escalado horse racing game

9. Rolling cans of dog food and baked beans

Get two cans of equal mass – one containing dog food (or cat food for cat lovers) and the other containing baked beans.

Hold them side-by-side at the top of a ramp and then let them go at the same time asking the class which one will reach the bottom of the slope first.

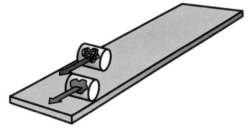

The can of dog food gets there first because the baked beans are moving within the other can, creating frictional forces which slow down the rate of rotation of that can and so making it roll slower.

Then try two cans of fizzy drink but shake one first. See which one wins in this case.

Age range: 11-18 depending on treatment
Apparatus required: •Wooden ramp about 1.5 m long •Tins of dog food, baked beans and two of fizzy drink

10. Friction between books

A very simple and yet impressive example of friction can be seen using two paper-backed books. It is best done with ones made from rougher poor quality paper.

Hold the books with their open sides facing each other and carefully interleave the pages so that about half of one book extends into half the other as shown by the diagram.

Then get two people to hold the books by their spines and try and pull them apart. There is so much friction between the pages that it is likely that the books will be damaged before they can be pulled apart – so be careful!

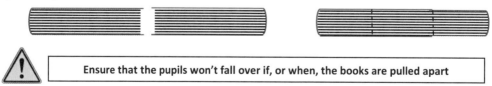

⚠️ **Ensure that the pupils won't fall over if, or when, the books are pulled apart**

Age range: 5-14
Apparatus required: •Two paper-backed books

11. Friction and sliding cups

The aim of this experiment is to give you an idea of the friction needed to slow things down.

Take a small plastic pot and put some weights in it. Gently slide it across the floor of your classroom.

Measure how far it has gone from where you let it go to where it stopped. Change the weights in the pot and try the experiment again.

Some of you may have watched the curling in the Winter Olympics – the stones they use behave in the same way as your pots on the floor.

Age range: 7-11   Apparatus required: •Tape measure •Plastic cups •Masses

INERTIA

General background information for this section:

The inertia of an object can be described as its reluctance to change the way it is moving. Bodies with high inertia (large mass) are difficult to move and stop. The Apollo astronauts found their own inertia a problem when walking on the Moon. The lower gravitational pull meant lower friction between their feet and the ground, so it was more difficult for them to overcome their inertia and stop. Heavy objects "floating" In orbiting spacecraft are similarly difficult to control.

1. Inertia – large mass and two threads
2. Helium-filled balloon
3. Inertia - car, tea set and blocks
4. Coin/card and beaker
5. Inertia and the linear air track

6. Wig wag – or the inertia balance
7. Water on an umbrella
8. Inertia of a rod
9. The bicycle wheel gyroscope
10. Inertia powered car

1. Inertia- large mass and two threads

Tape two 1 kg masses together and suspend them from a rigid support such as a beam using a piece of cotton. Then tie a second piece of cotton to the bottom mass. A sharp pull will break the lower piece of cotton while a gradual pull will break the top one. This demonstrates the effect of the inertia of the masses.

Theory:

When the bottom thread is pulled gently the tension in it is T while that in the top thread is T+Mg where M is the total mass of the two 1 kg masses. As the pull is gradually increased clearly the top piece of cotton will reach its breaking stress first. However, if the lower thread is jerked sharply the inertia of the masses prevents them moving before the cotton breaks.

$Ft = Mu$ and if t is small then F is large.

Age range: 14-18
Apparatus required: •Two 1 kg masses •Tape •Rigid support such as a beam
•Weak cotton - strong enough to support 2 kg but not much more!

2. Helium-filled balloon

Get a helium filled-balloon of the kind used for parties. Tie it to a 1 kg mass on the back seat of your car and then drive around.

Get a friend to go with you to observe the direction of motion of the balloon as you accelerate, brake and corner. It will move in the direction opposite to what you expect. This is a really fascinating demonstration which could be videoed for class use. Get your pupils to try and explain why it moves the way it does!

Maybe take one on a school trip in a coach or get the pupils to try it for themselves.

Age range: 11-18   Apparatus required: •Helium-filled balloon

3. Inertia - car, tea set and blocks

Another two simple demonstrations of inertia.

(a) Get an inertia-powered car running and then place it on a thin piece of cardboard that is lying on some styrocell beads. The car hardly moves while the card is moved backwards rapidly. An example of Newton's Second and Third Laws.

(b) Place a silk scarf on the bench and arrange a toy tea set on it. It is more impressive if some of the cups are full of water. Now pull the scarf out from underneath. The tea set should remain where it is. Trying it with light plastic toy cups and then with real ones demonstrates the effect of mass on inertia. Light ones have much less inertia and therefore move much more easily.

(c) Put a stack of three wooden blocks on the bench, one on top of the other. Give one of the middle blocks a sharp blow with a hammer. It should move out, allowing the upper block to drop vertically onto the lower one. It does not moving horizontally much because of its inertia.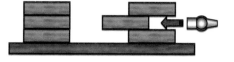

(d) Use a stack of four light plastic waste bins with plastic trays in between them, the lower one standing on a silk cloth. Pull out the cloth without the pile falling over.

Age range: 11-13
Apparatus required: •Inertia-powered car •Card •Styrocell beads •Plastic tea set •China cup •Milk bottle

4. Coin/card and beaker

This is a simple demonstration of inertia. A card with a coin on it is put on the top of a beaker. If you flick the card off sharply the coin falls into the beaker. The inertia of the coin makes it reluctant to move and the frictional forces between the coin and the card are too small to get it moving horizontally before it falls into the beaker.

Age range: 11-14   Apparatus required: •Coin •Card •Beaker

5. Inertia and the linear air track

An interesting extension to experiment three is to use a linear air track mounted on wheels! I use two old dynamics trolleys. Use a reasonably heavy rider (say 400 g) and a two-metre long linear air track. Put the rider on the track, turn up the air supply so that it floats and then pull the track itself – I use a weight hanging over a pulley. The inertia of the rider and the very low friction between it and the track will keep it motionless while the track moves under it! Make sure that you stop the air track before it falls off the bench, and have somebody to control the air hose!

Age range: 13 – 18
Apparatus required: •Linear air track •Rider •Pulley •Two small wheeled trolleys such as dynamics trolleys •Air supply •Thread •Mass

6. Wig wag – or the inertia balance

This is a classic experiment to compare the inertia of different masses. The apparatus is shown in the diagram. The tray fixed to two whippy metal strips is clamped to the bench and then displaced and allowed to oscillate - the frequency of oscillation can then be found.

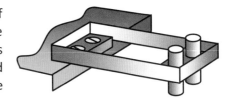

A 1 kg mass is now placed in one of the holes and the resulting frequency found. The procedure is repeated for up to three masses.

As you would expect, the frequency goes down as the mass is increased - but is this due to the weight of the masses or their mass? An effective way of showing this is to repeat the experiment with one of the masses, but suspend it by a thread so that it is hanging in the hole rather than resting on the base of the tray.

You should find that the oscillation period is unaltered, showing that it is the mass that governs the vibration rate and not the weight. In other words the frequency would be the same in an orbiting spacecraft or on the surface of the Moon as it was on the Earth. This makes it very useful as a timing device for astronauts.

Age range: 14-18
Apparatus required: •Wig wag and cylinders •G clamp •Stop clock •Retort stand •Thread

7. Water on an umbrella

This is a simple demonstration of inertia. Simply get an umbrella and sprinkle some water on it - you need a really waterproof surface to make this work well. (If your umbrella is old, try and get it re-proofed or else smear the surface with a little oil.) Now close the umbrella sharply - the water stays where it is due to inertia and so the umbrella comes away much drier.

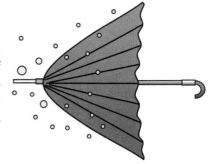

This is rather like a stationary car being hit from behind. The passengers remain where they are and the car moves off.

8. Inertia of a rod

 This should only be done as a demonstration with the teacher, and all present, wearing eye protection and being protected by safety screens.

(a) The Victorians were fond of a parlour demonstration that used inertia – although this one is not simply dependent on that. A 1.50 m dowel rod was balanced with its two ends resting on wine glasses. (See Figure 1)

The trick is to break the dowel rod by hitting it in the centre with a broom handle without breaking the wine glasses. It is a good idea to start the experiment by using a rod with a diameter of about three quarters of a centimetre. (See Figure 2)

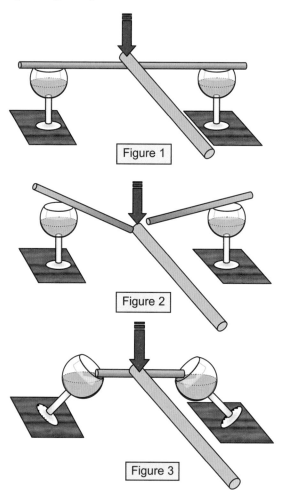

When the wooden rod is hit in the centre with the broom handle the shock waves travel outwards towards the two ends and the wine glasses.

This is just like the shock waves from an earthquake spreading out through the Earth's crust. If the rod is long enough they don't have time to reach the wine glasses before the wooden rod shatters.

However if the rod is short enough the shock waves reach the wine glasses before the rod breaks and the wine glasses fall over. (See Figure 3)

Figure 1

Figure 2

The variation described below is much less hazardous and just as impressive!

(b) As a safer variation of this, hang a dowel between two chairs by a piece of cotton at each end. Now hit it in the centre with a broom handle so that it will break without the threads breaking. The time of action of the force on the wood is short and it snaps before the force is transmitted along to the thread at both ends. The natural frequency of vibration of the rod is also lower for longer rods.

Figure 3

(The dowel may be hung from a support rod or directly from the two chairs.)

Two retort stands clamped to two benches could be used instead of the two chairs.

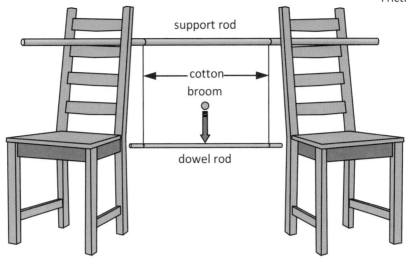

support rod

cotton

broom

dowel rod

Age range: 11-18 depending on treatment
Apparatus required:
•Wooden dowel rod (various diameters)   •Broom handle •Two lengths of cotton •Two chairs

9. Rotational inertia - the bicycle wheel gyroscope

There are some very impressive demonstrations of the inertia of rotating objects. One of the most simple and yet effective methods is to use a large gyroscope such as a small bike wheel that has had two wooden handles fitted to either side of the axle.

Get someone to hold the handles, wind a length of string round the axle, and then, using a strong pull, set the wheel spinning. Then ask them to hold it by just one handle and then change the direction in which the axle is pointing. It is very difficult because of the torque needed to alter the angular momentum of the wheel.

A number of fascinating experiments can be performed with this heavy gyroscope:
(a) get the pupils to try to pass it round the class while it is rotating, using only one hand each, and then ask them to abruptly change the axis of rotation
(b) get them to stand on a rotating table placed on the floor, hand them the spinning wheel with its axis horizontal and then ask them to turn the axis vertical
(c) suspend the spinning wheel by only one side of its axle, precession and nutation will result
(d) mount this spinning wheel in a case and get a pupil to carry it round the lab

 Beware of fingers being caught in the spinning spokes, or the wheel being dropped whilst being passed. Careful supervision is needed.

Age range: 13-18 depending on treatment
Apparatus required: •Rotating table •Bicycle wheel gyroscope •Length of cord

10. Inertia-powered car

Every school should have an inertia-powered car – often wrongly called a friction-powered car. The energy is stored in a flywheel within the car which can be clearly seen in the car in the photograph. This is 'powered up' by rubbing the wheels on the floor – this is where friction is used. This energy can then be used to drive the wheels so that the car moves.

Age range: 7-14   Apparatus required: •Inertia-powered car

VECTORS, MOMENTS AND STABILITY

General theory for this section:

The moment of a force is defined as the product of the force and the perpendicular distance from the line of action of the force to the pivot.

When an object is balanced, the sum of the clockwise moments (those trying to turn it in a clockwise direction) is equal to the sum of the anticlockwise moments (those trying to turn it the opposite way).

When an object is balanced, the vertical line from the centre of gravity passes through the point of balance and the object will topple over when this vertical line falls outside the base of the object.

1. Balancing forks and a pivot mechanism
2. Bottle top and door frame
3. Balancing a pencil and/or a snooker cue
4. Mop and back muscles
5. Action men and artists models in Physics
6. Shopping trolley
7. Balances - wooden coat hangers
8. Vectors and a rope
9. Male and female balancing
10. Mobiles to demonstrate moments
11. Arm muscles and levers
12. Centre of gravity of a pupil
13. Bear on bike
14. Moments
15. Centre of gravity and mass of a broom
16. The wooden spoon
17. Rolling up hill
18. Moving fingers on a long ruler
19. Pile of leaning blocks
20. Interesting balancing
21. The heavy bottom toy
22. Moments and a CD
23. The rolling spool

1. Balancing forks and a pivot mechanism

(a) The position of the centre of gravity of a system is vital for its stability. Fix two forks together, prongs to prongs, stick a cocktail stick through between the prongs and then balance the arrangement on the edge of a glass. (It helps to tape the prongs of the forks together). Finally set fire to the end of the cocktail stick over the glass. The wood burns, eventually going out at the edge of the glass.(It helps to tape the ends of the forks together.)

(b) A simple way of lowering the centre of gravity of a ruler when used for investigation of the law of moments is to use a rubber band to fix a ruler below a rod. The rod is then used as the pivot and is balanced on an aluminium yoke. This gets the centre of gravity below the point of suspension and makes balancing easier.

Age range: 11-14   Apparatus required: •Two forks •Cork •Glass •Ruler •Rubber band •Metal rod •Metal rod

2. Bottle top and door frame

The enormous effect of leverage can be shown by taking the cap off a bottle by holding it in the gap between the door and the frame. (Take care not to damage the door or its frame!)
It is worth giving some warnings about long levers giving too great an effect, such as the over tightening of both car wheel nuts and spark plugs with long-handled spanners! Trying to get them undone with a short arm spanner might prove impossible.

Age range: 11-14   Apparatus required: •Bottle with removable cap •Door

3. Balancing a pencil and/or a snooker cue

Why is it so much more difficult to balance a pencil than a snooker cue on your finger? This can be demonstrated by using a number of differently shaped rods - long, short, light, and heavy with a mass at the top or near the lower end - a pencil and a snooker cue. It is much easier to balance heavy rods or ones with a mass at the top such as a mop!

The ease of balancing is simply to do with how sensitively you can adjust the position of the centre of mass - a small movement of your hand will produce a large angular acceleration in a light rod.

Age range: 11-14 or older depending on treatment
Apparatus required: •Rods of different types - snooker cue, broom, pencil, metre ruler, six inch nail

4. Mop and back muscles

The following demonstration is a simulation of the enormous tension produced in the muscles of your back when you lean over. Tie a piece of string to the handle of a mop about a quarter of the way from the mop head. The head of the mop represents your head and the handle of the mop represents your spine. Drill a hole through the end of the handle furthest from the head and pivot it here, the head of the mop being at the top.

Now try and support the mop as it tilts by holding the string at a small angle to the handle of the mop (I am told that back muscles make an angle of only $10°$ with your spine!) The tension in the string represents the huge tension in your back muscles as you bend over. Bending at $45°$ produces a tension of over double your own body weight!

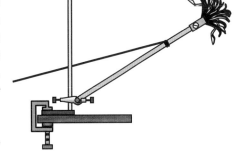

Holding something in your hands while you bend over into a car boot will increase the tension even further.

Theory:
The tension in string (back muscles) T is given by the equation: $T \sin A = mg \cos \theta$
where A is the angle of the string with the mop (back muscles with the spine) and θ is the angle that the mop handle (spine) makes with the horizontal. In the diagram the angle between the string and the mop has been exaggerated. The angle between your back muscles and your spine is less than $10°$.

Age range: 16-18
Apparatus required: •Mop •String •Newton meter •Metal rod for pivot •Retort stand and boss •G clamp

5. Action men and artists models in Physics

The stability of the human body and the variable position of its centre of gravity can be studied using wooden artists' models, action men or even Barbie dolls. Their ability to stand, bend and balance on the flat, on trolleys and even on rotating tables is much easier to investigate than using real people who might get hurt!

Age range: 11-14   Apparatus required: •Action man •Small wooden artists' model

6. Shopping trolley

This is an interesting example of everyday balancing. The trolleys are extremely stable and make a good example for the discussion of moments; the handles are almost directly above the back wheels. Have you ever tried to tip one up by pushing downwards on the back? Even if you put your full weight on the handles the trolley will not tip over. Even better if you can actually borrow one and bring it into the lab!

Age range: 11-18 depending on treatment
Apparatus required: •Shopping trolley!

7. Balances - wooden coat hangers

Wooden coat hangers make good simple balance arms. The hooks can be supported on a metal pivot and the design of the coat hanger gets the centre of mass of the system well below the pivot. Even wire ones will do if the masses that you are using for the balancing are not too great. They will probably need adjusting with a little plasticine first to get them to balance on their own.

Age range: 11-13   Apparatus required: •Coat hangers - wire or wooden

8. Vectors and a rope

A very simple introduction to the importance of the directional nature of a force can be given by using a rope held horizontally and pulled tight by two strong pupils – one pulling on either end. Now a relatively weak pupil should try to push down on the centre of the rope – it is quite easy to move it down no matter how hard the other two pull.

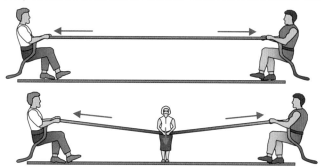

Initially it is quite easy to push the rope downwards because of the directions of all the forces. The men are pulling horizontally and when the rope is pushed down only a very small fraction of their 'pull' is trying to prevent the rope from going downwards.

However, it gets harder and harder the further down the centre of the rope gets. This is because of the increased vertical component of the tension in the rope that must be counteracted by a larger downward force in the centre.

Theory:
Downward force = 2TsinA where T is the tension in the rope and A is the angle that the rope makes with the horizontal. Say T = 200 N and A = 10°, i.e. a two metre rope pushed down in its centre by about 15 cm. This requires a downward force at the centre of only 34 N.

 This is best done outside on the grass to avoid injury if the 'pullers' fall over.

Age range: 16 – 18
Apparatus required: •Three students   •About three metres of rope •Newton meter as an extension

9. Male and female balancing

An interesting and amusing experiment on the balancing of the human body (that can be done with a man and a woman) is to get first a man and secondly a woman to stand facing a wall, three foot lengths away from it and with their hands behind their backs. Now ask them to bend forwards so that their nose just touches the wall. Women can usually to do this without overbalancing while men can't. Why is this?

An alternative method is to kneel down with your forearms on the floor, your elbows touching your knees and with a small object on the floor between your fingers. Now sit up, clasp your hands behind your back and see if you can touch the object with your nose. Women can do it – men can't. Why? Men have heavier upper bodies than women whereas women have relatively heavier hips.

Age range: 16-18   Apparatus required: •One male and one female

10. Mobiles to demonstrate moments

A lot of simple physics can be demonstrated with a child's mobile. It is instructive to design one both by trial and error and also by working out the moments required at each level. The ones with the more massive hanging objects tend to be better because they are more stable.

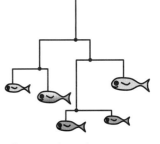

Age range: 11-13
Apparatus required: •Objects to construct a mobile •Cardboard •Balance •Stiff wire •Thread

11. Arm muscles and levers

A study of the lifting of weights by your arm is a good example of levers. The muscles of the forearm have a much greater tension in them than the weight you are lifting if the forearm is held horizontally. Get one of the pupils to try this by first holding the weight near their shoulder and then slowly extending their arm – the torque (turning effect) gets greater.

Theory:
The moment of a couple or torque = Force x perpendicular distance between the line of action of the two forces

Age range: 11-14
Apparatus required: •Forearm and masses - up to 5 kg is useful •Model forearm if possible

12. Centre of gravity of a pupil

You can find the centre of gravity of a pupil by the following method using a strong wooden plank, some bathroom scales and a brick (or block of wood) the same height as the scales.

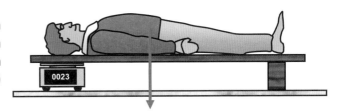

Put the plank down with one end on the block of wood or a brick and the other on the bathroom scales. Ask a pupil to lie on the plank with their heels over the pivot (brick). Record the reading of the scales. Take moments about the brick, having weighed the pupil first.

 | **This should be done on the floor of the laboratory.**

Theory:

Reading on scales x distance of scales from pivot = Weight of pupil x distance of pupil's centre of gravity from the pivot + Weight of plank x distance of centre of gravity of plank from the pivot. The weight of the plank can be ignored if you record the increase in the scale reading when the pupil lies down.

Age range: 11-16
Apparatus required: •Plank (2m long) •Bathroom scales •Metre rule •Brick or wood block

13. Bear on bike

There are many lovely toys that demonstrate why tight rope walkers puts out their arms to balance themselves or may even use a long pole. I have seen one of these in a toy shop in Venice. It was a model bear holding a balancing rod and riding a unicycle along a string. At either end of the rod were two wooden balls that dipped below the point where the wheel rested on the string, so that the centre of mass was below the point of balance. He moved quite easily along the string, being very well balanced by the rod.

Age range: 11-14   Apparatus required: •Bear on a unicycle or something similar •Taught string

14. Moments

A very simple demonstration of the effect of distance on the turning effect of a force can be demonstrated using a door. Get a small pupil to close the door by pushing with one finger placed near the outer edge of the door while the teacher pushes with all their force on one hand very close to the hinge! The effect of the distance of a force from the pivot is clear - the pupil usually manages to push the door closed!

With older pupils, get one of them to push the door such that their arm is at an acute angle with the door. It is much harder to open or close it. This emphasises the importance of the words "perpendicular distance" in the definition of the moment of a force.

Age range: 11-13 or 16-18 depending on treatment   Apparatus required: •Pupil and door

15. Using the centre of gravity to find the mass of a broom

This simple experiment emphasises that it is not just the mass on either side of a balance point that determines whether an object will be balanced, but also how it is distributed.

Hang up a broom by a string from roughly the centre of its handle so that the head will go down - the centre of mass of the broom being on the side nearest the broom head.

Now, by loading the other end with masses (m) bring the broom into a horizontal position. Locate the centre of gravity of the broom by removing the masses and adjusting the position of the string so that the broom balances.

Theory:
Force of weights x Distance of weights from pivot = Weight of broom x distance of centre of mass from pivot

Age range: 13-15
Apparatus required: •Retort stand and clamp •String •Broom •Slotted masses

16. The wooden spoon

Get a wooden spoon. Balance it on your finger to find the centre of mass. Mark this point and then cut the spoon into two pieces by cutting through the centre of mass. Fix a small piece of dowel rod so that the pieces can be joined together again. This makes a very instructive demonstration when you ask pupils which side of the spoon has the greatest mass – they invariably say that both pieces are the same since they balance at the centre of mass.

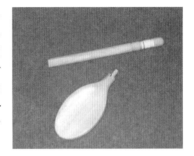

Prove that they are not by measuring their mass with a balance.

It is the moment of the forces on either side of the pivot that must balance so the 'bowl' of the spoon must be heavier than the handle because its centre of mass is closer to the pivot point on which the whole spoon was originally balanced.

Thin dowel rod

Age range: 11-13
Apparatus required: •Wooden spoon cut through its centre of mass and fitted with a dowel rod •Top pan balance

17. Rolling up hill

An interesting demonstration of the turning effect of a force is to make a tin roll up hill! Use a large, flattish cake or biscuit tin (one with a diameter of 30 cm and depth of 8 cm or so works well) and fix a hidden mass (such as a lump of plasticine) inside one rim and then show the pupils that the tin can rolls up hill. Of course you will start it so that the mass is slightly to the uphill side of the vertical, and the tin will only roll up hill until the mass reaches the lowest point - hence the advantage of a fairly large tin. See how long it takes them to spot what is going on without getting hold of the tin!

An alternative method is to use two large discs cut from thick sheets of polystyrene. A depression is made near their rims and a lump of plasticine wedged in it. The two discs are then stuck together - the loaded section being invisible!

Age range: 11-18 depending on the treatment
Apparatus required: •Plank to act as a ramp •Large tin with lid and lump of plasticine •Polystyrene

18. Moving fingers on a long ruler

This is a surprising demonstration of the effect of frictional forces and balancing. Balance a metre ruler or a broom handle on two fingers, the fingers being at different distances from the two ends. Then slide your fingers together - they always meet in the centre of the ruler as long as it is uniform - this is good for a discussion of moments.

Of course, if the rod is not uniform, such as a snooker cue, the two fingers will meet at the centre of mass. (See the example about the polar bear on ice!) It may work better with two round pencils – one held in each hand.

Theory:
The greater the distance of a finger from the centre of mass of the ruler, the smaller the reaction on it, and so the smaller the frictional force. The ruler will then slide more easily over this finger than the other, which is nearer the centre of mass. This situation continues until they are at equal distances, when both fingers move together.

Now try it with a 250g mass taped to one point of the ruler. This will move the centre of gravity of the ruler.

Age range: 11-18 depending on the treatment
Apparatus required: •Metre ruler or other long uniform rod •Two round pencils

19. Pile of leaning blocks

This demonstration looks at stability. Take some rectangular blocks, dominoes are ideal, and pile one on top of the other, setting each domino a little off centre compared with the one below it. How many can you pile up, and where is the centre of mass of the whole stack?

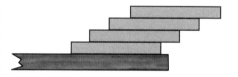

Theory
A mathematical rule can be found to give the greatest overhang for a given number of blocks, each of length L. It can be shown that the N th block can have a maximum projection of $L/(2N)$ relative to the block below. In other words the top, or first block can hang ½ its length over the second block, while the second block can hang ¼ of its length over the third and so on. For a large number (N) of blocks the sum of the series is $0.5(0.5772 + \ln N)$.

Age range: 11-18 depending on treatment
Apparatus required: •A number of dominoes or other suitable blocks •Ruler

20. Interesting balancing

(a) Balance two beakers of water on a lever balance and then put your finger in one of them. What happens? Relate this to Archimedes and upthrust. You can do this by using one beaker and a top pan balance (see the section on Archimedes).
(b) Put two pieces of taper in the end of a straw and, using a pin as a pivot, balance the arrangement. Now light the tapers - what happens? This can also be done with a candle which has been sharpened at top and bottom so that it can be lit at both ends while being pivoted in the middle. A fascinating rocking motion results.

Age range: 11-14
Apparatus required: •Balance •Beaker of water •Taper •Straw •Candle •Pin and cork
•Retort stand, boss and clamp

21. The heavy bottom toy

This toy can be used to demonstrate stability. It has a low centre of gravity and will always return to the vertical position if displaced.

Age range: 7-11

22. Moments using a CD and magnets

This is a delightfully simple way of demonstrating the law of moments and how the turning effect depends on the perpendicular distance from the pivot to the line of action of the force.

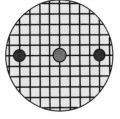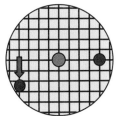

Take a CD and fix a grid scale to it as shown in the diagram. You will then need four small button magnets. These should be fitted in pairs either side of the CD and equal distances from the centre. Mount the CD and magnets on a horizontal axle (such as a glass rod or pencil) so that it balances.

Now move one of the pairs of magnets vertically downwards. Although the distance of the magnets from the axle has increased, the perpendicular distance from the axle to the line of action of the weight of the magnets is unchanged and the CD remains balanced.

Age range: 11-16
Apparatus required: •CD •Paper grid •Four button magnets •Retort stand and boss •Rod

23. The rolling spool

Take a cardboard cable spool about 40 cm in diameter similar to that shown in the photographs and fix a length of string to the central shaft.

First, set it up so that the string comes off the TOP of the shaft and try pulling the string. As you would expect you pull the spool towards you.

Now arrange it so that the string comes off the BOTTOM of the shaft. It may surprise you to find that the spool still rolls towards you! In both the above cases the string must be pulled horizontally. The critical point is when the line of action of the force in the string passes through the line where the two sides of the spool touch the table.

You may be able to prove this by considering moments about that point.

Age range: 16-19
Apparatus required: •Cable spool •String •Adhesive tape

(I am very grateful to Martin for the idea for this experiment.)

CIRCULAR MOTION

General theory for this section:
Centripetal force is the force that pulls or pushes an object from its straight-line path. It always acts towards the centre of a circle. The centrifugal force is the reaction of this force on the thing doing the pushing or pulling but not on the rotating object itself.

Centripetal force = mv^2/R where m is the mass of an object moving at a constant speed v round a circle of radius R

1. Model prop powered plane on a thread – bought at Heathrow Airport
2. The bath water and the plughole.
3. Shape of rotating liquid surface
4. Whirling bucket
5. Rotary water sprinkler with air
6. Rotating lawn sprinkler with water
7. Toy cars and loop the loop
8. Boat in box
9. Wall of death - fruit bowl and marmite lid
10. Fairground rides
11. Rounders bat on rotating table
12. The wire coat hanger and circular motion
13. Rotating candle
14. Back seat of a car
15. A simple centrifuge
16. Rotating jelly
17. Cress seed and rotating table - g forces
18. Rotation of rigid bodies and moments of inertia
19. Wall of death simulation
20. The lariat

1. Model prop-powered plane on a thread - circular motion

The theory of a conical pendulum can be very clearly demonstrated by using a model battery-powered plane that hangs from a pivot by a thread, the pivot being able to rotate. The battery drives a large propeller at the back of the plane, making it fly in a circle of radius r at a constant speed. It is also a good simulation of the chairs in fairground rides.

The faster the plane the bigger the angle (θ) that the string makes with the vertical. Measurements of θ, v, m and r are easy to make, and so the experiment could be used to find the acceleration due to gravity (g). The only problem is that it's difficult to stop!

Theory:
For a plane of mass m
Resolving vertically $mg = T\cos\theta$
Resolving horizontally $mv^2/r = T\sin\theta$
Therefore: $\tan\theta = v^2/rg$ and so $g = v^2/[r\tan\theta]$

Age range: 16-18
Apparatus required: •Model plane on thread and suitable support •Stop clock •Ruler

2. The bath water and the plug hole

Since this experiment can only be done at the place in the hemisphere where you live, the only hope of showing the differing direction of rotation in the different hemispheres is to get a video which shows the water going down the plug with the vortex rotating in opposite directions. What will be possible with a video link via the Internet! (This counter rotation in different hemispheres may now have been discounted as pure chance!)

3. Shape of rotating liquid surface

The shape of a rotating liquid surface can be found using the following experiment. Mount a glass beaker securely at the centre of a rotating table. (One of the best methods is to make a hollow circular aperture in a piece of wood into which the beaker will just fit and screw or bolt this to the rotating table.) Put warm melted wax in the beaker and spin it. As the wax cools and solidifies, a permanent record of the shape of the rotating surface will be produced. Using water or oil or wallpaper paste will give a temporary record.

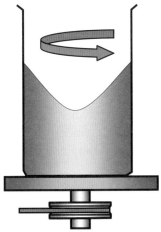

An alternative version is to use a bowl of sugar. The shape of the surface can be retained as long as you don't spin it too fast!

Theory:
Shape of the surface can be shown to be $y = \omega^2 x^2/2g + C$ where ω is the angular velocity and x the distance from the centre of rotation.

Age range: 16-18
Apparatus required: •Wax •Beaker •Rotating table •Motor and drive belt •12V variable D.C. supply

4. Whirling bucket

The classic centripetal force experiment. Put a little water in a plastic bucket – get hold of bucket and then swing the bucket in a vertical circle. As long as the rate of rotation is great enough the water stays in the bucket! Slowing the rate of rotation can get the water to almost fall out at the top of the path, and you can usually hear it slopping around at this critical point. An empty five litre plastic paint tine with about a litre of water in it works well.

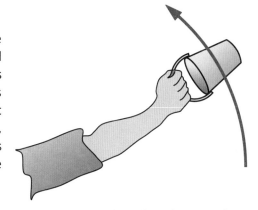

Mention that the water and bucket experience a centripetal force, but that there is also a centrifugal force - this is the reaction on the pivot, in this case your hand. Many extensions of this are possible, such as swinging a tray loaded with beakers by four strings! Plastic beakers are safer, but glass ones have more inertia and so are more stable.

Theory
The water and the bucket move in a vertical circle at a constant speed, and so although the centripetal force is constant the tension (T) in the string varies. It is greatest at the lowest point of the circle because of the differing contributions of gravity at different points of the circle.
Centripetal force = $mv^2/r = T + mg\cos\theta$ where θ is the angle that the string makes with the vertical, measured from the point where the bucket is at the top.

 Do not swing it too fast so that the handles of the bucket come off, and ensure that the bucket does not hit the floor at the lowest point of the circle. Do not use a metal bucket.

Age range: 14-18
Apparatus required: •Bucket •Water

5. Rotary water sprinkler

Fix an inflated balloon to the water inlet nozzle of a rotary lawn sprinkler and allow the balloon to deflate. Use this not only to show circular motion but also to measure energy conversion. I prefer to block up the vertical outlet if the sprinkler has one so that air only emerges horizontally.

6. Rotating lawn sprinkler

Use the lawn sprinkler again but this time fixed to a water tap. This is a good example of angular momentum. The momentum of the water leaving the sprinkler imparts an equal and opposite momentum to the central rotating head.

7. Toy cars and loop the loop

Toy cars on a plastic track can be used to demonstrate a number of ideas in mechanics. If the track can be bent into a vertical circle then loop the loop experiments can be performed.

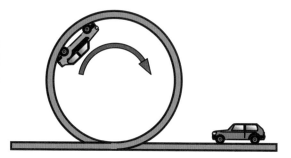

Theory:
Centripetal force = mv^2/r. This is provided by a combination of the reaction of the track (R) and the force of gravity (mg). At the top of the path the car can travel at its minimum speed since the centripetal force can be provided by gravity alone. $mv^2/r = R + mg$
The greatest reaction occurs at the bottom of the path where $R = mv^2/r + mg$

Age range: 16-18   Apparatus required: •Toy cars •Loop the loop track •Ruler

8. Boat in box

Put a small toy boat or a fishing float in a plastic bowl of water and spin it on a turntable - watch the motion of the boat or float as the spin rate is altered.

Age range: 14-16
Apparatus required: •Boat or fishing float •Plastic bowl of water •Turntable •Motor •TV camera helps

9. Wall of death - fruit bowl and marmite lid

This demonstration is a simulation of a motorcyclist on a wall of death at a fairground. Take a glass or plastic fruit bowl of diameter at least 30 cm to represent the Wall of Death and a lid of a jar to represent the motor cyclist (one from a Marmite jar works well). With a little practice the lid can be made to roll round the sides of the bowl on its edge and once moving can be kept going by a small oscillation of the bowl. It will roll round rapidly even though the sides of the bowl are kept vertical.

Age range: 16-18   Apparatus required: •Fruit bowl and marmite lid

10. Fairground rides

(a) Ride one - loop the loop

Using the loop the loop track with toy cars is a very good simulation of what happens in vertical fairground rides. The question is - how high up must you start the ride so that the cars just make the loop without falling off? It is difficult to demonstrate this exactly because of friction, but we can get an idea. Theoretically the car must start from a height which is 2.5 times the radius of the loop.

Theory:

At the top of the loop a = v^2/r = g if the car is not to fall off.

Therefore k.e at this height must be $\frac{1}{2}mv^2$ =$\frac{1}{2}mrg$. Potential energy = mg2r and so the total energy at the top of the loop is 2.5mrg. So if the car is to make the loop without falling off it must have had an initial potential energy of 2.5mrg and so must begin from a height of 2.5r above the base of the loop.

(b) Ride Two - the swinging chairs

What about the swinging chairs? These are chairs fixed to a central pillar by wires. As the rate of rotation is increased, so the chairs swing out further and further from the vertical. Do they all swing out the same amount?

You can make a simple model of the chair ride at a fair with chairs made from bottle tops. Mount it in the centre of a rotating table and then spin the table using a motor. (Alternatively use a battery powered electric drill with a plywood disc attached.)

It can be used to demonstrate the effect of different masses in the chairs by loading some with plasticine; you could make actual people shapes. The important thing is that the mass does not affect the angle of the strings to the vertical.

Theory: -

Consideration of the formula $\tan\theta = v^2/rg = r\omega^2/g$ (where v is the linear velocity and ω the angular velocity of the chairs) shows that all the chairs swing out the same amount regardless of their mass.

θ is the angle that the string makes with the vertical, v the speed of rotation and r the radius of the circle.

Age range: 16-18   Apparatus required: •Chairs model •Motor •Suitable power supply •Rotating table or electric drill with a plywood disc attached   •G clamps

11. Rounders bat on rotating table

Stand on a rotating table and swing a rounders bat to show the effect of conservation of angular momentum. This is a more effective extension of trying to rotate yourself on a rotatable table where moving your arms in one direction causes your body to move in the other - both coming to rest at the same time. Standing on the table yourself and very gently throwing a kilogram sand bag is another effective demonstration.

 | **Be careful about how and when the sandbag is thrown** |

12. The wire coat hanger and circular motion

Pull open a wire coat hanger so that it forms a square. File the end of the hook flat and then bend the hook until it points towards the opposite corner of the square. Balance a 1p coin on the hook, put one finger in the corner of the square opposite the hook and then spin the coat hanger in a vertical circle - the coin stays in place! This is a very simple but excellent demonstration of centripetal force.

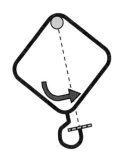

The force of the hook on the penny always acts towards the centre of rotation. The present record is five 1p pieces stacked on top of each other.

With only one penny balanced and with great care I have once even been able to bring the coat hanger to rest without the penny falling off. I am very grateful to the professor from the USA who first showed me this.

Age range: 14-18
Apparatus required: •Wire coat hanger with filed end •Pile of small coins

This is one of the finest experiments in the whole collection! It is impressive yet simple.

13. Rotating candle

On a turntable put a candle shielded by a glass tube such as a jam jar – the candle must be shorter than the height of the jar. Light the candle and rotate the turntable. Watch the flame! (A table with a diameter of 30 cm and a rotation rate of about 1 Hz is appropriate.)

Age range: 16-18

Apparatus required: •Rotating table •Motor •Jam jar •Candle •Blu tack®

14. Back seat of a car

Who falls into whose lap as you go round corners? The person nearest the centre of the curve travels on in a straight line whereas the one on the outside of the curve is pushed round by the side of the car to meet them. So it appears that the person on the inside falls into the other one's lap. This is similar to the effect on the clothes in a spin drier.

Notice that if the driver tries to corner too fast the car will roll outwards - the inner wheels leaving the ground first.

15. A simple centrifuge by whirling a container on string

A simple centrifuge can be made by whirling a plastic bottle round your head on a piece of string. Use a mixture of water and sand to show the separation. Experimenting with other liquids such as syrup and wallpaper paste makes an interesting extension to this experiment.

 The whirling is best done out of doors with the pupils standing at a safe distance.

Theory: For a mass m moving in a circle of radius r the centripetal force (F) = mv^2/r.

Age range: 14-18
Apparatus required: •Plastic bottle •String •Water •Wall paper paste •Sand

16. Rotating jelly - circular motion

The effects of centripetal forces on a rotating object can be shown impressively by making a circular jelly about 3 cm deep in a crystallising dish. When it is set empty it out carefully on to the centre of a polystyrene plate which is securely fixed to the centre of the plywood platform.

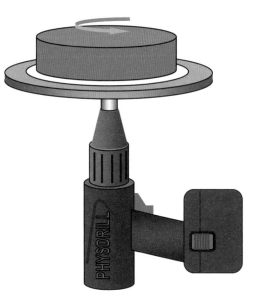

Slowly increase the rate of spin of the table. The jelly will flatten.

Further increasing the rate of spin will eventually make the jelly break up - the cohesive forces within it being less than the centripetal forces needed. It can be used to demonstrate why car tyres fly apart when they are spun too fast.

I was told that if you used some of the old forms of tyre remoulds you should not travel at more than 50 mph so as to reduce the risk of the tyres breaking up!

The jelly experiment also shows the shape of the liquid surface while rotating. It is useful to photograph it or take a video for later analysis.

Age range: 16-18 for real benefit
Apparatus required:
•Crystallising dish •Jelly •Polystyrene plate •Variable speed electric drill •Circular plywood platform with central bolt for fitting to the drill chuck

17. Cress seed and rotating table - g forces

Can we demonstrate the effect of the g force on a cress seed growing on a rotating table? We would have to rotate them for a week to make them grow outwards.

18. Rotation of rigid bodies and moments of inertia

It is instructive to investigate the effects of the moment of inertia with the following simple experiments:
(a) use discs of equal mass but of different mass distribution as energy sources
(b) look at the physics of inertia-powered toy cars and consider the full size version
(c) investigate the rotation of a heavy bicycle wheel

19. Wall of death simulation

Mount a vertical sided glass beaker or crystallising dish on the centre of a rotating table. (Use the electric drill and the plywood circle.) Set it spinning and carefully place a rubber eraser in it against the wall but not touching the bottom of the dish. The rubber "sticks" to the walls.

Age range: 16 – 18
Apparatus required:

•Rotating table •Glass dish •Safety screen •Adhesive (Blu Tack [®]) •Rubber eraser

20. The lariat

A loop of string or rope is wrapped round a wooden cylinder (or a tin can) fixed to a motor so that it can be rotated about a horizontal axis. The loop can be nudged off the cylinder and continues to rotate.

 Use a safety screen between you and the students, and wear eye protection.

Age range: 15-18
Apparatus required: •Loop of string or rope •Cylinder of wood or a tin can •Motor •Power supply
•Safety screen and eye protection

Additional theory

Angular velocity

When an object is travelling in a circle it has an instantaneous linear velocity, but it also has an angular velocity (ω). This is defined as the rate of change of angle with time and is usually expressed in **radians per second**.

For a rotating body that is rigid such as a CD or a wheel the angular velocity is the same at all points on the body while the linear gets greater as the distance from the centre gets larger. However, if the body is not rigid, like soup in a bowl that is being spun round, the angular velocity changes.

Motion in a vertical circle

If an object is being swung round on a string in a vertical circle at a constant speed the centripetal force must be constant, but because its weight (mg) provides part of the centripetal force as it goes round the tension in the string will vary.

Let the tension in the string be T_1 at the bottom of the circle, T_2 at the sides and T_3 at the top.

At the bottom of the circle:

$T_1 - mg = mv^2/r$ so $T_1 = mv^2/r + mg$

At the sides of the circle:

$T_2 = mv^2/r$

At the top of the circle:

$T_3 + mg = mv^2/r$ so $T_3 = mv^2/r - mg$

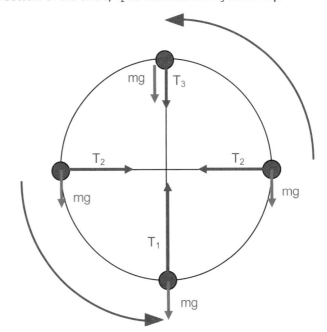

ROCKETS

General theory for this section

The propulsion systems of rockets depend on the laws of momentum conservation. For a solid or liquid fuel rocket, the greater the velocity of the exhaust gases the greater is their momentum and hence the greater the momentum of the rocket.

The calculation of the velocity of a rocket some time after its launch is a difficult problem, since the mass of the rocket is constantly changing and therefore even with a constant thrust the acceleration will not be constant. The velocity of the rocket when its mass is M can be shown to be:
Velocity of rocket $(v) = u - w \ln(M/M_0)$
where u and M_0 are the initial velocity and mass of the rocket and w is the velocity of the exhaust gases relative to the rocket.

    1. Carbon dioxide rocket
    2. Water powered rockets
    3. The firework rocket - upside down!
    4. Balloon rocket

1. Carbon dioxide rocket

The carbon dioxide rocket trolley is a superb piece of apparatus for the study of momentum. It is simply a 'sparklet' soda siphon bulb mounted horizontally on a small trolley. The side of the trolley is fixed to a piece of string that is looped round a retort stand on the floor. The idea is to use a pair of compasses with a short point to puncture the 'sparklet' bulb and allow the carbon dioxide gas to rush out, the reaction on the bulb making the trolley move off in the opposite direction - "orbiting" the retort stand at high speed!

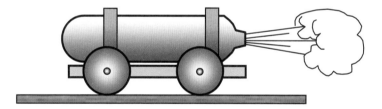

The size of the hole is critical. If it is too big, the gas comes out rapidly and it is all over too soon; too small and the result is a rather pathetic movement. Measuring the rotation rate in a circle of known radius can give the average velocity of the trolley.

Putting the trolley on a set of rails along the lab has produced some spectacular accelerations, but safety must be considered in case it leaves the track!

 It is very important to mount the cylinder securely on the trolley and to ensure that the pupils stand at a safe distance from the experiment.

Age range: 14-18 depending on treatment
Apparatus required:
•Carbon dioxide rocket trolley •Sparklet soda siphon bulbs •Pair of compasses or dividers •String
•Retort stand •Rulers •Stop clock

2. Water-powered rockets

There are two types, and both provide excellent demonstrations:

(a) A small plastic rocket that is filled with a little water, mounted on its pump mechanism and the air is pumped in. When sufficient air has been put in the rocket is launched - the high air pressure within the rocket ejects a stream of water and the rocket flies up.

(b) The second, and rather better version is simply a plastic drinks bottle with a set of fins and a valve - again air is pumped in, but this time the valve automatically releases the rocket when the pressure inside the bottle reaches a certain amount.

 This must be done in the open air. Beware of where the spent rocket will fall, and make sure that the rocket is not launched horizontally.

Age range: 14-18 depending on treatment
Apparatus required: (a) •Water rocket and pump mechanism
(b) •Plastic drinks bottle •Valve and fins assembly •Bicycle pump

3. The firework rocket - upside down!

 This teacher demonstration should only be done in the open air using safety screens. All present should wear safety spectacles and should stand well back. Never use a rocket containing star shells.

Mount a small firework rocket, one without star shells, pointing downwards and held loosely in a tube in a clamp on the top of a cheap top pan balance reading to an accuracy of one gram.

Light the rocket and stand well back behind the safety screen. The thrust of the rocket acts downwards and the reading on the top pan balance gives the thrust of the rocket during the firing. Use a TV camera if possible to record this for later analysis. The "toy" chemical rockets that are produced are sold with data sheets that give good force against time curves, and these can be used for analysis if you do not wish to do the rocket experiment yourselves!

Some safer alternatives would be to use a balloon, a soda siphon bulb or a plastic bottle containing dilute acid and chalk.

Age range: 16-18
Apparatus required:
•Firework rocket (small - without star shells) •Top pan balance •Small metal tin lid •Piece of hardboard to protect balance •Safety screen •Retort stand and two clamps •Launch tube to hold rocket

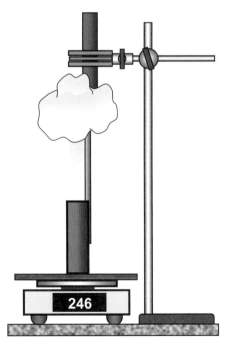

4. Balloon rocket

(a) Blow up a balloon and then release it so that it flies around the lab.

This is a classic demonstration of Newton's Third Law and the conservation of momentum. The momentum of the exhaust air is equal and opposite to that of the rubber of the balloon. The momentum of the complete system before release is zero and that after release must therefore also be zero.

I have found that it works better with a sausage shaped balloon.

(b) A variation of this simple experiment is to use a "tethered" rocket by fixing the balloon to a plastic straw which is threaded on a taut line across the lab. Keep the balloon closed with a clothes peg while you prepare the mount.

(c) The principle of action and reaction can be demonstrated by a variation of the balloon rocket. You will need two balloons - one with a short length of plastic tube (a centimetre or so) fitted in its neck. Now blow up the other balloon, close off its neck with a clip and fix it to the other end of the tube. Now open the clip. The inflated balloon does not fly around the lab - the emitted air produces a force on the other balloon which prevents it from moving.

(d) Another demonstration of this principle is to take a plastic straw - one with a flexible section - and bend it into an L shape. Pivot the top and blow into it through a tube - the emitted air will make the straw turn. Now fit a small plastic bag or a piece of cling film over the end. No air escapes - there is a force on the bag and the straw does not turn.

Age range: 11-14
Apparatus required:
•Balloons - at least one sausage shaped one •Plastic straw •Tight wire mounting •Clothes peg
•Plastic tube •Plastic straw

MISCELLANEOUS MECHANICS

1. Strength
2. Bi-filar suspension
3. Sycamore seed propeller
4. Unrolling a carpet - whiplash
5. Cotton reel tank
6. Energy in a balloon
7. Viscosity of air - oscillating table tennis ball
8. Satellite orbits
9. An interesting double pulley
10. Boomerang
11. Yo Yo
12. Tops
13. Party popper
14. Planetary orbit
15. Straw and potato
16. Hoffnung – the bucket of bricks
17. Racing-car tyres - different kinds of rubber
18. Lung volume
19. Weight suspended from a wheel - SHM
20. Creaking furniture - plastic cups
21. Rollers
22. Monkey and bananas
23. The torsion balance
24. Rotating soap film
25. Ropes
26. Propeller on a wooden stick
27. Three coins
28. Horseshoe and cocktail stick
29. Toy divers
30. Building bridges competitions
31. A rubber sheet for gravitational fields
32. Air brakes - trolley with card sail
33. A simple clamp
34. Simple pulley model
35. Centre of percussion of an object
36. Perpetual motion
37. Hunter on ice
38. Picking up objects - back to the wall
39. Large balloon – mass of air
40. Keys and matchbox over a dowel
41. Air brakes and a propeller
42. Collisions - ball bearings
43. Water diving - unstable equilibrium
44. Efficiency of a bicycle
45. Conservation of angular momentum
46. The reflection of a power ball
47. Air pressure and marshmallows
48. Marble tracks
49. Rolling double cone
50. Whirlywings
51. Human energy demands

1. Strength
Squeeze a set of bathroom scales to find the strength of your hands. Don't lean on it.

Age range: 8-13
Apparatus required: •Bathroom scales

2. Bi-filar suspension
This is a useful oscillation experiment for students at higher level. A metal rod is suspended horizontally by a thread at each end and is made to oscillate in a horizontal plane by displacing one end.

Age range: 16-18
Apparatus required: •Two retort stands •Thread •Metal rod •Stop clock •Ruler

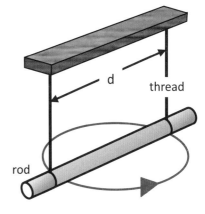

3. Sycamore seed propeller
This is simply a plastic propeller on a short stick. It demonstrates the principle of a propeller very well. Spinning it the right way by moving it between the palms of your hands makes it fly across the lab.

4. Unrolling a carpet - whiplash

A roll of carpet can be made to give a whiplash effect as you unroll it. It makes a useful introduction to the effects of whiplash of a head in car crashes, and hence the need for head rests in cars.

5. Cotton reel tank

This is a very old toy that can be made from a cotton reel, a slice of candle, an elastic band and a couple of matchsticks. A picture is shown in the diagram. It makes a useful example of energy conversion - stored energy in the rubber band is converted to kinetic energy in the cotton reel tank.

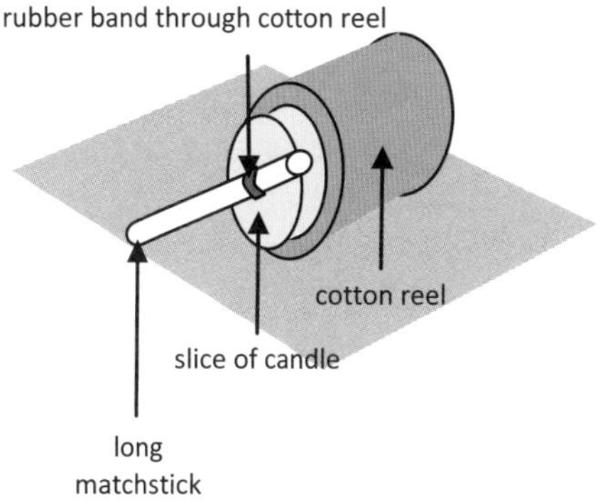

rubber band through cotton reel

cotton reel

slice of candle

long matchstick

Age range: 11-14
Apparatus required: •Cotton reel •Match sticks (one long one) •Rubber band •Lolly stick

6. Energy in a balloon

Work out the energy in a blown up balloon either by calculation or by the energy released and converted to kinetic energy on a linear air track. Or by how much it takes to pump it up. If you pop it, how much energy goes into the kinetic energy of the fragments and how much into the sound?

What is the energy in a stretched rubber sheet? How much energy is stored in a gas when its volume and pressure change?

Age range: 11-18 depending on the treatment
Apparatus required: •Balloons •Linear air track etc.

7. Viscosity of air with an oscillating table tennis ball

The viscosity of air and its damping nature can be investigated by using a table tennis ball fixed to a length of thread and used as a pendulum.

8. Satellite orbits

The idea of this experiment is to draw a scale diagram for a satellite in orbit 200 km above the Earth's surface (with 1 mm representing 2 km) - that is with an orbit radius of 6600 km, 3.3 m when scaled down. A section of orbit is drawn using a pencil fixed to a 3.3m length of string and the tangent to the arc is drawn at one point.

The distance that the satellite would fall in 120 s is found using $s = 1/2gt^2$ (using t = 120 s and assuming that g is constant up to 200 km above the Earth's surface). The distance round the orbit where such a drop occurs is measured and then the fraction of a whole orbit is worked out. The time for one whole orbit can then be found.

It is important for the students to realise that the only piece of data that turns this into a real value for the satellite orbit from just a large drawing is the value for g.

Age range: 15-18
Apparatus required: •Pencil •3.5 m of string •Large sheet of paper such a drawer lining paper •Metre ruler

9. An interesting pair of pulleys

This intriguing problem uses two single pulleys. The lower pulley has a thread hung over it with a 100g on one end and a 200g mass on the other. This pulley is attached via a second thread over a second and upper pulley, which is fixed to a retort stand, to a mass of 300 g (with a little plasticine added to compensate for the mass of the first pulley). Since the masses at the two ends of the thread over the upper pulley are equal, ask the students what happens when the masses are allowed to move.

With the masses quoted here the large mass moves downwards with an acceleration of g/17.

To demonstrate this it is better to start off with the small masses being almost equal, otherwise their acceleration is too great.

Theory:
The theory for the general case is surprisingly complex. It can be shown that the large mass will descend if $-(m_1-m_2)^2 > 0$, which is never true, therefore $a_1 < 0$.

Using the values for the masses given above:
Let the acceleration of the lower masses be +a and –a and the acceleration of the 300g mass be A. For simplicity we will take g as 10 ms^{-2}.
300 gm mass: 3 - 2T = 0.3A   200 gm mass: 2 - T = 0.2(a-A)   100 gm mass: T - 1 = 0.1(a+A)
From these three equations we can show that:
A= 0.5/0.85 = 0.588 ms^{-2}

Remember that we have taken g = 10 ms^{-2}, 10/17 = 0.588 so the acceleration is g/17.
If you take g = 9.81 ms^{-2} the acceleration becomes 0.577 ms^{-2}.

Age range: 16-18, the analysis being suitable for mathematicians taking Mechanics at A level
Apparatus required: •Two single pulleys •Set of slotted masses with three hangers •Thread •Retort stand •Clamp •Nail •TV and video to record the motion for later analysis or three light gates

10. Boomerang

It is not safe to throw a wooden boomerang inside the lab, but it makes a superb demonstration for the discussion of fluid flow when thrown outside. Hold it vertically with the concave side facing away from you. Polystyrene boomerangs can be used inside the school in a hall or gym.

11. Yo Yo

This is a good example of conservation of angular momentum and its transfer to linear momentum. The analysis of the motion is quite complex.

12. Tops

These are just rather nice. They can be used to demonstrate rotational motion or energy conversions - many of them will either play a tune or turn upside down! The theory of the inverting top should provoke some useful discussion.

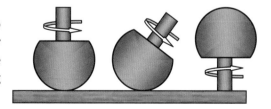

13. Party popper

This is a good example of energy conversion - and is just a bit of fun! You can use one to demonstrate various types of energy conversion.

14. Planetary orbit

Use a conical pendulum to simulate a planetary orbit or better still the decay of a satellite orbit when it encounters the friction of the upper atmosphere.

The decay of an orbit can also be demonstrated by using a large glass funnel. The satellite is represented by a marble spiralling in - analogous to the action of a satellite being affected by air friction in the atmosphere.

15. Straw and potato

Get a potato and cut it in half. Then try and push a plastic straw through one of the halves from the flat side. It's no good - the straw just bends. Now drive the straw sharply into the flat side of the potato - it should now go straight through. A shout as you drive the straw through usually wakes up a sleepy class!

Age range: 13-18 depending on treatment   Apparatus required: •Potato •Plastic straw

16. Hoffnung – the bucket of bricks

The recording of Gerald Hoffnung at the Oxford union has a wonderful account of a bricklayer. He has a bucket of bricks at the top of some scaffolding and tries to get it to the ground. The resulting account as the bucket, initially heavier than him so pulling him off the ground and then splitting open as it lands, spilling out the bricks is fascinating and hilarious. It makes superbly entertaining material for the resultant forces and pulleys section of any 16-19 course.

17. Racing-car tyres - different kinds of rubber

On a dry racetrack racing cars use slick tyres. They are smooth and so before the start they are warmed up by using heated jackets and then by repeated swerves on the track to create heat from friction. This melts a small quantity of rubber and so they feel sticky to the touch. While the track stays dry this 'stickiness' gives them a good grip. Not so effective on a wet track!

18. Lung volume

It is possible to get an estimate of your lung volume by blowing into water filled measuring cylinders that have been inverted over a tank of water. The amount of water blown out gives an approximate value for your lung volume.

Age range: 11-13
Apparatus required: •Sink full of water •A number of large measuring cylinders or cans

19. Weight suspended from a wheel - SHM

Suspend a weight by a long string from the rim of a bike wheel. Rotate the wheel and use the distance from the ground as a measure of the SHM. Measurements of the sideways movement of the weight are also worth taking.

Age range: 16-18
Apparatus required: •Bicycle wheel mounted on an axle •Thread •Weight (such as a pendulum bob)

20. Creaking furniture - plastic cups

This demonstrates the expansion and contraction of furniture at night as the house cools down. We do the reverse - a warming up. Get two plastic cups and glue them together in the fridge with their tops together. Take them from the fridge to the lab - they should warm up and creak as they expand!

21. Rollers

This experiment involving rolling two cylinders down a plane, one with a heavy axle and one with a heavy rim (both the same total mass), can be used as either an interesting demonstration for the younger pupils to make them think, or as an analysis of moments of inertia for the older students. The can with a heavy centre accelerates faster than one with a heavy rim. Use tins loaded with extra mass at different points.

Theory:
Moment of inertia of a solid cylinder (the heavy axle) = $Mr^2/2$ where r is the radius of the axle
Moment of inertia of the heavy rim = Mr^2 where r is the radius of the can

Age range: 13-18 depending on treatment
Apparatus required: •Ramp •Two cans loaded one at the centre and one at the rim

22. Monkey and bananas

A monkey hangs on to a weightless rope that is passing over a frictionless pulley. On the other end of the rope is a bunch of bananas of exactly the same mass as the monkey. What happens if the monkey begins to climb the rope towards the bananas?
The bananas also move upwards with the same acceleration as the monkey. If the monkey now lets go of the rope both the bananas and the monkey fall - the distance between them remaining the same. If the monkey now grabs hold of the rope again - it may burn its hands - they both come to rest.

I am grateful to a colleague who suggested a further twist to this problem. What happens if the monkey reaches across and starts to eat the bananas?

23. The torsion balance

A home-made torsion balance made by a wire stretched between two supports with a light rod such as a plastic straw fixed to it at right angles can be used as an accurate balance. (A clamp can be a useful way of tensioning the wire.) It can also be used to demonstrate an accurate method of force measurement or investigation of the shear modulus of a metal

Age range: 16-18
Apparatus required: •Wire •Two retort stands bosses and clamps •G clamps •Light rod or plastic straw •Slotted masses (light)

24. Rotating soap film

Use a tin can with a soap film across the end and with its axis horizontal so that the soap film is vertical. Fix the can to an electric drill and spin it. The film should be illuminated by a 100 W lamp from behind a translucent screen.

Age range: 11-18   Apparatus required: •Soap solution •Electric drill •Tin can •Lamp •Screen

25. Ropes

You are asked to remove two ropes from a warehouse. The problem is that the two ropes are suspended through two small holes in the ceiling. The idea is to cut down as much rope as possible - the holes are too small for you to get your hands through and the height of the holes above the ground is too great for you to jump down from there without serious injury!

One possible solution: Climb up one rope - cut the other near the ceiling, tying the piece that you cut off to your rope near the top. Make a loop in the remaining piece of the other rope and then feed the cut off piece through it. Hold on to this piece and your rope together, and then cut your rope near the ceiling. Holding onto both ropes, slide down and then pull the double rope down through the loop!

26. Propeller on a wooden stick

This wonderfully simple toy is just a serrated edged stick of about 1cm^2 cross section, about 20 cm long and with a thin wooden propeller nailed to one end, but the Physics in it is fairly complex. Rub a small piece of dowel along one edge of the serrated part of the stick, and the propeller will rotate. Rubbing it along the other side can make the propeller rotate the other way.

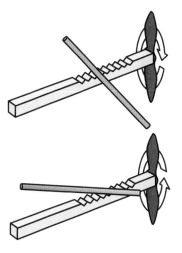

Theory
Elliptical standing waves are set up in the rod caused by the asymmetric vibrations due to the serrated edge.

27. Three coins

The conservation of momentum and Newton's cradle can also be demonstrated by three coins on the table. Place two together, holding one down with your finger. Slide the third coin towards this coin so that a collision takes place. The third coin comes to rest while the first coin flies off.

A larger scale version of this can be demonstrated in a game of croquet. Place two croquet balls in contact with each other and put your foot on top of one of them. Then strike this ball with the mallet – the free ball moves off.

28. Horseshoe and cocktail stick

A cardboard horseshoe stands leaning against a cocktail stick as shown in the diagram. The problem is to pick up the horseshoe and the cocktail stick with just the other cocktail stick without touching anything with your hands except the second stick.

One possible solution: Push the second stick between the inclined one and the horseshoe. Allow the horseshoe to fall forwards slightly so that the supporting stick protrudes below it, resting on the other stick. Then use this to pick up both the first cocktail stick and the horseshoe.

Age range: 11- Adult
Apparatus required: •Cardboard horseshoe shape •Two cocktail sticks

29. Toy divers

Some toyshops sell plastic toy divers which you can blow into via a tube to make them rise, or suck to make them sink. They are rather like variable Cartesian divers.

30. Building bridges competitions

This is worth doing both for general interest and for a study of the structures sections of syllabuses. It is a useful way of getting the students to think about moments and vector analysis. Plastic straws are quite good. Fixing them together is a problem - we have even sewn them together with thread!

31. A rubber sheet for gravitational fields

A rubber sheet fixed over an old bike wheel (with the spokes removed) makes a very good demonstration of a simulated gravitational field. The sheet should be fixed to the wheel by a piece of string tied tightly around the rim.

A set of slotted weights hanging from the centre of the sheet allows you to simulate the change in mass of the central object (planet or star) very easily. Then just roll in a ball bearing (to represent an orbiting satellite or planet), and try to get it to move along a tangent to a circle about the central mass. Using a single heavy ball bearing in the centre rather than the slotted masses shows an effect on both the central mass and that approaching from the outside since the central mass moves because it is not so massive as the weights.

The depression of the sheet as a heavy ball bearing rolls across it simulates the curvature of space formed by the gravitational field of a massive object.

An alternative method is to use a large coffee tin with the bottom cut out and with one end covered with a sheet of cling film. The whole apparatus can then be placed on an OHP so that it can be seen by the whole class.

Age range: 16-18
Apparatus required: •Bicycle wheel with the spokes removed •Thin rubber sheet •Set of slotted masses •Various ball bearings

32. Air brakes - trolley with card sail

As an extension to the investigation of a toy car running down a ramp try using air brakes. Tie a piece of thread to the car and wrap the other end round a glass rod that stands in a test tube. Fix a piece of card (postcards are ideal) to the top of the rod to act as an air brake. As the car runs down the ramp the rod rotates, so rotating the card. Investigate the effect of different sized pieces of card on the acceleration of the car. Suggest plotting a graph of the square of the velocity after a given distance against the inverse of the area of the card.

Age range: 11-18 depending on treatment
Apparatus required: •Toy car •Cardboard •Timing mechanisms •Wooden board to act as a slope

33. A simple clamp

We have used two small blocks of wood joined with a bolt and wing nut as holders for all sorts of small items - they are especially useful for pendulum threads and hacksaw blades. The pressure on the item held can be altered by tightening or loosening the nut, so enabling a thread to be pulled through while still supporting a pendulum bob.

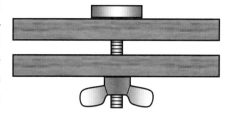

34. Simple pulley model

An interesting and surprising example of the mechanical advantage of a pulley system can be shown by the following demonstration. Two rods are held parallel by two people (a couple of retort stand rods will do fine for this). A piece of string is tied to one and then looped a few times round both.

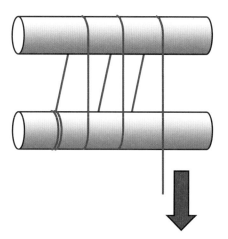

If you hold the other end of the string you will be able to pull the rods together no matter how hard the people holding the rods try to prevent you. If there is little friction between the rods and the string, the more loops you can make the better it will work.

You should see that the result is exactly analogous to a real pulley system with a large velocity ratio and hence a large mechanical advantage for a given efficiency.

Theory:
For a pulley system   Efficiency = Mechanical advantage/Velocity ratio

Age range: 11-16 depending on treatment
Apparatus required: •Two pieces of broom handle, towel rail or retort stand rods •Smooth string

35. Centre of percussion of an object

Suspend a 1 m ruler from the 5 cm mark on a matchstick. Hit it sharply with a hammer two thirds of the way down the ruler from the match. What happens?

Try this at a variety of points and relate to the forces felt by games players in cricket, baseball and rounders.

Age range: 14-18
Apparatus required: •1m ruler •Retort stand, boss and clamp •Match stick •Hammer

36. Perpetual motion

A disc of wood is mounted so that its centre is held by an axle in the wall of a tank of water, half the disc being in air and the other half in water. The side in the water experiences an upthrust. (We will assume that there is a perfect frictionless seal so that no water leaks out!) Why doesn't the disc rotate?

37. Hunter on ice

This is an interesting example of equal and opposite forces. Imagine that you are standing on a frozen lake holding a rope, the other end of which is tied to a sleepy polar bear!

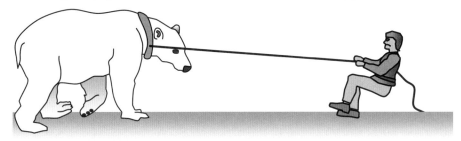

You pull on the rope and if there is negligible friction you and the bear both move - as you would expect. Because of its greater mass the bear accelerates less rapidly than you do, but where do you meet? In fact it can be proved that if there is no friction you and the bear will always meet at the same place where $md_1 = Md_2$. Your mass is m and you move d_1; the bear, mass M, moves d_2.

38. Picking up objects with your back to the wall

An interesting example of balancing and the centre of mass of the human body can be shown by getting a pupil to stand with their heels against a wall and then asking them to pick up an object placed say half a metre in front of them. This is not possible because of the position of the body's centre of mass. You cannot counterbalance the 'forward lean'.

39. Large balloon - mass of air

Use a large rubber balloon - one that you can blow up to a diameter of over 30 cm - to measure the mass. (One with a volume about 0.03 m^3 contains about 36 g of air.) There may be a problem here, however. What about the change of pressure as the balloon is inflated?

40. Keys and matchbox over a dowel

Tie a bunch of keys to one end of a length of thread and a matchbox to the other. Loop the thread over a piece of dowel rod fixed horizontally in a boss. Hold the matchbox so that it is on the same level as the dowel rod with the keys hanging vertically down wards. Let go. The keys fall and the matchbox swings down, but the thread wraps itself around the dowel rod.

Age range: 11-18 depending on treatment
Apparatus required: •Retort stand and boss •Wooden dowel rod •Match box •Thread
•Bunch of keys or 50g mass

41. Air brakes and a propeller

A very good demonstration of air brakes is to make a windmill from a set of card vanes fixed in a cork which is then mounted over a glass tube with a closed end. This tube is fitted loosely on a glass rod. A thread wrapped round this is hung over a pulley and fixed to an accelerating mass or to a car on a ramp. Differing damping effects can be produced by changing the size of the vanes.

Age range: 11-15
Apparatus required: •Cork •Cardboard •Glass tube •Glass rod and pivot •Thread •Car •Ramp •Pulley

42. Collisions - ball bearings

Use a magnet and two ball bearings - one large and one small. Roll them together towards the magnet with the large one in the lead. A 'magnetic gun' results. (See the magnetic accelerator)

43. Water divining - unstable equilibrium

Is this really all it is - unstable twigs? A fascinating investigation could result here.

44. Efficiency of a bicycle

Mount the bicycle upside down and by measuring the mechanical advantage and its velocity ratio work out the efficiency of the bike. The mechanical advantage is found by hanging a mass on one of the pedals while finding out the force applied at the rim of the wheel to counteract the weight of the mass using a Newton meter.

The velocity ratio is calculated by measuring the distance moved by a point on the rim of the wheel for one rotation of the pedal.

 Do not allow pupils to spin the wheels at high speed as serious damage to fingers may result.

Theory
Efficiency of the bike = [Mechanical advantage/Velocity ratio] x 100

Age range: 14-16
Apparatus required: •Bicycle •Sets of large slotted masses •Newton meter •String •Retort stands and clamps

45. Conservation of angular momentum

This can be demonstrated by a number of simple experiments.
(a) Stand someone on a rotatable table with their arms outstretched. Give them a gentle push so that they start rotating and then ask them to pull their arms into their sides - the rate of spin increases since their moment of inertia has decreased, and the spin rate must get larger to conserve angular momentum. (It works even better if they hold a kilogram mass in each hand!)
(b) Use a conical pendulum fixed to the top of a broomstick. The pendulum bob is given a push so that it begins to move in a circle, the string wrapping itself round the stick and the rotation rate increasing as the radius of the orbit gets less.
(c) A cylinder is fixed to a string that is suspended from a beam. The cylinder is held on its side and spun round. As it falls with its axis vertical the rate of spin increases.
(d) Stand a pupil on the rotating table outside the laboratory and get them to throw a 1 kg sandbag. They will rotate in the opposite direction to that in which the sandbag is thrown.

 Always stand the rotating table on the floor. Make sure that the sandbag is thrown gently, and that the rest of the class stand well back.

Age range: 11-16 Apparatus required: •Rotating table •1 kg sandbag •Cylinder •String

46. The reflection of a power ball

Find a hard floor and a flat topped table. Throw a power ball (without spinning it) so that it hits the floor just outside the table and then bounces up under the table and hits the underneath of the table top (see diagram).

There is nothing unusual about this, but it is when the ball hits the underneath of the table top that something rather strange happens. Instead of reflecting off at the same angle the ball returns along its original path!

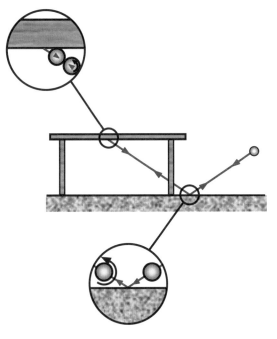

This can be explained by thinking about the spin of the ball. When it hits the ground at an angle the frictional force between the ball and the ground makes the ball spin (as shown in the inset). As it hits the underneath of the tabletop it is this very spin coupled with another frictional force that returns the ball along its original path.

Now try wetting the ball. This lowers the friction, reduces the spin and the ball bounces out at the far end of the table!

This is a fascinating experiment on collisions. I have yet to experiment using different balls such as table tennis balls, hockey balls and tennis balls.

Age range: 16-19
Apparatus required: •Flat topped table •Power ball •Hard floor

47. Air pressure and marshmallows.

Put some cylindrical marshmallows in an empty wine bottle. Then use a 'vacuvin' and stopper to reduce the air pressure in the bottle. As you do so the marshmallows will expand because the air within them is at a greater pressure than the air in the bottle.

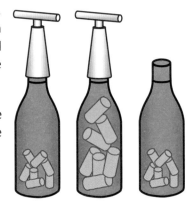

When air is allowed back into the bottle by taking out the stopper they will 're-inflate'. This is a good example of the change in the volume of a gas with pressure.

Age range: 11-16
Apparatus required: •Wine bottle •Vacuvin and stopper •Cylindrical marshmallows

48. Marble tracks

There are a number of mechanics experiments where you will need to roll marbles down a track – to investigate collisions, to measure g, to check the best shaped path to give the shortest transition time between two points and so on. Two possible tracks are:

(a) a length of plastic tubing with an internal diameter a bit larger than a marble

(b) a piece of plastic electrical trunking (either the base or the clip-on cover) – the width of this could be either a bit bigger or a bit smaller than a marble depending on whether you want the marble to sit in the track or roll along the top

Both these items can be bought really cheaply from most DIY shops.

Age range: 11-19   Apparatus required: •Plastic tubing •Electrical trunking

49. Defying gravity – a rolling double cone

Make a double cone out of wood by fixing two funnels together 'face to face'. Make two slanted and tapering support ramps so that you have the arrangement shown in the diagram. When the double cone is put on the lower end of the ramp it seems to roll uphill – apparently defying gravity.

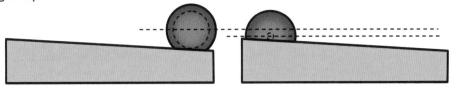

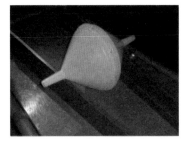

This can be explained by thinking about what is happening to the centre of gravity of the rolling double cone. At the bottom of the ramp the cone is supported near its centre and so its centre of gravity is high (See diagram 1). At the top of the ramp the cones are supported nearer their tops and so their centre of gravity is lower (See diagram 2). The double cone has actually rolled so that its centre of gravity is nearer the ground.

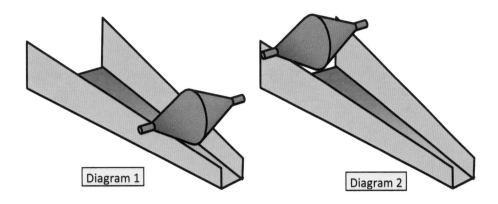

Diagram 1

Diagram 2

Age range: 11-18
Apparatus required: •Double cone •Ramp

50. Whirlywings

These make a fascinating basis for an investigation for pupils and teachers of almost any age – from six to sixty years of age! A whirlywing is simply a rectangular piece of paper or card. You hold it with the long side horizontal and with the plane of the whirlywing almost vertical and then drop it. As it falls it spins about its long axis.

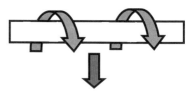

Investigations can include the effect of size, shape or material on the distance flown, the time of flight or the shape of the path. The aerodynamics of the whirlywing can be investigated by older students.

Interested students might try making a revojet – a plane with each wing a rotating whirlywing. I am grateful to Bob for this idea.

Age range: 6 – 60
Apparatus required: •Rectangular piece of paper or card •Scissors •Ruler or tape •Stopwatch

51. Human energy demands

How much energy do we need to take from food in each 24 hours? The answer depends very much on the sort of people we are particularly on our age and our work.

Some needs are:

BOYS AND GIRLS	Kilojoules per day		TEENAGERS	Kilojoules per day	
				BOYS	GIRLS
0-1 year	4200		11-14 years	11500	
2-6 years	6300		15-19 years	14700	10500
7-10 years	8400				

ADULTS	MEN	WOMEN
Lying in bed all day	7400	6300
Working 8 hours per day:		
Light work	12000	9500
Heavy work	15000	12500
Very heavy work	21000	

PREGNANCY	
Early months	10000
Late months	11500
Nursing the baby	12500

Activities	Kilojoules per minute
Resting in bed	4
Washing, shaving, dressing	14
Walking	21
Standing	7.5
Cycling	28

Power of the heart	1W
Power of the brain	20 W
Power of a 15 year old student	around 350 – 700 W

ELASTICITY

General theory for this section:

An object obeys Hooke's Law if the deformation is directly proportional to the applied force. For example this will apply to a piece of copper wire being stretched by small loads - the actual maximum load depends on the cross sectional area of the wire.

The Young modulus (E) for a material is a measure of how much it will stretch. This is given by the equation E = FL/eA where e is the extension, L the original length, F the applied force and A the cross sectional area of the wire. For steel the Young modulus is 2×10^{11} Pa.

1. Uses of elasticity
2. Bending of a beam
3. The belly flop
4. Glass
5. Energy stored in a rubber band
6. Shear stress
7. Bungee jumping
8. Elasticity of rubber when cooled
9. Stretching a sock or tights
10. Strength of paper and string
11. Elasticity of rubber molecules
12. Heating in stretched rubber
13. Whirling springs and Hooke's Law
14. Silly putty
15. Creatures and granite
16. Electric strain gauge

1. Uses of elasticity

The following is a list of the applications of elasticity that I have found useful when introducing the topic: A bouncy castle, space hopper, elastic in clothes, bridges, trampolines, trainers, cricket bats, aircraft wings, your muscles, your skin, car bumpers, crash helmets, car and bike suspension and fishing line. Some mountain bikes actually have air suspension forks!

2. Bending of a beam

As a practical example of bending and shear stresses bend a metre ruler in the laboratory by supporting it at either end and then loading it at its centre. Investigate the effect on the depression of changing both the load and the length of the beam.

A rather nice extension of this uses a filament of glass drawn out from a glass rod, the filament being in the centre of two much fatter end sections. The rod should be held horizontally by its end and then the filament in the centre loaded with masses. A quite surprising deformation can be produced.

 All present require eye protection and safety screens should be used. Dispose of the broken glass with care.

Theory:
The depression of the centre of the beam when it is loaded at its centre is proportional to the load and to the length of the beam cubed

Age range: 16-18
Apparatus required: •Slotted masses •String •Metre rule •Two knife edges on bosses •Retort stands •Ruler mounted vertically in base clamp •Glass rod with central filament section •Safety screen •Goggles

3. The belly flop

An idea of the very high compressibility modulus of water can be gained from talking about how painful it is to do a "belly flop" into a swimming pool. It's actually only 100 times worse to launch yourself on to a slab of concrete if the water does not part to let you enter!
Bulk modulus of concrete = 100×10^{11} Pa   Bulk modulus of water = 1×10^{11} Pa

Age range: 16-18

4. Elasticity of glass

The elastic nature of glass can be seen in old windows. The weight of the glass makes it "creep", the lower portion of the pane becoming fatter than that above it. Glass is much easier to break when it is scratched - the scratch provides an initial dislocation which then spreads easily when under stress.

Glass fibre may be bent in a circle while a glass block can only suffer small angular deformation before it shatters. This is because of the difference in length between the two sides of the specimen – small for the fibre but large for the block for a given angle of deformation.

5. Energy stored in a rubber band

You may know that if a rubber band is stretched considerably, beyond its elastic limit, it will not return to its original length. This can be shown by adding masses to the lower end of the band and then removing them carefully - recording the corresponding extensions. I have found it better to cut the band into one straight length, giving greater extension for a given mass.

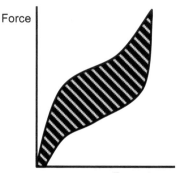

The non-recoverable energy absorbed by the rubber band may be worked out by finding the area of the hysteresis loop produced by the force-extension graph. It is instructive to calculate the velocity of projection of a paper pellet by a rubber band both with and without allowance for the energy that cannot be recovered. A very rough estimate of the energy stored in a rubber band can be gained by firing a ball upward from a rubber band stretched by a known amount. You should mention the effects of air resistance in both experiments.

 Long stretched rubber bands can cause severe eye damage on 'fly-back'. Eye protection should be used.

Theory:
Non recoverable energy absorbed by the band = Force x Distance = area inside the hysteresis loop

Age range: 14-18
Apparatus required: •Rubber band •Slotted masses •Ruler •Base clamp to hold the ruler vertical from the floor •Retort stand and clamp •Suitable clamp for holding the rubber band •Safety spectacles

6. Shear stress

This can be demonstrated in a number of ways, and it should be pointed out that it is this type of stress that is most likely to be encountered in machines and buildings.
(a) You can show it clearly with a simple pack of playing cards. If the top card is slid sideways while being pressed down on the cards beneath the whole pack will exhibit shear. Don't use cards that are too slippery!
(b) Make a sausage of plasticine and twist it at one end while holding the other end steady.
(c) Clamp a metre rule to the desk and twist that.
(d) Show how you can rotate your arm - mainly the wrist.

Age range: 16-18
Apparatus required: •Pack of playing cards •Sausage of plasticine •Ruler •Arm

7. Bungee jumping

This can be simulated by using a long piece of elastic and a mass, doing the experiment over a stair well if possible. Elastic bought from a haberdasher's works well or you might try unravelling a piece of climbing rope. Can you get the length right so that the mass just stops before it hits the ground?

Age range: 14-18   Apparatus required: •Long length of elastic •Masses

8. Elasticity of rubber when cooled

Many of us will have seen, or heard about, the wonderful demonstrations of the change of elasticity of rubber when cooled in liquid nitrogen. However reasonable results can be obtained by using dry ice (solid carbon dioxide). Try cooling a piece of rubber tube in solid carbon dioxide for a minute or two and then hitting it with a hammer – the rubber shows a marked change in its elasticity and will shatter under the impact. The change in elasticity of a squash ball and a rose petal when put in the solid carbon dioxide is also worth investigating.

 Gauntlet style leather gloves and eye protection are needed when handling dry ice (solid carbon dioxide). Safety screens should be used to protect against flying fragments.

Age range: 11-18
Apparatus required: •Squash ball •Rubber tubing •Flower petal •Hammer •Carbon dioxide cylinder and cloth

9. Stretching a sock or tights

This experiment relates elasticity to something practical - clothes!
Take some tights - one leg will do - and fix them to a clamp. Load the bottom end with weights and record the force and resulting extension. (Forces of up to 150 N are needed to give a reasonable extension.) Slowly remove the weights and record the extension as they are taken off. Tights are very good; they stretch a lot when loaded and also show a hysteresis effect which apparently disappears when they are washed!

Age range: 14-18
Apparatus required: •Tights (one leg will do!) •Masses •Retort stand, boss and clamp •Ruler

10. Strength of paper and string

This is an interesting couple of experiments to demonstrate the difference between the shape of a specimen and the way forces are applied to it.

(a) Try and stand a sheet of paper on one end with a 100 g mass on top - the paper collapses. Now roll the paper into a tube - it will easily support the weight of the 100 g.

(b) Hold a piece of string vertically with the 10 g mass tied to the top - let go and the mass falls as the string collapses. Now hold the string from the other end so that the mass is at the bottom - the string easily supports it.

Age range: 11-18 depending on follow up   Apparatus required: •Paper •100 g and 10 g masses •String

11. Elasticity of rubber molecules

Stretch a piece of rubber until it becomes difficult. At this point the rubber molecules should have untangled themselves and be aligned along the direction of stress. You will now probably notice that the band looks a little paler and the surface texture may have changed. Now put a pin through the rubber and move the pin about a bit. The rubber will break apart along the line of stretch, which is also along the line of molecules, showing that there is a lower strength between molecular chains than along them.

Age range: 14-18
Apparatus required: •Two clamps •Retort stands etc. •Large slotted masses (up to 5 kg) •Pin •TV camera if possible

12. Heating in stretched rubber

Put a piece of balloon rubber between your lips and stretch it. As it is stretched you will notice an increase in temperature unlike what happens with a gas - expansion usually means cooling. Alternatively use a rubber band about 1 cm wide. Holding a length of a centimetre or so between your thumbs and forefingers, pull it sharply and then place it quickly against your top lip. The heating effect is very noticeable. Is it that the molecules in the rubber have become more ordered and so they give off heat energy - resulting in a cooling? Blu tack ® works as well.

A strip of rubber cut from a balloon is first stretched and then held against your forehead. This feels warm and when it is allowed to contract it cools down.

Age range: 16-18   Apparatus required: •Rubber balloon •Rubber band • Blu tack ® •Scissors

13. Whirling springs and Hooke's Law

Fix a rubber bung to the end of a spring and spin it in either the vertical or horizontal plane. To measure the force you can use a spring balance fixed in the line with a string. Alternatively calculate the value by measuring the radius of orbit and the speed of rotation. Record the reading on a TV camera if possible for slow analysis later.

Age range: 16-18
Apparatus required: •Helical spring •Rubber bung •Ruler •Stop clock •Spring balance •TV camera

14. Silly putty

This is wonderful stuff and is available in many toyshops so if you see some - buy it! Stocks may not last. There are two different types:
(a) this type glows in the dark especially after being irradiated with ultra violet
(b) this type changes colour when it is heated.
Both types have the same elastic properties. If a ball of it is held by one side it will creep (slowly sag), if dropped it will bounce, and if hit with a hammer it will shatter. Another example of the application of a large impulse is if you hold a piece in your hands and then pull it sharply. It will snap – reminiscent of a severe muscle pull!

 Eye protection should be worn and a safety screen used to protect against flying fragments. Short wave u.v lamps should only be used where direct radiation is screened from the eye by a sheet of glass or opaque material.

Age range: 11-18
Apparatus required: •Silly putty •Hammer •Ultra violet lamp •Eye protection •Ultra violet goggles

15. Creatures and granite columns - leg strength, height and g

(a) We are made the way we are because of the gravitational pull of our planet. What would the design of other creatures be on planets with widely differing g values? Animals living on planets with very high g values would be expected to have thick legs while those of similar mass that lived on small planets with low g values could be supported by spindly legs!

While we are thinking about creature design, what about considering if animals would black out if they had a long neck and turned round too quickly.

Bone is actually amazingly strong - the compressive breaking stress of solid bone being only about a third that of steel! (170×10^6 Pa) A piece of chicken bone can be investigated to show this strength. Eye protection and a safety screen are essential to protect you from flying splinters. The bone is held vertically in a clamp and weights placed on the top of a small platform resting on the bone.

 Eye protection and safety screen(s) will be needed to protect all present from flying fragments of bone.

(b) Granite columns

The maximum possible height of a granite column on Earth is around 7800m. Higher than this and it will shatter under its own weight.

Simulate this by a column of damp sand. Put a tin lid on top and load this with masses until the sand column gives way. This should occur at the base. Another way of doing this is to use jelly. Make a tall jelly in a gas jar, measuring cylinder or glass tube. Pour it out vertically and see how much can be outside the support of the tube before it splits apart.

Theory:
Breaking stress = hρg   where h is the height of the column and ρ its density

Age range: 16-18
Apparatus required: •Sand •Water •Masses •Tin lid •Chicken bone •Jelly •Safety goggles and safety screen

16. Electric strain gauge

A simple model of an electric strain gauge can be made by an arrangement similar to that used for investigating the stretching of fishing line. Take a 2m length of resistance wire (such as nichrome) and clamp one end to the bench. Pass the other end over a pulley and hang a weight on the end. Measure the resistance between two points on the wire as far apart as possible either by using a sensitive ohmmeter or a voltmeter and a microammeter. (Do keep the current low – you do not want any heating effect.) Now increase the load and a change in the resistance of the wire should result.

 If pupils do this they should be aware that the wire might get hot enough to burn their skin or ignite paper etc.

Age range: 16-18

Apparatus required: •Nichrome wire (2m) •Set of weights •G clamp •Bench pulley •Ruler
•Ohmmeter or voltmeter and microammeter

SURFACE TENSION

General theory for this section;

Surface tension is known to be due to intermolecular attractions in the liquid surface and these forces produce a skin effect on the surface. The forces between individual pairs of molecules are very small, and so in a definition of the surface tension we consider the effect of a large number of molecules in a line in the surface.

Think about a line of unit length drawn in the surface of the liquid and think of the forces acting on the molecules in that line. Clearly the forces will act in all directions in the surface but we will consider only those components of force acting at right angles to the line. The force on the whole line is the sum of all the forces on the individual molecules. Notice that any given molecule is in equilibrium due to equal and opposite forces acting on it. This force per unit length is called the surface tension of the liquid.

Pressure difference across a curved liquid-air surface of radius R = 2T/R where T is the surface tension of the liquid.

1. Wax on a kitchen sieve	10. Floating a needle
2. Surface tension - glass blocks and water	11. Glass, coin and credit card
3. Capillary rise and perpetual motion	12. Beer glass and handkerchief
4. Surface tension and soap solution	13. The double bubble
5. Giant bubble recipe	14. Camphor boat
6. Boat and surface tension	15. Diameter of a molecule
7. Simulated water drops	16. An air bubble in free fall
8. Rotating dish	17. How full is a glass?
9. Soap bubbles	18. Strength of a soap film

1. Wax on a kitchen sieve

This is a very good demonstration of surface tension. Immerse the sieve very briefly in hot wax to get a thin coating on the wires. Then pour water into the sieve - due to surface tension the water will not pass through the greasy holes. The angle of contact between the water and the wires has been increased to more than 90° and so the water will not wet the wires.

 The wax is best melted in a water bath rather than by direct heat. If heated directly great care is needed to prevent ignition of the liquid wax or vapour.

Age range: 11-18 depending on treatment
Apparatus required: •Kitchen sieve •Wax •Suitable container in which to heat the wax

2. Surface tension - glass block with water in between

Take two glass blocks and put a few drops of water on the surface of one of them and then press the two blocks together taking care to spread out the water film over the whole of the intervening surface. The very thin layer of water between the blocks gives a large pressure difference across the curved surface of the water between them and makes it very difficult to pull them apart.

Theory:
Pressure difference = 2T/r where T is the surface tension of water and r is the radius of curvature of the water surface.

Age range: 11-18 depending on treatment
Apparatus required: •Two rectangular glass or acrylic blocks •Water

3. Capillary rise and perpetual motion

You could try to demonstrate perpetual motion by taking a capillary tube and dipping one end into water with the top bent over so that the open end of the tube is less than the height of the capillary rise in the tube. The idea is that water rises up the tube by capillary action, and the open end allows water to fall on to a small paddle wheel. It won't work of course because at the end of the tube the water surface becomes convex, so preventing any water leaving the tube - a pity!

4. Surface tension and soap solution

The effect of soap or meths on the surface tension of water can be shown very easily by this simple experiment. Cover the bottom of a tray with a thin layer of coloured water (a mm or so). Touch the water surface with a glass rod dipped in meths or soap solution. The water springs away leaving the bottom of the tray dry.

Age range: 11-18 depending on treatment
Apparatus required: •Tray •Water •Soap solution or meths

5. Giant bubble recipe

A number of experiments concerning bubbles are more impressive if a "strengthened" solution is used. To make these giant bubbles and sheets of soap film the following recipe is suggested. You can not only blow big bubbles (diameter over 30 cm) but also make wonderful soap films on a frame made from four plastic straws that can be made to oscillate, demonstrating slow SHM.

Age range: 11- 18 depending on treatment
Apparatus required: •You will need to make a mixture of 100 ml of bubble bath, 400 ml of tap water (this may be a little too much), 200 ml of gelozone (available from health food shops) and 50 ml of glycerine.

6. Boat and surface tension

Take a rectangular plant tray and fill it with clean water. Find a light aluminium food tray that is almost as wide as the plant tray and float it on the water. Touch the water surface behind the boat with a finger moistened with a little soap solution. The boat should be pulled along the tank by the greater surface tension of the water in front of it.

Theory:
Net accelerating force on the front of the boat = LT where L is the length of the front of the food tray and T is the surface tension of the water.

Age range: 11-18 depending on treatment
Apparatus required: •Plant tray •Rectangular aluminium food tray •Water •Soap solution

7. Simulated water drops

The shape of water drops can be simulated by fitting a thin rubber sheet to a ring clamp (diameter about 10 cm) and then filling the sheet with water - the rubber becomes distended giving the shape of a water drop.

8. Rotating dish

A splendid soap film can be formed on a crystallising dish which, as it is spun on a rotating table, will give different thicknesses of soap film (thinner near the centre and thicker towards the edges) and therefore produce different colours due to interference within the film. Use the improved giant bubble recipe and view the result with a TV camera if available.

Age range: 11-18 depending on treatment
Apparatus required: •Crystallising dish •Rotating table and suitable power supply • Blu tack ®
•Soap solution •TV camera (optional)

9. Soap bubbles

Soap bubbles have a number of uses in school Physics. They can be used in experiments on surface tension, in a simulation of Millikan's experiment, for the estimate of the size of a molecule as well as for interference effects. The beautiful colours in the films are due to the path differences for different colours of light.

An upper limit of the size of the soap molecule can be gained from the fact that a soap film or a soap bubble goes black when it is about to break. They are then so thin (less than one wavelength of light) that the only path difference is due to the phase shift of π on reflection at one face and none because of interference due to their thickness.

Age range: 11-18   Apparatus required: •Bubble solution •Blower

10. Floating a needle

The ability of a water surface to support small objects such as insects can be demonstrated by using this experiment with a needle. Rest the needle on a piece of filter paper and then lower them gently so that they float on the surface of water in a beaker. The filter paper eventually becomes waterlogged and then sinks leaving the needle floating. Adding soap will make the needle sink as it reduces the surface tension of the liquid. An alternative version is to try floating a razor blade.

Theory:
The water surface is depressed so that the needle is held up by the two surface tension forces (2LTcos A where L is the length of the needle and A is the angle that the water surface makes with the vertical where the needle rests on it).
Weight of needle (mg) = 2TLcos A.

Age range: 11-18 depending on treatment
Apparatus required: •Filter paper (the more absorbent the better) •A needle •A razor blade
•Beaker of water •Soap solution

11. Glass, coin and credit card

Fill a glass to the brim with water. Put a credit card on the surface and then place a coin on the overhanging section of the card. The surface tension will hold the card on to the water.
(Thanks to Tim for this idea)

Age range: 16-18   Apparatus required: •Glass •Water •Credit card •Coin

12. Beer glass and handkerchief

Push a handkerchief into an empty beer glass and then half fill the glass with water (or beer!) Then stretch the wet handkerchief tightly over the top of the glass, and hold it using a rubber band (a) and put a plate on top (b).

Now turn the glass upside down (holding the plate in place) (c) and then - keeping the handkerchief tightly stretched - remove the plate (d).

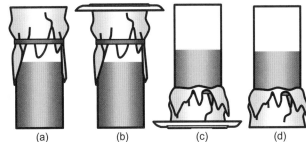

(a)   (b)   (c)   (d)

The water stays in the glass because of surface tension effects within the layer of water touching the handkerchief.

Age range: 11-19
Apparatus required: •Beer glass •Handkerchief •Plate •Rubber band •Water (or beer)

13. The double bubble

The pressure difference in different sized bubbles can be shown by the following experiment. Join a length of glass tubing to each side of the top of a T piece junction using a short length of rubber tubing with a tube clip over it. Blow a different sized bubble on each of the two ends of the T piece of glass tubing in turn, closing the clip to seal off the bubble. When both bubbles are blown open the clips to join the two but sealing off the arrangement from the air with a third clip at the base of the T piece. The big bubble gets bigger and so less curved while the small bubble gets smaller and so more sharply curved - the pressure equalises as the curvature of the two spherical surfaces becomes the same.

Theory:
Pressure difference across the curved surface of a soap bubble = $4T/r$ where T is the surface tension of the bubble liquid and r is the radius of the bubble.

Age range: 11-18 depending on treatment
Apparatus required:
•T piece •Glass tubing •Rubber tubing •Three tube clips •Soap solution

14. Camphor boat

This experiment shows the lowering of the surface tension of water by a piece of camphor (a drop of soap solution will work equally well in its place). A small piece of camphor is put in a notch at the back of a piece of thick card shaped as a boat and floating on water. As the camphor dissolves, the greater surface tension of the water at the front of the boat pulls it along.

Age range: 11-13
Apparatus required: •Camphor granules or Soap solution •Cardboard •Water in a sink or tank

15. Diameter of a molecule

The traditional oil drop experiment. Firstly you need a shallow tray filled with clean water - the cleanliness of the surface may be achieved by pulling a pair of waxed rods apart over the surface starting at the centre. A light dusting of lycopodium power is now sprinkled on the surface. A drop of oil is formed on a wire and its diameter (2r) measured. A TV camera used here instead of a travelling microscope makes life a lot easier.

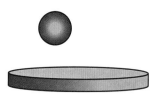

This drop is now placed on the water surface - it spreads out and the diameter (2R) of the resulting disc of oil formed on the water is measured. The thickness of the film (h) can then be calculated and the diameter of an oil molecule cannot be greater than this.

Theory:
Volume of oil film ($\pi R^2 h$) = volume of oil drop ($4/3(\pi r^3)$)   Therefore $h = 4/3(r^3/R^2)$

Age range: 11-13
Apparatus required: •Tray •Water •Powder •Oil •Wire holder •TV camera or travelling microscope or a scale graduated in half mm •Waxed rods •Ruler

16. An air bubble in free fall

Take a small plastic bottle (preferably flat sided to avoid distortion), fill it about three quarters full of water and screw the top back on.

Now throw it gently upwards and observe what happens to the air as the bottle falls towards the ground (catch it before it hits it!) You will see that the air forms a roughly spherical bubble in the centre of the water.

Theory: The air and the water are both in free fall. As it falls the air bubble tries to adopt the volume with the smallest surface area, in other words a sphere. (I am grateful to Randel for this idea.)

Age: 14-18   Apparatus required: •Small flat sided plastic bottle •Water

17. How full is a glass?

The effect of a convex meniscus can be shown by this simple experiment. Get one of the pupils to fill a glass with water. Now show that you can put in quite a bit more water, or some lead shot, without it overflowing - the convex meniscus keeps the water in place.

Age range: 11-18 depending on treatment
Apparatus required: •Glass •Water •Sand or lead shot

18. Strength of a soap film

Soap films will 'put up with' a lot of rough treatment before they break. You can push a wet finger or a wet knife through a soap film, but a dry object will burst it. Most surprising is that a stream of water will pass through a soap film and the film will still be there.

Age range: 11-18
Apparatus required: •Soap solution •Wire frame •Water

FLUID FLOW AND VISCOSITY

General theory for this section:
There are basically two principles involved here:
(a) Bernoulli's law which relates to the lowering of pressure in a moving fluid
(b) Stokes' law which relates to the terminal velocity of objects falling through a fluid
The viscous drag on a sphere of radius r falling at its terminal velocity (v) through a fluid of viscosity $\eta = 6\pi\eta rv$

1. Fluid flow - ink and glycerol
2. Viscosity and falling dust
3. Stokes' Law
4. Fluid flow in tubes
5. Balancing balls
6. The physics of the frisbee
7. Styrocell beads in a snowstorm
8. Throwing a ruler - Bernoulli

9. Ball in funnel
10. Moving a ball in the air
11. Cotton reel and card
12. Table tennis balls and egg cups
13. Blowing between two sheets of paper
14. Terminal velocity and mass
15. Paper glider

1. Fluid flow - ink and glycerol

Fill a measuring cylinder or gas jar with glycerol and put a thin layer (a few mm) of blue ink on the top. Drop a ball bearing into the jar. As it falls some of the ink is collected by it and the streamlines round the falling ball are clearly visible as it moves downwards. With care the ink can be pipetted up again so making the glycerol reusable!

Age range: 14-18
Apparatus required: •Tall measuring jar •Glycerol •Ink •Pipette •Ball bearing

2. Viscosity and falling dust

Relate the viscosity of the air to the speed of fall of light and heavy rain, builders' dust falling slowly in a room and the fall out after the Chernobyl disaster across Europe. Heavy rain hurts more than light rain - the droplets are not only bigger but also fall faster. ($6\pi\eta rv = mg = 4/3\pi r^3\rho g$). Calculate the rate of fall of the different particle sizes. Try it with styrocell beads in water. Basically we are looking for the terminal velocity of the particles.

3. Stokes' Law

The effect of viscous drag on a sphere can be investigated by dropping ball bearings through glycerol. Alternatively you can watch bubbles rising through a fizzy drink, syrup or glycerol.

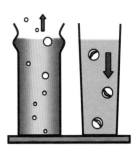

Theory:
When the balls (radius r) are falling at their terminal velocity (v) through a fluid of coefficient of viscosity η the drag due to the viscous effect of the fluid is equal to the difference between their weight (mg) and the upthrust (U)
$mg - U = 6\pi\eta rv$

Age range: 15-18
Apparatus required: •Tall measuring cylinder •Glycerol •Stop clock

4. Fluid flow in tubes
Compare the viscosities of a number of different liquids by allowing them to flow down through glass tubes. It has been suggested that you could make a clock from a tin of syrup - graduated by how long it takes the syrup to run out!

Age range: 14-18
Apparatus required: •Various liquids – water, syrup, glycerol •Tin with a hole in the bottom •Glass tubes of various diameters •Stop clock •Filter funnel •Rubber bung with a hole in the centre for attaching the glass tube to the filter funnel •Short length of rubber tubing •Tube clip

5. Balancing balls
Balance a polystyrene ball or a table tennis ball on top of a vertical jet of water from the tap or a vertical jet of air from an air blower. The first one is messier! With the air jet it is possible to bend the jet at quite an angle with the vertical - showing that it is not simply the upward force of the jet that keeps the ball up. Try a balloon on the air jet! A hairdryer acts as a good air blower.

Theory:
The rapidly moving stream of air forms a lower pressure region that keeps the balls within it.

Age range: 14-16
Apparatus required: •Air jet •Retort stand and clamp •Various polystyrene balls •Table tennis ball •Light rubber ball •Beach ball

6. The physics of the frisbee
Use one of these to show fluid flow and pressure decrease in the fast moving stream of air over the frisbee. Simply throw the frisbee and talk about the way it moves.

7. Styrocell beads in a snowstorm
A further demonstration of viscous drag can be made by pouring some styrocell beads into a jar full of water, putting on the lid and then turning the jar upside down. The beads fall slowly due to the viscosity of the water (Stokes' Law) and simulate a fairly good snowstorm. (Christmas fun!)

Age range: 11-14
Apparatus required: •Styrocell beads •Jar with screw top lid (the taller the better - plastic bottle will do) •Water

8. Throwing a ruler - Bernoulli
Throw a 30 cm ruler by holding it in the centre horizontally and then flipping it about its long axis. The resulting spinning motion should make it curve up or down. Compare this motion with top and bottom spin of a table tennis ball.

Age range: 13-16   Apparatus required: •30 cm ruler

9. Ball in funnel

Another simple demonstration of the lowering of pressure in fast-moving air streams is to put a table tennis ball on to the bench and place a glass funnel over it. Attach the funnel to an air blower and switch on the airflow. The ball will be pushed up into the funnel and the rush of fast-moving air between the ball and the funnel creates a pressure difference and holds the ball in the funnel despite the fact that the funnel is held upside down!

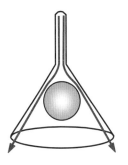

Age range: 15-18
Apparatus required: •Air blower •Table tennis ball •Glass funnel •Rubber tubing

10. Moving a ball in the air

The bending of the path in air of a spinning table tennis ball, tennis ball, cricket ball or rounders ball can be shown very clearly by the following experiment. Put a polystyrene ball or a table tennis ball into a cardboard tube with one end covered and with an internal diameter just a little greater than that of the ball itself.

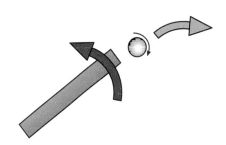

Holding the tube by one end, swing it smartly so that the ball is thrown out. The side of tube will give the ball a spin about a vertical axis and it should curve across the lab. Deflections of at least a metre in a distance of ten metres can easily be obtained. It is even better outside where you can throw it faster. Using a polystyrene ball and covering the inside of the tube with sandpaper works well.

Theory:
As the spinning ball moves through the air the flow of air past it will be more rapid on one side than on the other. This creates a difference in pressure between the two sides of the ball and so the ball moves into the area of lower pressure.

Age range: 14-18
Apparatus required: •Polystyrene ball or table tennis ball •Cardboard tube about 70 cm long

11. Cotton reel and card

Put a pin through a card and put this in the tube in the centre of a cotton reel. Blow through the other end of the cotton reel. The fast moving layer of air emerging between the cotton reel and the card creates low pressure, and this pressure difference holds the card on to the reel.

Age range: 14-18   Apparatus required: •Cotton reel •Cardboard •Long (2 cm) pin

12. Table tennis balls in egg cups

Blowing across the top of a table tennis ball which is resting in an egg cup is a very simple way of showing the reduction in pressure in a moving fluid.

Put a table tennis ball in an egg cup. Place another egg cup nearby and ask someone if they can transfer the table tennis ball to the other egg cup without touching it. The art is to blow sharply across the top of the ball. The lower pressure in the air stream draws the ball into the airflow where it will be given a sideways force which will move it into the other cup.

A certain amount of practice is needed.

Age range: 16-18
Apparatus required:
•Table tennis balls •Egg cups
•Puff!

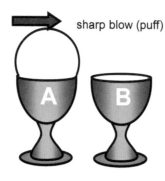
sharp blow (puff)

13. Blowing between two sheets of paper

One of the simplest demonstrations of reduced pressure due to fast-moving air is simply to hold two sheets of paper vertically, one in each hand, and then to blow down through the gap between them. The lowering of the pressure in the moving air (Bernoulli Effect) explains why they are drawn together.

Theory:
When a fluid is in motion the pressure within the fluid varies with the velocity of the fluid if the flow is streamlined. This pressure variation is a consequence of Bernoulli's theorem proposed in 1740. This states that:
The pressure within a fast-moving fluid is lower than that in a similar fluid at rest or moving slowly.

This effect can also be seen when two tall heavy lorries travel along rapidly side by side and are drawn together. The same effect has also been experienced at sea between two ships. This also explains the vibration of the reed in an oboe; the fast moving air stream between the two reeds causes lower pressure between them and so forces them together. Changes in this pressure cause the reeds to vibrate.

The shape of the cross-section of an aircraft wing is designed so that the velocity of the air above the wing is greater than that below it. A region of low pressure is therefore created above the wing and so the aircraft experiences an upward force known as lift.

Racing cars have inverted aerofoils so that the force is downwards, thus increasing the force between the car and the road

Age range: 13-16
Apparatus required: •Two sheets of paper

14. Terminal velocity and mass

The effect of mass on terminal velocity can be investigated using a number of cup cake paper cases. These are dropped singly or nested in groups of two, three, four and so on. The outer shape of one or more cups is almost the same and so the only variable is mass. You can drop them from the same height and time how long they take to reach the ground or alternatively experiment with different heights until each combination of cup cases reaches the ground at the same time.

I am very grateful to Donald Simanek for the initial idea for this experiment.

Theory:
When a body is falling at its terminal velocity the vertical forces on it are balanced and so drag force (F) = weight of body = mg. It is usually assumed that when a body is moving through a fluid such as air the drag force (F) on it is proportional to the velocity of the body squared (v^2).

Therefore: $F = mg = kv^2$, but if the body is falling at its terminal velocity it will be moving with constant velocity and so to find the distance (d) that it falls in a time t we can use the simple equation: $d = vt$

Therefore: $d = t[\sqrt{(mg/k)}]$

So if d_1 is the distance fallen in a time t by one cup case (mass = 1) and d_3 the distance fallen in a time t by three nested cup case (mass=3) then: $d_3/d_1 = \sqrt{3} = 1.732$. So if we want to have the cup cases hitting the ground at the same time we must drop them from different heights – in the ratio of the square root of their masses.

If we drop them from the same height, the ratio of the times taken for one and three cup cases to reach the ground is:

$t_1/t_3 = \sqrt{[m_3/m_1]} = 1/\sqrt{3} = 0.58$

Age range: 11-19   Apparatus required: •Paper cake cups •Ruler •Stopwatch

15. Paper glider

To make the paper glider you need an isosceles right angled triangle of paper. The long edge is then bent over twice – each bend being about 0.3 cm wide. This is then bent round in a circle to join the two pointed ends forming a shape rather like a bishop's mitre. The end is then bent upwards to give the shape shown in the photograph. If you hold the paper near to the bent up tail and then let it go it will float across the room covering a distance of many metres.

There are many possibilities for investigating the range with different types of paper, size of bend, and angle and size of the "tail". Older students can study the fluid flow through the glider.

Many thanks to Ian for this idea.

Age range: 7-18   Apparatus required: •Triangle of paper •Ruler •Stopwatch

VIBRATIONS AND WAVES

General theory for this section:
The RATE of vibration is called the **FREQUENCY** and is measured in **HERTZ**. A frequency of 1 Hz is a rate of vibration of ONE oscillation per second. To measure high frequencies we use kilohertz (kHz) (1 kHz = 1000 Hz) and megahertz (MHz). [1 MHz = 1 000 000 Hz].You may have met frequency scales before - on a piano or on a radio. The frequency of middle C is 256 Hz and that of FM radio about 100 MHz.

Large, heavy or slack objects vibrate slowly and have a low frequency.
Small, light or tight objects vibrate quickly and have a high frequency.

1. Skipping rope - only certain frequencies
2. Standing waves on plates - the drum
3. Waves and refraction
4. Standing waves
5. Wave motion
6. Phase changes
7. Standing waves and a toothbrush
8. Melde with white elastic
9. Vibration
10. Standing waves on a vertical slinky
11. Speed of waves along a rope
12. Standing waves and gas flames
13. An oscillating floating cylinder

1. Skipping rope - only certain frequencies

Two people stand opposite each other and try swinging a skipping rope, or wobbling a stretched rubber tube. They will find that are only certain frequencies that are allowed. No matter how hard they try, not all frequencies are possible.

The fundamental frequency and two additional harmonics are shown in the diagram. These harmonics are easier to produce if the rubber tube is moved in a slightly circular way - rather like actual skipping. (I have found the rubber tubing easier to control than the rope.)

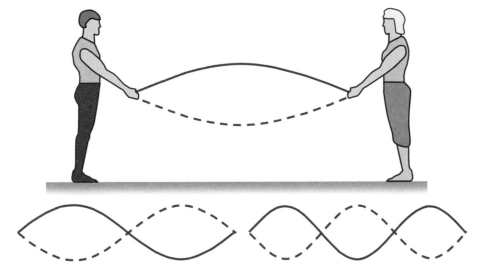

Theory:
When the rope or cord vibrates with its fundamental frequency (the lowest) the length of the cord is one half of one wavelength. For higher modes of oscillation the length is equal to a whole number of half wavelengths.

Age range: 14-18   Apparatus required: •Skipping rope •Rubber tubing (Bunsen burner tubing is fine)

2. Standing waves on plates - the drum

These can be studied using a metal plate fixed on the top of a vibration generator. (Even stiff card will do.) Sprinkle some dust on the plate and then vary the frequency of oscillation of the vibration generator. Standing wave patterns should be seen on the plate. With the vibration generator switched off some interesting sounds may be heard when a musical box is placed on the plate and set going. The plate will resonate at certain frequencies.

Age range: 16-18
Apparatus required: •Drum or stretched membrane •Vibration generator •Metal plate •Dust or talcum powder •Musical box

3. Waves and refraction

A useful way to explain the way light waves behave in reflection and refraction is to compare them to water waves. Water waves slow down as they pass from deep to shallow water and light waves slow down as they pass from air to glass. As waves move up a steadily sloping beach they slow down and their wavelength is reduced, the frequency of the waves remaining unaltered. If the angle of incidence is anything but zero (in other words if the waves hit the boundary at any angle to it other than a right angle) then the waves will bend - refract – and their direction of travel will be changed. This is explained by realising that one side of the wave front hits the join before the other and so slows down first, causing a change of direction.

Driving a car from sand on to a tarmac road at an angle gives exactly the same turning effect. This can be demonstrated by using a toy car running on to an area of sand on a perspex sheet. Total internal reflection can be seen!

Age range: 13-16   Apparatus required: •Toy car •Perspex sheet •Sand •Overhead projector (optional)

4. Standing waves

A small-scale version of standing waves in sound can be performed using a piezoelectric buzzer and a microscope slide. Set up the buzzer facing the slide and move the slide towards it and away from it - recording the positions of the nodes and antinodes with a small microphone.

Age range: 14-18   Apparatus required: •Piezoelectric buzzer •Microscope slide •Stands •Microphone

5. Wave motion

The motion of a tuning fork and the sound waves produced by it can be observed using the following arrangement. Tape together three or four bar magnets all aligned the same way and put them in a coil of wire of around 3000 turns connected to a cathode ray oscilloscope.

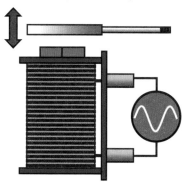

Now vibrate a tuning fork over the magnets. The fork becomes magnetised and so induces a potential in the coil which can be seen on the oscilloscope. Using a storage oscilloscope module will enable the waveform to be studied at leisure. The beats formed between two tuning forks of similar frequency may also be studied using this method by striking them and then holding them both over the magnets.

Age range: 16-18
Apparatus required: •Four strong bar magnets •Tape •Oscilloscope •3000 turn coil •Leads

6. Phase changes

To demonstrate the phase change that occurs on reflection of a wave use two ropes, one with its far end fixed to a post and the other with a free end - such as a ring sliding along a vertical rod like a retort stand. A pulse is sent along each rope and is reflected from the far end. The phase change of π only occurs on reflection from the fixed end; a crest is reflected back as a trough. This is not the case with the free end nor is it for a water wave hitting the side of a harbour wall - the particles of water are free to move up and down and so no phase change occurs here.

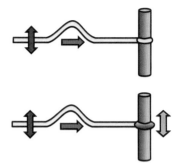

Age range: 16-18   Apparatus required: •Ropes •Broom handles

7. Standing waves and a toothbrush

This is a very simple method of demonstrating standing waves.

Remove the brush part of an electric toothbrush and fix a length of light elastic thread to the metal vibrating rod. Fix the toothbrush in a retort stand (this gives it more stability than holding it in your hand) and then hold the other end of the elastic thread. It is even possible to buy toothbrushes with dual speeds.

Pull the thread gently and then switch on the toothbrush. If you adjust the tension correctly you will produce standing waves on the elastic thread. Changing the tension will give different harmonics.

This is a simple experiment that removes the need for an expensive vibration generator.

Age range: 11-16
Apparatus required: •Electric toothbrush •Elastic thread •Retort stand boss and clamp (optional)

8. Melde with white elastic

The standing waves on a string are very well demonstrated by using a piece of white elastic fixed to a vibration generator, looped over a pulley and attached to a mass to give it tension.

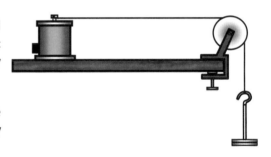

The vibration generator is switched on and the elastic is then viewed with a stroboscope. It is easy to change the tension by adding more mass.

Theory: Frequency (f) = $(1/2L)(T/m)^{1/2}$ where T is the tension of the elastic and m its mass per unit length.

 Stoboscopic lighting may induce photo-epilepsy in some individuals. Check that no-one present is affected in this way. If so they will need to leave the room.

Age range: 14-18   Apparatus required: •Vibration generator •White elastic •Stroboscope •Slotted masses

9. Vibration

The variation of pitch with vibrating mass can be clearly shown by the following simple experiment. Hold a ruler over the edge of the bench and twang it. The ruler vibrates, producing a note. The pitch of the note can be varied by sliding the ruler further on or off the bench.

Changing from a wooden ruler to a plastic one demonstrates the dependence of thestiffness of the vibrating object on the note produced. This can be used as a simple demonstration of vibration, or for more advanced work, to investigate the equation of a vibrating cantilever - using a metre ruler loaded with masses.

Plotting log T against either log M or log L where M is the mass on the ruler, L is the length of the ruler protruding over the bench and T is the period of oscillation will enable the student to predict the equation of the motion.

Age range: 13-16   Apparatus required: •Rulers of different thicknesses and materials

10. Standing waves on a vertical slinky

Hang a metal slinky spring from a beam and fix the lower end to a vibration generator. By adjustment of the frequency of the vibration generator very good standing waves may be set up in the slinky. It is helpful to mark the nodes with coloured tape.

The frequency required is usually a few Hertz. As an extension try the experiment using a plastic slinky. Compare the frequencies needed to set up standing waves in the steel and the plastic.

Theory: The distance between nodes (points of no vibration) is one half a wavelength.

Age range: 16-18
Apparatus required: •Vibration generator •Signal generator
•Slinky spring •Coloured sticky tape

11. Speed of waves along a rope

Mount two identical thick ropes side by side across the lab, one end of each rope fixed to the wall and the other hanging over a pulley with a mass on the end to tension the rope. Put a piece of folded card over each rope at the same distance from one end. Hit the ropes at the same point with a broom handle and observe the folded card. The rope with the greatest tension will carry the vibrations faster and the card on this rope will jump off first.

Theory

Speed of waves along the rope = $(T/m)^{1/2}$ For a rope with a mass per unit length (m) = 0.1 kg and tension 50 N the speed = $22ms^{-1}$, for tension (T) = 20 N speed = 14 ms^{-1}.

Age range: 16-18
Apparatus required: •Two lengths of thick rope •Two pulleys • Masses • Card • Broom handle

12. Standing waves and gas flames

Another wonderful demonstration of standing waves uses the apparatus shown in the accompanying diagram. A metal pipe has a row of fine holes drilled along it and a small loudspeaker fitted to one end. The loudspeaker is connected to a signal generator. A gas supply is connected to the other end.

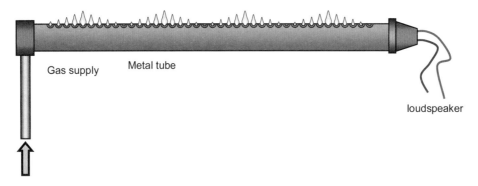

Gas is passed into the tube and the gas coming out of the holes is lit. When the loudspeaker is turned on, a series of standing waves is formed in the pipe and their position and displacement are shown by the height of the flames along the tube. If a musical signal is applied to the speaker the waves will 'dance'!
(I am grateful to Eilish who first showed me this experiment)

 There must be no leaks, except through the flame holes and so the loudspeaker and gas supply tube are best permanently sealed to the tube. Gas pressure has to be carefully controlled to limit the flame height. Beware of a very hot tube even after the gas has been turned off. The tube should be checked for leaks before each use and must be flushed with gas for 20 seconds before ignition. This 'flushing' should be done with adequate ventilation to ensure no build up of gas in the room and before the pupils arrive.

Age range: 16-19
Apparatus required: •Metal pipe about 3 cm in diameter and 2 m long •Drill with 1.5 mm bit for the holes •Small loudspeaker and signal generator •Connector for the gas supply •Leads

13. An oscillating floating cylinder

This is a fascinating experiment and I am grateful to Martin who first showed me this.

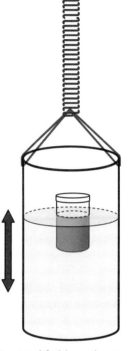

Cut the top off a large plastic drinks bottle so that you have effectively a large beaker. Pierce two holes at opposite ends of a diameter, thread a loop of string through the holes and then fix this loop to a long helical spring. Half fill the 'bottle' with water. In the water float a plastic film canister – loaded with sand so that it floats upright and painted to show the water level when it is floating at rest. (See diagram)

What happens if we allow the 'beaker' to oscillate up and down on the spring?
At the bottom of each oscillation will the canister:
(a) always float with the same volume submerged as in the rest position?
(b) float with less submerged – higher in the water?
(c) float with more submerged – deeper in the water?

It actually always floats with the same amount submerged.

Theory:
The depth at which the wooden block or straw floats depends on both its weight (not its mass) and the upthrust on it. The upthrust depends on the weight of water displaced. Thus, as the acceleration of the jar and the block change, the weight of the block and the upthrust on it change 'in direct proportion to each other; as a result, the depth at which the block floats remains unchanged as the apparatus oscillates.

Objects undergoing acceleration behave in the same way as they would in a gravitational field. As the jar and its contents oscillate, they have an acceleration which is due to both the constant gravitational field of the Earth and the varying acceleration due to the simple harmonic motion of the oscillation.

As the jar moves upwards, its net acceleration is greater than that of the Earth's gravitational field and as it falls its acceleration is less than that of the Earth's field. On the downward part of the motion, it is as if the jar were on the Moon, where the gravitational acceleration is less than on Earth: 1.63 m/s^2, about 16.7% that on Earth's surface.

Oscillating the beaker on Earth is really only the same as changing the gravitational pull – it is a good example of the equivalence of gravitational and inertial frames.

Age range: 16-19, adult

Apparatus required:
•Long helical spring •2 litre plastic drinks bottle •String •Film canister with sand or plasticine •Water
• Scissors or knife for cutting bottle •Straw loaded with plasticene as an alternative to the canister

DOPPLER EFFECT

General theory for this section:

When a source of waves and an observer are moving towards or away from each other there is an observed change in frequency of the wave received by the observer. This change (Δf) is given by the equation $\Delta f = fv/c$ where v is the relative velocity of source and observer, and c is the velocity of the waves.

If the source is moving towards the observer the waves are "squashed up", so the wavelength is made smaller. The faster the source moves the more the waves are squashed. With sound this means that the pitch of the sound that you hear is increased, and with light the colour of the light that you see is shifted towards the blue end of the spectrum.

If the source is moving away from the observer the waves are "stretched out", and so the wavelength is made larger. The faster the source moves the more the waves are stretched. With sound this means that the pitch of the sound that you hear is decreased, and with light the colour of the light that you see is shifted towards the red end of the spectrum.

The change in frequency is much more noticeable in sound than it is with light. This is because the speed of light is so much greater than the speed of sound.

1. Doppler buzzer
2. Doppler velocity with microwaves
3. The Doppler duck
4. Beats and the Doppler Effect

5. Applications of the Doppler Effect
6. A chocolate factory and the Doppler Effect
7. The moving tuning fork
8. Doppler Effect – whistle and funnel

1. Doppler buzzer

An easy way to show the Doppler Effect with sound is to use a whirling piezo electric buzzer. Connect a small buzzer to a battery or power supply by some long wires which should be taped securely to the buzzer, hold the battery in your hand and then swing the buzzer round your head. For wires a metre and a half long (or more) a really good Doppler effect is produced. You should ask the pupils whether they think that the person actually spinning the buzzer round will hear the Doppler Effect or whether the change of pitch is only audible to somebody else.

It is also interesting to ask if it matters how close to someone you stand. Clearly it does - the nearer you are the more the interval between high and low pitch will be changed. Instead of the piezo-electric buzzer you can use a small speaker.

You could also try using a mobile phone with a suitable ring tone held in your hand and swung round at arm's length – it sounds like bagpipes!)

Theory:

For an emitted frequency of 300 Hz and a rotation rate of two a second in a one metre radius circle the frequency shift is 11.5 Hz, a change of pitch of a little under a semitone at that frequency.

 A length of cord or string should be attached to the buzzer or loudspeaker so that, if a break does occur in the electrical connections, it cannot 'fly off' and cause damage or injury.

Age range: 16-19 Apparatus required: •Piezoelectric buzzer •Power supply or battery pack •String •Two 2m leads •Electrical tape

2. Doppler velocity with microwaves

The frequency shift due to the reflection of a wave from a moving object (due to the Doppler Effect) is very easy to show using the 2.8 cm microwave apparatus. Set up the transmitter and receiver side by side, pointing the same way, with the receiver connected to an amplifier and speaker. Put a sheet of cardboard mounted vertically in a base clamp in front of the amplifier and receiver. Now move a sheet of metal backwards and forwards on the other side of the card. The Doppler shift is easily heard as a note from the loudspeaker.

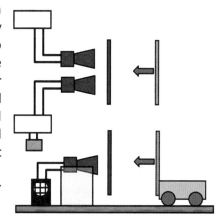

Swishing a metre ruler is especially effective. The faster the ruler moves the higher the pitch.

It will work with just your hand and without the card if done in a lab with good reflections from the walls. The police radar speed trap frequency is apparently has the same frequency as that use in school microwave kits with wavelength (λ) of 2.8 cm!

If the output is connected through the amplifier to an oscilloscope a very much more sensitive demonstration results - any movement in front of the card gives a large trace on the screen. The actual shape of the trace can then be seen easily.

Theory:

The microwave transmitter produces a beam of microwaves, some of which is reflected from the stationary sheet of card into the receiver while some passes through and is reflected back to the receiver from the moving object. The waves from the moving object suffer a Doppler shift - an increase in frequency if the object is moving towards the card and a decrease if it is moving away. The two signals are fed to the amplifier and the difference signal is what appears at the speaker.

Frequency shift (Δf) = 2fv/c

Age range: 16-18
Apparatus required: •2.8 cm microwave transmitter and receiver •Power supply •Loudspeaker •Amplifier unit •A4 cardboard sheet mounted vertically in a base clamp •Metre ruler and metal plate •Oscilloscope

3. The Doppler duck

I use a clockwork duck with paddling feet to generate waves in a tank and to show the Doppler Effect. As the duck moves along, the ripples in front of it get compressed while those behind it are spread out - the longer the tank the better. I have often thought that a bath in the lab would be very useful!

A TV camera mounted above the tank is especially helpful to show this effect to a large group.

Age range: 16-18
Apparatus required:
•Water tank •TV camera
•Clockwork plastic duck

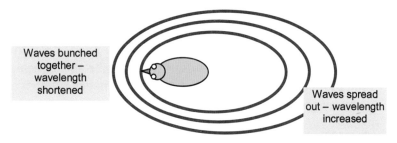

Waves bunched together – wavelength shortened

Waves spread out – wavelength increased

4. Beats and the Doppler Effect

The Doppler change of pitch can be used to give beats between two signals. For the two sources two signal generators are needed, feeding outputs to two small speakers, one loudspeaker being mounted on a dynamics trolley (the rider on a linear air track is an alternative). If the frequencies of the two signal generators are adjusted to give beats, then by moving the dynamics trolley the beat frequency can be made to change. This is an exact simulation of the police radar speed trap and is a sound version of experiment 2.

Age range: 16-18
Apparatus required: •Two small loudspeakers •Dynamics trolley or Linear air track •Leads •Two signal generators

5. Applications of the Doppler Effect

1. Galactic red shift – lines in the spectra of receding galaxies are shifted towards the red
2. Plasma temperatures – broadening of spectral lines from fast moving atoms
3. Doppler burglar alarm – reflected signal from a moving object such as a person
4. Rotation of the Sun – shift in frequency due to recession and approach of solar limbs
5. Radar speed trap – shift in frequency of the reflected wave from a moving car
6. Speed of blood flow in the body – shift in frequency of signal reflected from moving blood

6. A chocolate factory and the Doppler Effect

A good analogy to help to explain the Doppler Effect is to imagine that you are working in a chocolate factory packing chocolates that come to you down a steadily moving conveyor belt. At the other end of the belt another person puts the chocolates on the belt at a steady rate. The chocolates therefore reach you at the same steady rate at which they were put on.

Now imagine that the other person starts to walk slowly towards you alongside the conveyor belt, still putting chocolates on at the original steady rate. You can see that you will receive the chocolates at a faster rate because after putting a chocolate on the belt your partner walks after it and when the next chocolate is put on the belt it will be closer to the first chocolate than if he or she had not moved. You will also receive chocolates at a faster rate if you walk towards the other end, collecting chocolates as you go while your partner stays still.
Walking the other way will mean an increasing separation of chocolates and a drop in the rate at which you receive them - the Doppler Red Shift.

In this analogy the chocolates represent the crests of a wave, the rate at which they are put on the belt the original frequency of the source, the rate at which you receive them is the observed frequency, your speed (or your friend's speed) is the speed of the observer (or source) and the speed of the belt represents the speed of the waves.

7. The Moving Tuning Fork

A very simple demonstration of the Doppler Effect is to use a tuning fork mounted on a small sounding box. You simply hold the box in your hand, strike the tuning fork and then move it towards or away from the class. They will easily be able to hear the change of pitch.
Good musicians may be able to estimate the change of pitch and so a rough measurement of the speed of your arm could be made.

Age range: 14-18
Apparatus required: •Mounted tuning fork •Striker

8. Doppler Effect – whistle and funnel

A very simple way of showing the Doppler Effect is to use a whistle and funnel. You will need to find a cylindrical whistle and fix a funnel into the mouthpiece. Then tie a length of string to them as shown the diagram. The funnel and whistle should then be whirled round your head with the open end of the funnel leading.

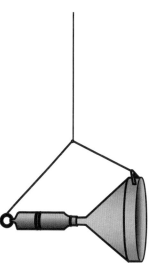

Theory:
As it moves through the air enough air will go into the funnel and then through the whistle to make a note. This note will alter as the speed of rotation is changed.

Get someone to stand a few metres away from you and listen to the note that they hear. As the whistle moves towards them the pitch of the note will increase and when it moves away it will decrease. The funnel and whistle can be swung in either a horizontal or vertical circle.

Age range: 16-19

⚠ This should be done outside if space in the laboratory is limited. Ensure that pupils are a safe distance away.

Apparatus required:
•Plastic funnel •Cylindrical whistle (an old fashioned police whistle is ideal) •String

Further general information about the Doppler Effect

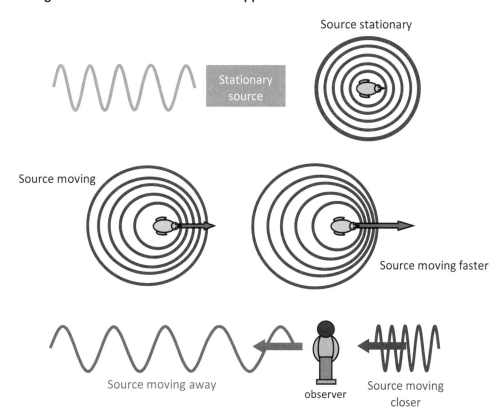

Source stationary

Stationary source

Source moving

Source moving faster

Source moving away

observer

Source moving closer

RESONANCE AND DAMPING

General theory for this section:

Resonance

Any object, such a child's swing can be made to vibrate if it is given a push, but you find that if the frequency of the push has one particular value the amplitude of the oscillation of the swing builds up - this is known as resonance. Put another way, if the driving frequency is equal to the natural frequency of the oscillating system then resonance results.

Damping

There are two types of damping:

(a) Internal - where the amplitude of oscillation of an object reduces due to internal forces

(b) External - where the amplitude of oscillation of an object reduces due to external forces such as air or liquid

Either of these may produce light damping where the oscillations die away very slowly, critical damping where they die away fairly quickly in less than one oscillation or heavy damping where the object takes a long time to reach its equilibrium position without oscillating

1. Mechanical resonance - hacksaw blade
2. Coupled pendulums - Barton
3. Air damping
4. Resonance between buildings
5. Standing waves
6. Resonance in a rod
7. Resonance and earthquakes
8. Resonance again

9. Tacoma Narrows Bridge
10. Resonance - tambourines
11. Resonance curves and damping
12. Coupled pendulums - two SHM
13. Feedback
14. Coupled oscillations and resonance
15. Resonating plank

1. Mechanical resonance - hacksaw blade

Mechanical resonance can be demonstrated very well by using a 30 cm long hacksaw blade mounted vertically in a base clamp. Oscillate it by using a vibration generator pressing against the lower part of the blade and load the top of the blade with a lump of plasticine. To get the different resonance frequencies alter the frequency of the vibration generator until the hacksaw blade makes large oscillations. Use two five-kilogram masses placed behind both the vibration generator and the clamp to keep the arrangement steady or clamp it all to the bench.

Vary the mass of plasticine to give different resonant frequencies. Values in the 10 Hz to 20 Hz range are to be expected.

Another variation of this resonance experiment is to mount the hacksaw blade horizontally directly on to the vibration generator. It then becomes rather like the ruler twanged over the edge of the bench.

Age range: 16-18
Apparatus required: •Vibration generator •Signal generator •Hacksaw blade •Two large masses or G clamps •Two base clamps •Plasticine

2. Coupled pendulums – Barton's pendulums

Set up a series of light pendulums all suspended from the same tight string. Fix one heavy pendulum to the string - the same length as one of the light pendulums. Now displace the heavy pendulum. Resonance will occur between the heavy pendulum and the light pendulum of the same length. All the pendulums will move with phase differences between them and the heavy pendulum.

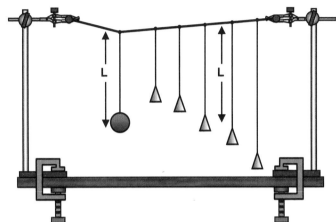

The traditional pendulums are lead spheres and paper cones, but I have found that polystyrene balls are very suitable for the light pendulums.

Age range: 16-18
Apparatus required:
•Five light pendulums
•One heavy pendulum
•String
•Two retort stands
•Two G clamps

3. Air damping

Suspend a mass from a spring. Fix a large cardboard disc above the mass. It is convenient to use the hanger from a set of slotted mass and have the disc resting on the base of the hanger with another mass on top to hold it in place. Pull the mass downwards and allow it to oscillate. You will need a spring with a spring constant that allows an initial amplitude of some 20 cm to show this effect well. As a demonstration a slinky spring works very well. The effects of air damping can then be easily investigated by measuring the decay in amplitude as time passes.

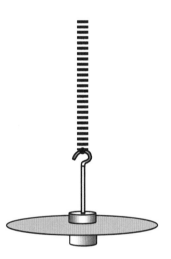

For the older students a graph of the natural log of the amplitude against the number of oscillations enables the equation of the motion to be found, namely $A = A_o e^{-kn}$

A further investigation can be carried out using discs of different diameters.

Age range: 16-18
Apparatus required: •Helical spring •Slotted masses •Cardboard disc about 30 cm in diameter •Ruler in a base clamp

4. Resonance between buildings

I used to live in a house that was joined to my neighbours' by a garage. Each house had identical large open plan lounges. When he used his stereo in his lounge I could hear it loudly in mine. The sound was transmitted along the joining beams to my house. The transmission of the bass frequencies was particularly unpleasant, the low frequency booming resonating in the large volume of the room!

5. Standing waves

As a demonstration of standing waves and resonance use a vibration generator mounted upside down connected to a signal generator. Hang a spring from it and attach a mass to the lower end of the spring. This arrangement enables the resonant frequency of the system to be altered easily by changing the suspended mass. The resonant frequency can be found by changing the frequency of the vibration generator and looking for the largest oscillation of the mass. The period can be compared with that given by the formula for the natural period of oscillation of a spring $T = 2\pi(e/g)^{1/2}$, where e is the extension of the spring when a mass m is hung on it at rest.

An alternative version of this experiment is to have the weight hanging from the spring that is then attached to a thread over a pulley coming up from the vibration generator, which is placed on the ground below it.

Age range: 16-18
Apparatus required:
•Pulley •Vibration generator •Signal generator •Thread •Helical spring
•Slotted masses and hanger •Retort stand and clamps

6. Resonance in a rod

Take a metal rod; one about a metre long and with a diameter of 0.5 cm is about right. Hold the rod in the centre with one hand and then stroke the rod with the thumb and forefinger of the other hand, having rubbed them with rosin. The rod will then "sing". To get a good resonance you will have to grip the rod quite tightly.

The wavelength of the sound produced is half the length of the rod so if the rod is too short you won't be able to hear the sound.

Age range: 13-18   Apparatus required: •Aluminium rod 1m long and 0.5 cm in diameter •Rosin

7. Resonance and earthquakes

This experiment suggests two different methods of simulating the effect of an earthquake.
(a) A set of dowel rods of different lengths (or hacksaw blades) topped with different amounts of plasticine is mounted in a board. The board can then be shaken to simulate an earthquake. Some of the rods will vibrate strongly (showing resonance) depending on the frequency of vibration of the board.

(b) Stick a set of paper rings of different diameters on a card. The rings represent different sizes of buildings. Then shake the card. If you get the shaking frequency right one ring resonates. Varying the shaking frequency will make different rings resonate. Rings of card and aluminium foil can also be used to represent buildings made of different materials.

Age range: 14-18   Apparatus required: •Dowel rods •Plasticine •Board •Card •Paper •Aluminium foil

8. Resonance again

A further example of resonance using the vibration generator is to suspend a spring from a retort stand. Hang a weight on it and fix another spring below the weight. Fix this spring to a vibration generator and switch on. Adjust the frequency of the vibration generator to give resonance.

Age range: 16-18
Apparatus required: •Vibration generator •Signal generator •50g mass
•Two short helical springs (3 cm x 1 cm unextended) •Retort stand, boss and clamp •G clamps

9. Tacoma Narrows – resonance in bridges

This classic video clip of the collapse of this bridge is a must for all Physics departments. It shows the resonance collapse of the bridge due to the effect of high winds on the special structure of the bridge. Notice the man leaving his car. The millennium bridge across the Thames in London suffered badly from resonance effects when it was first opened and had to be stiffened to prevent it swaying.

Resonance can be a problem to all suspension bridges. In fact when I used to go to secondary school part of the route was across a small suspension footbridge over the river Severn in Shrewsbury. If two or three of us went across together, a suitable heavy walking speed would get the bridge swinging. The local army cadets were told to fall out of step when crossing it! They didn't always obey orders!

Age range: 13-18

10. Resonance - tambourines

Fix one tambourine by its rim in a clamp with its skin vertical and hang a light polystyrene ball so that the ball just touches the skin of the tambourine. Now hold a second identical tambourine parallel with the first and close to it, and strike this second tambourine. The resonance effect with the first should make the ball swing away from the skin.

Age range: 13-18
Apparatus required: •Polystyrene ball on thread •Two tambourines •Retort stand, boss and clamp

11. Resonance curves and damping

The nature of sound that can be made by blowing across the top of a milk bottle or twanging a tuning fork makes a good demonstration of the relation between the damping of an oscillating system and the shape of its resonance curve. The milk bottle has a broad resonance curve but heavy damping. The tuning forks have a sharp resonance but light damping, and so the oscillations take a long while to decay. The decay of the sound can be measured with a microphone and a storage oscilloscope or with a computer sensor.

Age range: 16-18
Apparatus required: •Milk bottles •Tuning fork mounted on a resonant box •Microphone
•Storage oscilloscope or computer sensor

12. Coupled pendulums - two SHM
Suspend a filter funnel by four threads so that it is able to oscillate in two planes. Put your finger over the funnel outlet and fill the funnel with sand. Now oscillate it over a sheet of paper. The pattern formed shows SHM in two directions.

Age range: 14-18
Apparatus required: •Filter funnel •Thread •Sand •Retort stand, bosses and clamps

13. Feedback
Feedback is the phenomenon where part or all of the output of a system is fed back to the input and affects it. A simple demonstration of this is as follows and is an effect that many of us have heard from the public address system at sports days or while trying to set up a sound system for a concert or play. Put a microphone in front of a speaker driven by an amplifier. The slightest noise will produce the high-pitched whistle denoting feedback.
There follows two analogies, one of positive feedback - where the feedback increases the output, and one of negative feedback - where the feedback decreases the output.
Positive feedback: a snowball rolling down a hill - the bigger it is the bigger it gets.
Negative feedback: a stream full of leaves or mud flowing through a narrow gap - the more leaves that get stuck the slower the water flows and the more leaves get stuck and so on.

14. Coupled oscillations and resonance – the Wilberforce pendulum
This device is simply a mass suspended by a spring. It has three modes of oscillation:
(a) a swinging motion
(b) a vertical oscillation along the axis of the spring
(c) a twisting motion
If these last two modes can be made to have the same fundamental frequency, energy can be transferred between them. The way of varying the torsional oscillations without varying the mass is to have a wooden disc with four bolts imbedded in it and projecting radially. On each of these is a nut, and if the nuts are moved in or out the moment of inertia of the disc is changed but not its mass.

Age range: 16-18
Apparatus required: •Spring •Slotted masses •Wooden disc with four bolts and nuts fitted as described

15. Resonating plank.
A man walks across a field carrying a long plank on his shoulder. At each step the plank flexes a little (a) and the ends move up and down. He then starts to trot and as a result the plank bounces up and down (b). At one particular speed resonance will occur between the motion of the man and the plank and the ends of the plank then oscillate with large amplitude.

(a)   (b)

SOUND

General theory for this section

Sound waves travel through the air by the air molecules vibrating backwards and forwards. This 'backwards and forwards' motion of the molecules in a sound wave means that sound waves are **LONGITUDINAL WAVES**. The faster the vibration, the higher the pitch of the note, and the bigger the vibration the louder the note.

On the Moon where there is almost no air, sound would not travel from one place to another. You could see an explosion but not hear it.

1. Wine glass
2. Continually rising pitch that gets nowhere
3. Sea shell amplification
4. Wood blocks - musical scale
5. Playing a hose pipe
6. Playing a saw
7. Sound transmission under water
8. Singing tube
9. Increase in pitch as a bottle is filled
10. Sharp and flat!
11. Chicken - resonance with rubbed string
12. Tea chest and washboard - music
13. Dog whistle and dog
14. Two tunes in the orchestra
15. Musical jars
16. Velocity of sound - echo method
17. Paper cup telephones
18. Difference tones
19. Reflection of sound
20. Sound transmission under water (2)
21. Bell in bell jar
22. Balloon guitar
23. The refraction of sound
24. Dominoes and sound transmission
25. Playing a straw
26. Reflection of sound 2 (i = r)
27. Sound – a set of simple experiments
28. Making sounds louder
29. Musical notes
30. The sensitivity of your ears
31. Sound in different materials
32. Reverberation time in a concert hall
33. Energy in a vibrating tuning fork

1. Wine glass

Playing a wine glass makes an interesting introduction to sound and resonance. Partly fill a wine glass with water and moisten your finger with a little meths to get rid of any grease. Rub your finger round the rim of the glass to make it sing. (If you put wine in the glass you can moisten your finger in the wine.) The water writhes and shakes because of the vibrations which you can actually feel in your finger. (Don't press too hard – you don't want to break the glass.)

Good effects can be achieved if you apply a steady pressure between your finger and the glass, firmly enough to get the stick-slip motion needed to produce the sound but not enough to break the glass and cut yourself! Changing the amount of liquid in the glass gives a change in the pitch of the note. Glasses with differing amounts of liquid can be used to play a tune.

Age range: 11-13
Apparatus required: •Wine glass •Meths (or a little violin or cello rosin)

2. Continually rising pitch that gets nowhere

A wonderful demonstration of the physiology of the human ear is the technique of a continuously rising note which does not actually get anywhere. This strange sensation can be produced by introducing harmonics.

129

3. Sea shell amplification

Listen to a sea shell. The rushing sound which seems to be like the sea is the result of the tiniest of sounds being amplified in the shell. These tiny sounds from around you cause resonance effects within the shell. This explains why different shells give sounds of a different pitch. The louder the noises around you the louder will be the sound of the 'sea' in the sea shell. Don't spoil the magic of the effect for the young by too much explanation!

Age range: 5-13
Apparatus required: •Sea shell

4. Wood blocks - musical scale

Cut up a series of hardwood blocks, with their dimensions as follows. All are of the same cross section 3 cm x 0.5 cm and their lengths should be 22.0 cm, 22.8 cm, 24.2 cm, 25.8 cm, 27.2 cm, 28.3 cm, 29.5 cm and 30.5 cm. Drop them one at a time onto a hard floor so that one end hits the floor slightly before the other. The effect is like a xylophone.

Age range: 11 - 18 depending on treatment   Apparatus required: •Wooden blocks cut to size

5. Playing a hose pipe

The dependence of the length of a pipe on the fundamental pitch that it emits when played can be impressively demonstrated by this experiment. Fit a clarinet mouthpiece into one end of a hose pipe. Play an ascending scale by chopping off lengths of the pipe with a pair of loppers having first calculated the lengths required for a good scale and marked them on the hose pipe. As it gets shorter the fundamental frequency of the pipe gets higher and so up goes the pitch. It has one big disadvantage as a musical instrument for the twenty-first century - you can't go back down again unless you are very good at sticking pieces of hosepipe together!

Age range: 11-13
Apparatus required: •Length of marked hose pipe
•Clarinet mouthpiece •Loppers

6. Playing a saw

A good example of the effect of tension on the notes produced by a musical instrument can be obtained by playing an ordinary saw. Hold the saw between your knees, bend it into an S shape and then play the smooth edge with a bow! With luck and practice flexing the saw allows tunes to be played - I have managed part of Three Blind Mice!

It is worth emphasising that there is no need for amplification - the large surface area of the saw means that a lot of air is set in motion and a loud and rather ethereal noise is produced.

 | **Reduce the hazard of cuts from the saw teeth by sticking a length of thick carpet tape over them.**

Age range: 11-13
Apparatus required: •Saw •Cello bow •Towel as protection for your legs •Rosin

7. Sound transmission under water

You can try this with a speaker in a glass funnel covered in cling film and a microphone in a plastic bag. Remember to insulate all the connecting leads.

Age range: 11-13
Apparatus required: •Small speaker in a glass funnel •Thin plastic membrane •Tank of water •Microphone in plastic bag

8. Singing tube

There are two methods of producing sounds from a simple tube.

(a) One is just a plastic tube that you spin round your head, and the sound you get is formed in the same way as blowing across the open end of a milk bottle. As the tube moves, the rush of air across the open end gives a sound. Differing lengths resonate at differing frequencies.

(b) The other one is more complex. Set up a glass or metal tube (about a metre long and with a diameter around 5 cm) vertically in a clamp. About 10 cm from the base fit a piece of copper gauze across the tube, and then heat the gauze strongly until it glows red-hot. Remove the flame. The tube should emit a loud singing note that lasts for some time. This is due to the expansion and contraction of the air in the tube as the copper cools down.

It is important not to allow the tube to heat up much. If it does, the effect is much less strong as all the air in the tube becomes hot and the contraction effects are not so pronounced. For this reason a metal tube is better than a glass one because it can be cooled quickly and the heat can be conducted away through its walls. A cardboard tube will also work.

An interesting extension is to use a cooling collar used for wine and wrap it round the tube. Moving this up and down will alter the pitch of the note emitted.

Theory:
As the copper gauze cools, the air around it contracts sharply and a shock wave is set up in the tube, thus forcing the air within the tube into oscillation. Usually the fundamental note for the tube is produced (L = λ/2), but I have obtained harmonics (L = λ). The position of the copper gauze is fairly important - no effects being produced if it is too close to the end of the tube.

 Take care not to shatter the glass tube or ignite the cardboard tube with the Bunsen flame.

Age range: 11-18 depending on treatment.
Apparatus required: (a) •Plastic tube (b) •Glass tube •Copper gauze •Bunsen •Retort stand and clamp

Extension experiments
Use a metal tube with two layers of gauze inside. This version can be used as described, but it has the advantage that it can also be heated from the side to avoid melting the gauze.

Both metal and glass tubes only work when they are held upright with the gauze at the bottom. Turbulence during heating and cooling sets up vibrations within the tube. Hot air rises so the gauze must be at the bottom of the tube.

9. Increase in pitch as a bottle is filled

The effect of the volume of a musical instrument on the pitch can be shown very easily by filling a bottle with water. As the water goes in, the air in the bottle is excited and a sound is produced. This sound increases in pitch as the bottle gets fuller, so there is less air to vibrate.

Age range: 11-13
Apparatus required: •Milk bottle and a supply of water

10. Sharp and flat!

The tendency of wind instruments to go sharp when taken into a warm concert hall is also due to this effect, since the fundamental frequency of a pipe increases as the speed of sound in air increases, and this happens when the temperature of the air rises.

Notice that the density of the gas has no effect on the sounds heard from stringed instruments.

11. Chicken - resonance with rubbed string

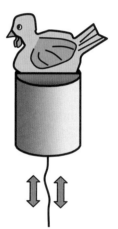

Take about 5 cm of cardboard tube (diameter also about 5 cm) and cover one end with stretched tracing paper. Fix a piece of thread through this. Make a chicken cut out that fits into the other end of the tube. Put rosin on your thumb and forefinger and gripping fairly tightly pull them down along the thread - a reasonable clucking and squawking sound can be made with practice! It is a very good example of resonance and amplification.

If you are ever in Prague these are sold by the street sellers in the castle (2002).

Age range: 11-13
Apparatus required: •Chicken made from cardboard tube and tracing paper •Rosin •Thread

12. Tea chest and washboard - music

The skiffle groups from the 1950s used two simple pieces of apparatus to make sound - the tea chest bass and the washboard. Both make interesting demonstrations. The bass in simply an inverted tea chest with a broom handle fixed vertically to one side. A piece of string from the top of the broom handle to the centre of the tea chest makes the string of the instrument. Changes in pitch are obtained by bending the broom handle. There is plenty of resonance from the large volume of air in the tea chest.

Rubbing a wooden plectrum across the ridges of a washboard produces a really good set of vibrations.

Age range: 11-13
Apparatus required: •Tea chest •Broom handle •String •Washboard

13. Dog whistle and dog

It would be nice to be able to use a dog whistle and a real dog to see their reaction to the ultrasonic waves produced by a dog whistle.

14. Two tunes in the orchestra

I have been told of a piece of classical music where two different parts of the orchestra play different tunes which when heard together sound like a third tune! I believe that there is a Haydn symphony where this effect can be heard.

15. Musical jars

Fill a row of jars with different amounts of water and play a scale and then a tune. It gets better with practice! See experiment 1.

16. Velocity of sound - echo method

The measurement of the speed of sound is easy to do using the echo method. Snap the clapper boards together outside in front of a distant building and record the time it takes for the echo to return. I use the school wall with a distance of nearly 200 m, giving a "there and back" distance of 400m. The advantage of this method is that it uses not only a larger distance for the sound to travel (giving a longer time interval which is easier to measure) but also eliminates wind errors.

A minor additional detail - it also keeps all the class together in one place, both those doing the timing and the person using the clapper boards!

The discussion of the result should lead on to mentioning that the temperature of the air also affects the speed of sound - it being faster in hot air since the molecules are moving faster.

Theory:
Velocity of sound in a gas depends on the velocity of the molecules of that gas (v) since the sound waves are transmitted by the motion and collision of the gas molecules.
This is given by the equation $1/2(mv^2) = kT$ and so $v = (3kT/m)^{1/2}$ where k is the Boltzmann constant $(1.38 \times 10^{-23}$ $JK^{-1})$.
Therefore the speed of sound in a gas depends on (i) the absolute temperature T and (ii) the mass of the individual molecules of that gas - in other words the type of gas.
Sound waves therefore travel faster through a hot gas which has light molecules.

Wear ear defenders.
The use of a starting pistol that looks like a revolver is now prohibited in schools.

Age range: 11-18
Apparatus required: •Long measuring tape •Stop clocks •Clapper boards

17. Paper cup telephones

Take two paper or plastic cups, and make a hole in the base of each. Then thread a 3 m long piece of cotton through the hole to join the two together, fixing the cotton to the base of the cups with tape. Now pull the thread taught, and speak into one of the cups, while someone else listens with their ear to the other one. The vibration of the air within the first cup is transmitted first to the cup and then to the thread. At the other end the vibration of the thread is passed to the second cup that then amplifies the sound. Try both changing the length and tension of the string and using wire instead of string.

You can extend this to the idea of a loudspeaker by putting a large coffee tin on a vibration generator to amplify the sound produced by a signal generator or radio.

If you cross the strings of two sets of paper cup telephones so that the strings touch, a multiple way conversation can be heard!

Age range: 11-13
Apparatus required: •Paper or plastic drinking cups or two small tins •Thread •Coffee tin •Vibration generator •Radio

18. Difference tones

The superposition of sound can be shown by using a referee's whistle with a hole on either side, or an old police whistle. (I have one from the 1940's given to me by my grandmother.) Blow into it and you will hear a note that is the combination of the tones from the two sides. My whistle gives a minor third output. Now bring your finger up to one of these holes to reduce the volume from that side, and finally to cut it out altogether - you will hear a change in the overall pitch.

Theory:
Superposition of two simple harmonic motions $y_1 = a\sin(2\pi f_1 t)$ and $y_2 = a\sin(2\pi f_2 t)$
Final wave form: amplitude $(y) = 2a\cos 2\pi(f_1-f_2)t/2 . \sin(2\pi(f_1+f_2)t/2$

Age range: 11-18 depending on treatment
Apparatus required: •Two-hole referee's whistle or police whistle

19. Reflection of sound

You can demonstrate this using two large concave mirrors with a small speaker at the focus of one and a microphone at the focus of the other. The intensity received by the microphone is then shown using an amplifier and an oscilloscope. Alternatively just put your ears at the focus of the second mirror.

Even simpler is to hold a large concave mirror up in front of you and move it inwards towards your face as you speak. When the distance between your mouth and the mirror is equal to the radius of curvature of the mirror a loud sound will be received by your ears.

Age range: 11-16
Apparatus required: •Two large concave mirrors - diameter around 45 cm •Microphone •Amplifier •Oscilloscope

20. Sound transmission under water (2)

Lie in a bath, and tap the side of the bath under the water with either your feet or a piece of wood. Now turn on to your side so that one of your ears is below the water surface. The sound will be much louder in that ear. The greater density of water means that the molecular vibrations are transmitted much more effectively through it.

Age range: 11 - 15
Apparatus required: •Bath •Water

21. Bell in bell jar

To demonstrate that sound needs a medium through which to travel suspend a bell in a bell jar and then evacuate it using a vacuum pump. This has the disadvantage that the bell vibrates mechanically, sending vibrations along the connecting wires. Standing the bell jar base plate on a sheet of foam rubber helps to reduce vibrations through the bench.

As an alternative use a piezo-electric buzzer suspended by threads and connected to a battery within the bell jar.

It would be good if the experiment could be done in a vessel that could be evacuated simply by allowing water to run out.

Age range: 11 - 13
Apparatus required:
•Bell •Bell jar •Vacuum pump •Sheet of foam rubber •Piezo-electric buzzer •Wire and battery •Thread

> **Eye protection required. Only bell jars designed to be evacuated should be used. Ensure that there are no cracks or chips in the glass which could cause the jar to implode when evacuated. Safety screens should be used to protect those present.**

22. Balloon guitar

You can make a really good balloon guitar using some very simple materials. You need a balloon, a length of wood, two nails and a piece of string. Fix the string to each end of the wood using the nails so that the string is loose. Blow up the balloon, and push it under one end of the string as shown in the diagram. Now push down on the string to force it on to the wood.

If you pluck the string a note can be made. Just like a real guitar the shorter the string the higher the note, so moving your finger closer and closer to the balloon will give you higher and higher pitched sounds. The balloon acts like the tea chest in a string bass – amplifying the sound.

push down here

(Thanks to Sue for the idea for this experiment)

Age range: 11-14
Apparatus required: •Balloon •Piece of wood •Two nails •String

23. The refraction of sound

This can be clearly demonstrated using a signal generator, a balloon filled with carbon dioxide, a microphone and an oscilloscope. The balloon acts as a lens, focusing the sound.

Age range: 14-16

Apparatus required: •Carbon dioxide cylinder •Balloon •Signal generator •Loudspeaker •Microphone •Oscilloscope

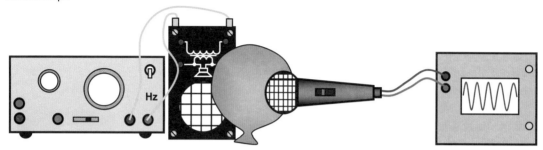

24. Dominoes and sound transmission

Dominoes can be used as an analogy to show that sound travels faster in a solid than in a liquid. Stand two lines of dominoes, one with the dominoes close together (this is the solid) and one with the dominoes further apart (this is the liquid). Knock over the first domino of each line, and watch the speed at which the 'pulse' travels down the two lines. It will move faster down the line with the dominoes close together. Sound travels faster in a solid than it does in a liquid.

'Solid'   'Liquid'

Age range: 11 – 16   Apparatus required: •Set of dominoes

25. Playing a straw

Flatten one end of a plastic straw. Cut the end as shown to make a mouthpiece – and blow through this end. (It works better if the 'mouthpiece' is a little behind your lips.) You should get an oboe-like note. (An oboe has a double reed rather like the two sides of the end of the straw.)

You can now get a friend to cut pieces off the straw while you are blowing.

As the straw gets shorter and shorter the pitch of the note will go up. Halving the length should increase the pitch by one octave.

If you do a control experiment first using another straw you can mark the places to cut it and so play a scale. If you can find one straw that will slip over the first one you have a slider, and so tunes can be played by moving the slider in and out. You could make a slider out of a tube of paper.

Age range: 11-14   Apparatus required: •Plastic straws •Scissors

26. Reflection of sound (2)

Mount a piece of hardboard vertically and lay two cardboard tubes on the bench in front of it. 10cm diameter tubes that have been used for carpets are ideal. Put a clockwork watch or clockwork kitchen timer in one tube, and put your ear against the open end of the other tube. When the angles between the two tubes and the hardboard are the same you should hear a loud ticking proving, that the angle of incidence = angle of reflection for sound.

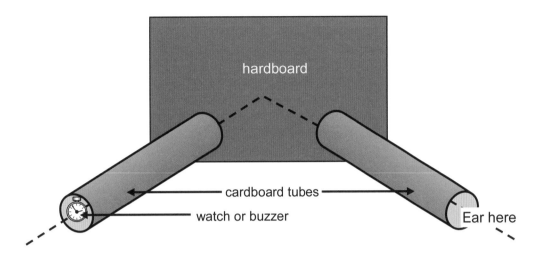

Age range: 11-14

Apparatus required: •Two large diameter cardboard tubes •Sheet of hardboard •Protractor •Clockwork watch, clockwork 'egg timer' or small electric buzzer

27. Sound – a set of simple experiments

The following list is a set of simple experiments that demonstrate that sound is made by vibrating objects.

They could be done as a circus for the pupils or by the teacher demonstrating them and asking the children to come up and try for themselves.

1. Put some small pieces of paper or rice grains on a drumhead and then hit the drum with your hand or a drumstick. The paper and the rice will vibrate (jump about).

2. Strike a cymbal, and then hold it close to your ear. If you touch the cymbal with your ear you can feel the vibrations.

3. Hit a cymbal, then get hold of the edge between your finger and thumb. You can feel the vibrations stop as you grip harder, and as they do the sound also stops.

4. If you stop the cymbal vibrating by putting the edge of it against your chest the sound it makes will stop as well. Link this to the damping of sound by rooms with soft walls and the echoes made from the hard stone walls in churches.

5. Fill a shallow tray with water, and then touch the edge of the tray with a vibrating tuning fork. Waves can be seen moving across the water surface.

6. Play a comb – you can feel the vibrations through your lips as you blow through the paper.

7. Hold a ruler down on the table with your hand so that it sticks out over the edge of the table, and then twang the ruler with your other hand. You can see the ruler vibrating, and as you make the ruler shorter you can hear the sound change. The shorter the ruler, the higher the pitch.

8. Hold your hand in front of a powerful disco type speaker. You should be able to feel the vibrations in the air. If you have an old speaker with no covering lay it down with the cone facing upwards and put some small polystyrene balls in it. Now connect it to a radio or CD player and turn it on. Loud music or speech will make the balls jump around.

9. Put your hand against the body of a cello, double bass or a piano while it is being played. You can feel the vibrations in the wood.

10. Twang a rubber band – you can hear a sound and also see the band vibrating.

11. Half fill a bowl of water, and touch the surface with a vibrating tuning fork. You will see water waves spreading out from the point of contact as the water surface vibrates.

12. Take a two-litre plastic bottle full of water (or lemonade) and knock it with your knuckles about half way down. You will hear a sound but also see a lovely pattern of vibrations on the water surface.

13. Hold a piece of thin card between your thumbs, and blow on its edge. You should be able to make a note and will be able to feel the vibrations in your thumbs.

14. If anyone in the school has a brass instrument get them to play it. They feel the vibrations in their lips as they make a sound. Even just using the mouthpiece on its own is good enough.

15. Get the children to walk away from a source of sound and stop when they can't hear it any more. The energy is spread out as the distance is increased, and so less is getting into their ears.

16. Whispering shows that quiet sounds are more difficult to hear than loud ones.

17. Cover your ears with some kind of muffler or large headphones. If you get someone else to make a noise you won't be able to hear it.

18. Tie two lengths of string to a metal cooker shelf grid. Make loops in the other ends of the string, put these round your index fingers and then put your fingers in your ears so that the grid hangs vertically. Get someone else to tap the grid with a ruler. You should hear a loud bell-like sound. The sound waves are being transmitted along the strings directly to your ears.

19. Put a small folded piece of paper on a violin, guitar or cello string, and then pluck or bow the string. The paper will jump about showing that the string is vibrating. You could always make a simple 'guitar' with two nails fixed into a piece of wood and with a rubber band stretched between them. Small pieces of paper bent over the band will jump off when the band is 'twanged'.

28. Making sounds louder - musical box and tin can

Try playing a small musical box on its own and then hold it against the base of an empty tin can. The sound is much louder because all the air in the tin can is vibrating as well rather than just that against the 'prongs' of the musical box.

It might be worth actually fixing a musical box to the base of the tin with small bolts. It makes it much easier to hold.

Putting the musical box on a table or a wood panelled wall also works very well. The whole table and panelling vibrates, giving a much louder sound. (Thanks to Ruth for this idea)

Putting a glass with the open end against a wall and then putting your ear on the closed end will help you hear sounds through the wall!

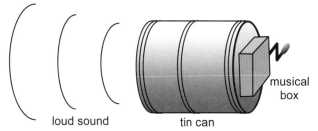

loud sound   tin can   musical box

Age range: 7 - 14
Apparatus required: •Small musical box •Tin can •Glass

29. Musical notes

The frequencies of notes in music have a precise relationship with each other. It is these ratios between one note's frequency and the next that makes combinations of notes pleasant to listen to. Notice that if you increase the pitch by one octave the frequency doubles. Using a 'key note' we can build up the whole scale. The notes shown are part of the 'equally tempered scale'.

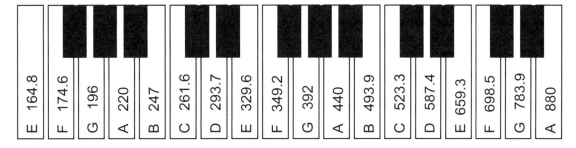

164.8	174.6	196	220	247	261.6	293.7	329.6	349.2	392	440	493.9	523.3	587.4	659.3	698.5	783.9	880
E	F	G	A	B	C	D	E	F	G	A	B	C	D	E	F	G	A

(Note: the frequencies shown on the keys are based on the musicians' scale with A = 440 Hz)

30. The sensitivity of your ears

Take two plastic ridged whirling tubes, and fix them together end to end with tape. Get one pupil to hold them so that the open ends are pressed to their ears. Another pupil then stands behind them, supporting the tube, and scratches along the ridges close to the join. Ask the first pupil which side of the join is being scratched.

They will be able to tell, although the difference in distance from the scratched section is only about 3 cm and the difference in time for the sound to reach each ear is only about 0.0001 s.

Age range: 7-14   Apparatus required: •Two plastic ridged whirling tubes •Tape

31. Sound travelling through different materials

This experiment is designed to show how well sounds travel through different materials and how some materials can be used to insulate us from unwanted sounds.

The difficulty is not providing a sound source, that can be a radio, but finding a method of measuring the amount of sound being transmitted by the material. If the school has a sound level meter this would be an ideal measuring device. Sometimes these may be borrowed from local authority education departments.

Alternatively we would have to use a microphone and a recording device that you can play back at a preset value.

(a) Put the battery-powered radio in a cardboard box covered with thick polystyrene with one open side. Then cover this open side with different materials. Simply get the pupils to judge which covering absorbs the most sound or use the sound level meter.

(b) Put your ear against a table. Another member of the class taps the table and you can hear the sound travel through the material of the table to your ear. Try this with different tables – what about the stainless steel tables in the school kitchen? You could refer to sound proofing of buildings – polystyrene foam or fibre glass.

(c) Put a battery-powered radio in a sealed box, and immerse it in water. The radio can still be heard – the sound has had to travel through the water to reach your ear. Talk to the children about whales and dolphins – they transmit sound to each other through water.

(d) Wrap up a mobile phone, and listen to the sound of the ring tones with different types of wrapping and different numbers of layers.

32. Reverberation time in a concert hall

The reverberation time gives an idea of the echoing nature of the room. It is the time taken for the sound level to fall to 10^{-6} of its original value (a drop of 60 dB). For symphonic music the best reverberation time is 2.0s; Symphony Hall in Boston, one of the finest concert halls in the world has a reverberation time of 1.8s with a full audience.

Symphony Hall in Birmingham is probably even better. This hall has large doors set in the upper tiers of the hall which can be opened or closed – so 'tuning' the hall to vary the reverberation time. When the doors are open the hall is more sound absorbent and when they are closed more sound is reflected so the reverberation time is longer.

33. Energy in a vibrating tuning fork

When you tap a tuning fork to make a sound the vibrations in the fork are very small. However you can show that it is vibrating, and so contains energy, by using a small polystyrene ball. Suspend the ball by a thread and then lightly touch the ball with the vibrating tuning fork. It will swing away violently, clearly showing that the fork is vibrating.

Age range: 7-14
Apparatus required: •Small (0.5 cm diameter) polystyrene ball •Thread •Support •Tuning fork

GEOMETRICAL OPTICS

GENERAL OPTICS

1. Optics and the smoke box
2. Sources of light demonstration lesson
3. The camera obscura
4. Distorted drawing
5. Absorption in glass - long pieces
6. Metallised film - one-way mirrors
7. Object and image
8. Variable power lens
9. The silvered bicycle reflector
10. Light reflection in a cube
11. Bent pencil in water
12. Refractive index - TV camera
13. A floating image
14. Christmas tree balls
15. Defects of lenses
16. Non lateral inversion - mirrors at 90°
17. Image position
18. Bending of wood - the optical lever
19. Real and apparent depth - sideways block
20. Pinhole camera - 360°
21. Interesting refractive indices
22. Kaleidoscope
23. Shadow films
24. Refraction and romance
25. Mirage machine

GENERAL OPTICS

1. Optics and the smoke box
Shine light through a plate with holes in it into a glass-fronted box full of smoke. The path of the rays through various lenses placed in the box can easily be followed. Smoke can easily be made by burning a piece of sacking, rag or corrugated cardboard in a smoke generator - available from beekeepers.

Age range: 13-16
Apparatus required:
•Smoke-tight box with one glass side •Smoke generator •Large (10 cm diameter) lenses

2. Sources of light demonstration lesson
I have found this an attractive way of introducing the topic of optics. We "look" at a number of different sources of light such as the Sun, matches, a Bunsen flame, iron filings and magnesium in the flame, a sodium chloride stick in the flame, a glowing wire, an electric light bulb, a low energy discharge tube, gas discharge tubes (hydrogen, cadmium, sodium, neon, xenon, and helium), an LED, a laser and an ultra violet light. The different colours of the sources, the time for which they shine and the energy losses can all be considered.

Impressive effects using ultraviolet light can be obtained from shining it on the following:
Silly putty, washing powder, nails, stage make-up, luminous watches and toys, security pens.

> **Lamps emitting short wave u.v have clear envelopes and require shielding from the eyes with a sheet of glass. Lamps with dark envelopes pose a minimal risk to the eyes but exposure should be kept to a minimum. The lasers used in schools are kept so bright that the aversion response - blanking – makes them safe to use and 'laser goggles' are not required. However, pupils should be warned not to look at the laser beam either directly or by reflection.**

Age range: 11-13

Apparatus required: •Laser •Matches •Bunsen •Iron filings •Magnesium •Electric light bulb
•Gas discharge tubes •Low energy lamp •LED •Ultraviolet light

3. The camera obscura

Small holes in shutters or blinds can give amazing views of outside scenes on the wall. It is really a pinhole camera on a very large scale. It is usually just the round disc of the Sun that can be seen, but actual views can sometimes be obtained. I have seen one formed through a small hole in a blind in a hotel room in Sorrento in Italy. An inverted image of a whole mountainside was formed on my bedroom wall as the sun "rose" over the hills near Vesuvius. Images of the Sun can often be seen in a wood where the sunlight reaches the ground after passing through small holes between overlapping leaves. The photograph shows this happening.

Age range: 11-13   Apparatus required: •Sunlight •Room with a fine hole in a blind

4. Distorted drawing

Two interesting phenomena:

(a) Reflection from a curved surface. Make a drawing of an object by looking at its reflection in a curved surface, such as a polished tin can, and then view the drawing the same way.

(b) Make a distorted drawing so that it is only clear when viewed from an angle to the picture. A very good example of this is the skull in Holbein's painting 'The Ambassadors' which is in the National Gallery in London.

5. Absorption in glass - long pieces

To demonstrate the absorption of light in glass get a series of 'off cuts' of different length from your local glazier. Shine light through the glass in the plane of the strip, and measure the change of intensity with length using a light dependent resistor (LDR). Use this to discuss the attenuation of light in glass fibres.

Age range: 14-18 depending on treatment
Apparatus required: •Long strips of glass with rounded edges •LDR •Light source •Ohm meter

6. Metallised film - one way mirrors

This reflective film has a number of uses. The best source of it is in shops selling wrapping paper - they often have some in a variety of colours and I have even seen some with reflection diffraction gratings. In optics it makes a very good one-way mirror depending on which side is illuminated more strongly. When viewed from the highly illuminated side it looks like a mirror, but when viewed from the less well-illuminated side it is possible to see through it to the brightly lit area.

It is also used by marathon runners to conserve heat after a race and so could also be part of the chapter on heat radiation experiments.

Age range: 11-18 depending on treatment
Apparatus required: •Sheet of metallised plastic •LDR for light transmission experiments

7. Object and Image

To show lateral inversion in a plane mirror use a pair of model cars - one British and one Continental with their steering wheels on different sides. Reflect them in a plane mirror to show that they appear laterally inverted.

8. Variable power lens

Use a plastic bag containing liquid, the curvature of which can be varied by squashing and stretching to simulate the way the muscles of the eye change the shape of the eye lens. Experiments will suggest the correct sort of radius of curvature to give you a reasonable focal length.

Theory:
The focal length (f) of a lens with spherical surfaces of radius r_1 and r_2 and of material of refractive index n placed in air is given by the equation:
$1/f = (n-1)[1/r_1 + 1/r_2]$.

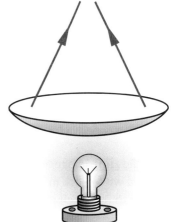

A very large version of this can be made by using a piece of transparent plastic or rubber sheet stretched tightly over the rim of a bicycle wheel. Pouring water into the top makes the plastic sag and if a lamp is put below the sheet an image can be formed on the ceiling of the lab. The sheet needs to be thin enough to distend with a relatively small amount of water otherwise the focal length is too great for any room but a high hall - like a sports hall!

Age range: 11- 18 depending on treatment
Apparatus required:
•Plastic bag •Bicycle wheel without spokes •Thin rubber sheet (as clear as possible) •Lamp

9. The silvered bicycle reflector

Get a clear plastic bicycle reflector made of pyramids of plastic, and silver paint one side (spraying it with aluminium paint is fine). Look into it - you see a completely black reflector. This is simply the reflection of your retina. Since each "hole" between the pyramids acts like a corner of a reflecting cube the light is simply reversed in direction.
(I am grateful to Roy for this fascinating demonstration.)

10. Light reflection in a cube

Note how light behaves when reflected from the inside of the corner of a cube. It is reversed in direction irrespective of the original direction of the incident ray of light. Three plane mirrors can easily be fixed together to give a right-angled corner. This explains why reflectors on bikes are made like this - the light from a car's headlamps is reflected back to the driver no matter from what angle it hits the reflector.

11. Bent pencil in water

One of the simplest methods of showing refraction in a liquid is to put a pencil in a glass of water and look at it from the top. The effect of refraction is clearly seen. The pencil appears to be bent - the end of the pencil seeming much nearer the surface than it should be. This can be used to explain the difficulty of reaching into water to pick something out - your judgement of direction is impaired by the refraction.

Age range: 11-13   Apparatus required: •Beaker of water •Pencil

12. Refractive index - TV camera

Float an object in water in a flat-sided plastic tank, and view from outside with the TV camera placed so that it looks precisely along the water surface. Some of the block will be seen through the air and some through the water. The refractive index may be worked out by measuring the dimensions of the two views of the block from the TV screen. (Refractive index = Real depth (in this case in air)/Apparent depth (in this case through the water.)

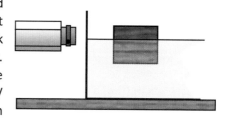

Age range: 13-18 depending on treatment
Apparatus required: •Rectangular plastic tank •TV camera •Wooden block to float in the tank

13. A floating image

Wave a white stick in mid air at the focal plane of a slide projector. The image on the slide will appear to be hanging in space, demonstrating the persistence of vision of the human eye.

14. Christmas tree balls

It is well known that the formulae for curved mirrors only apply if the reflecting surface is restricted to the centre of the mirror – i.e. to rays close to the axis. A good example of the distortion produced if this condition is not fulfilled, and when there is a reflection from a large part of a spherical surface, can be seen by using the coloured balls used for Christmas tree decorations. Using a TV camera would show the effects to a large audience.

Age range: 16-18   Apparatus required: •Christmas tree balls •TV camera if available

15. Defects of lenses

Use a lens of large diameter (10 cm if possible) and plot the image position as the lens is rotated about a vertical axis with respect to the object.

Age range: 16-18   Apparatus required: •Large lens with a diameter of at least 10 cm

16. Non-lateral inversion - mirrors at 90°

If you look at the image across the join of two mirrors that have been placed at 90° to each other you will not see any lateral inversion.

Age range: 11-16
Apparatus required: •Two plane mirrors fixed at 90° to each other •TV camera if available

17. Image position

Mount a small plane mirror vertically on the bench with a board writer standing in front of it. (The board writers should be a cm or two higher than the mirror.) You will see the image of the board writer in the mirror. Move a second board writer behind the mirror until the top of it seems to coincide with the image of the first one from whatever direction it is viewed (There is no parallax between them.) The second board writer is now at the image position of the first.

Age range: 11-13   Apparatus required: •Plane mirror mounted vertically •Two board writers or pencils

18. Bending of wood - measurement with a light beam – the optical lever

Use an optical lever to detect the bending of a bench. This can be done by fixing a small mirror to the bench and then reflecting a beam of light from it so that a spot is formed on the wall. It works especially well if the scale is on the other side of the lab. Now lean on the bench. The beam of light is deflected through twice the angle of deflection of the table and the spot moves. This method can also be used to detect the bending of walls if someone leans on them or the deflection of some ceilings if somebody walks overhead. The use of a light beam as a pointer is especially good since it has "zero" mass.

Age range: 11-18 depending on treatment   Apparatus required: •Plane mirror •Fine beam of light •Ruler

19. Real and apparent depth - sideways block

This experiment uses the real and apparent depth principle in a simple way to determine the refractive index of a block. Lay a glass or acrylic block on its side on a sheet of paper, and look at the base of the block through one side. It is then easy to mark the apparent depth of the block by measuring the length of the shiny part on the sheet of paper under the block.

Theory: Refractive index of the glass block = Real depth/Apparent depth

Age range: 11-13   Apparatus required: •Glass block •Sheet of paper •Pencil

20. Pinhole camera - 360°

It is simple to take a photograph with a pinhole camera by substituting the paper screen with a piece of photographic paper. However an interesting extension of this is to take an 'all round' photograph. Mount a toilet roll in the middle of a box with a pinhole in each of the four vertical faces of the box. In the dark room, or in a light proof bag, wrap photographic paper around the toilet roll tube.

Expose the film outdoors by uncovering the holes for up to 30s in overcast conditions but around 10s in sunlight. Develop and print the paper. A 360° picture should be obtained. A positive print can be formed by placing the negative print face downwards on the bench in the dark room (using only the safe light) on top of another sheet of photographic paper with its sensitive side uppermost. Then switch on the ordinary light for about 30 seconds and print as normal.

Age range: 11-13
Apparatus required: •Pinhole camera with centre mounted cylinder •Photographic paper •Dark room and chemicals

21. Interesting refractive indices

Some liquids have a refractive index almost equal to that of glass (about 1.5). Glass objects put in these liquids will seem to disappear.
Glycerine n = 1.47, castor oil n = 1.48, xylene n = 1.51, bath and body works shower gel = 1.51

 Dimethlybenzene (xylene) is flammable, harmful by inhalation and, in contact with the skin, will cause skin irritation so contact should be avoided.

22. Kaleidoscope

Two mirrors in a tube. Put two slices of pre-cut mirror in a cardboard tube, which can be a toilet roll. (It might even be worth trying to make your own mirrors from cards and kitchen foil.) Paint the inside of the tube matt black.

Fix the two mirrors together first along their long edges and then slide them into the tube.

The cover with the viewing hole is then fixed on the top of the tube, leaving the 'bottom' of the tube open.

A few small objects such as beads should be scattered on the paper and then viewed from above.

You can buy one of these but it is a useful exercise for the children to make one.

Alternatively use two strips of mirror and a strip of thick card or hardboard the same size as the mirror strips and bind them together in a triangular shape with an elastic band. You should first paint your piece of wood with matt black paint.

Age range: 7-14   Apparatus required: •Two rectangular plane mirrors •Cardboard tube •Glue

23. Shadow films

A really good and wide-ranging activity is to make a shadow film. There will be many skills involved – painting the screens, designing and cutting out the characters, choosing the thickness of the paper for the screen, choosing the right light source, writing the script, mounting the characters and understanding why we need to hold the characters AGAINST the screen.

The cut-out cardboard characters are fixed to thin dowel rods with either glue or a drawing pin.

Age range: 7-11
•Apparatus required:
•Dowel rod
•Cardboard
•Thin kitchen lining paper
•Drawing pins
•Glue or BluTack®

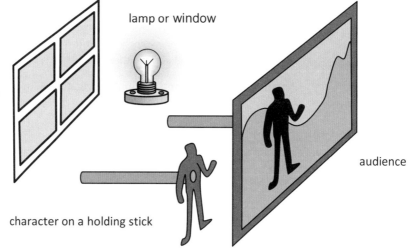

lamp or window

audience

character on a holding stick

24. Refraction and romance

Imagine that a young couple are sitting at a table on a far off beach. He asks her to marry him and gives her a gold ring with a large mounted diamond. She does not immediately accept but drops the ring into her glass of water – the diamond disappears, but she can still see the gold ring. She refuses his offer – why?

The 'diamond' is not diamond at all but glass. The refractive index of glass is similar to that of water and so the 'diamond' disappears. A real diamond has a refractive index that is very different from water and so would remain visible.

If you can't get a diamond the following experiment is even better because the solid and liquid suggested have a much closer refractive index. You can just see the word PYREX in the third photograph.

Get a flat sided plastic bottle and fill it with cooking oil. Float a pyrex test tube in the top. Then, using a thin wooden rod, push the tube down so that it fills with oil and sinks. It will disappear because the refractive index of pyrex and cooking oil are almost identical! (Clear baby oil also works well.)

Age range: 14-18 Apparatus required: •Flat sided plastic bottle •Cooking oil or clear baby oil •Pyrex test tube •Thin wooden rod

25. The Mirage machine

This fascinating double mirror demonstrates the production of an image in space. You reach down to try and pick up the space shuttle, toy animal or car and find that although you can see it you can't touch it! The lower photo is a close up showing both the object (the smaller space shuttle) and its image (the larger space shuttle).

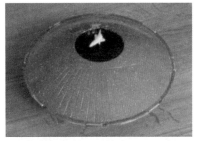

Shine a fine beam of light from a torch on to the image. The image seems to be illuminated although there is 'nothing there'. The light actually goes through the image and is reflected back by the mirrors.

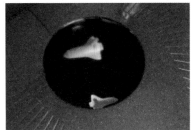

Theory and teaching notes
What you actually see is the image of the object formed in space by the double curved interior of the mirror box. This real image appears to be sitting on the top of the box.

Age range: 7-18   Apparatus required: •Mirage machine

TOTAL INTERNAL REFLECTION

The following series of experiments deal with the critical angle and total internal reflection.

General theory for this section:

When light meets the boundary between two transparent materials it will be refracted, but if it is travelling in the material with the greater refractive index and the angle of incidence is greater than the critical angle (c) it will be reflected back into the first material.

The critical angle is defined by the equation $n = 1/\sin c$ where n is the refractive index of the first medium. (This simplified equation assumes the second material to be air)

26. Colour of tanned legs under water
27. Critical angle - semicircular block
28. Total internal reflection - TV camera
29. Cat's eyes
30. Fibre optics
31. Corner of a glass block

32. Light along a water jet
33. Mirage
34. Total internal reflection and soot!
35. Optical wave-guide - prism entry
36. The floating coin
37. Mirror in tank - refraction

26. Colour of tanned legs under water

Have you ever noticed why tanned legs look less tanned as they go from air to water? Is this a layer of air bubbles on them? The light is continually reflected internally within the water, making objects in it look brighter.

27. Critical angle - semicircular block

Shine the light from a ray box or a laser into a semicircular block towards the centre of the flat side. It therefore enters at right angles to the curved side and so suffers no refraction at this point. Twist the block about the centre of the flat side so as to increase the angle of incidence of the light within the block with this side and so find the critical angle. Further increase will give total internal reflection.

Age range: 11-13
Apparatus required: •Ray box •Semicircular perspex block

28. Total internal reflection and the TV camera

Use a rectangular straight-sided plastic tank with some water in it (the one used for wave demonstrations is ideal). Point the camera upwards towards the underside of the water surface from outside of the tank. A splendid silvery surface can be seen.

Apparatus required: •Rectangular straight sided plastic box •TV camera •Laboratory jack •TV

29. Cats eyes

This is an excellent example of total internal reflection. They are visible from all directions like the corner of a reflecting cube. This also explains how bicycle reflectors work. If the bike reflector was simply a flat mirror then the beam would only reflect into their eyes for one position of the car – in fact you would only see the bike if it was directly in front of you. If the bike was to one side the reflection would not meet their eyes and the bike and rider would effectively disappear.

However, real bike reflectors are not plane. The back of the reflector is made of a large number of small tetrahedrons set together so that there are dips in between, in the shape of a corner of a right angled cube.

30. Fibre optics

Some uses of fibre optics - communications, endoscopy, security fences (you can't cut the optical fibre without the security guard knowing about it if they are watching a TV programme which has been transmitted down the fibre), lighting models. A torch or lamp using strands of glass or plastic is a simple and cheap way of demonstrating the use of fibre optics.

31. Total internal reflection - corner of a glass block

Use a beam of light from a ray box to show that you cannot get light to cross the corner of a right-angled glass block. Looking across it will simply show you the apparently silvered surface at the other face.

The photograph of the fish tank in my dentist's waiting room shows the internal reflection in a fish tank clearly.

32. Light along a water jet

This is a pretty example of total internal reflection. Get a piece of glass tube bent into a right angle to use as a water jet. Mount it in a clamp and attach it to a water tap by a length of rubber tubing. Set up a small lamp just behind the bend, and switch on both the flow of water and the lamp. The light will flow along the water path giving a gleaming patch where the water hits the base of the sink. It behaves just the same as the internal reflection along an optical fibre.

Age range: 11-13
Apparatus required: •Light source •Clamp •Sink or bucket •Water jet from L shaped glass tube

33. Mirage

A good demonstration of a mirage can be obtained by burying a few (up to six) immersion heaters in a tray of sand. Switching these on will give a mirage in the hot air above the sand.

Age range: 11-16   Apparatus required: •Six low voltage immersion heaters •Six power supplies

34. Total internal reflection and soot!

(a) This can be demonstrated by using a test tube immersed in water. The sides of the tube look silvery. A better and more controllable version is to use a glass tube. Put the tube in the water while holding your finger over the upper end to prevent the tube filling with water. It is full of air and so looks silvery just like the test tube, but when you take your finger off the water flows in and the silvery effect disappears.

(b) A further example of total internal reflection can be shown by blackening an egg with soot from a candle flame. Immerse the egg in water - it looks silvery because of the thin film of air that is trapped within the soot, only to be seen to be black when it is lifted out.

(c) An alternative demonstration is to use a table tennis ball and cover it with soot. When placed in water it will appear silvery due to the air film that clings to the soot giving total internal reflection.

Age range: 11-13
Apparatus required: (a) •Beaker •Test tube •Glass tube   (b) •Egg •Beaker of water •Candle

35. Optical wave-guide - prism entry
A prism fixed to the side of a plastic tube or piece of glass makes an easy way of demonstrating how light may be introduced into an optical wave-guide.

36. The floating coin
Put a coin in the bottom of a bowl and fix a cardboard tube at an angle so that it points above the coin and so that the coin cannot be seen through it (alternatively direct a TV camera to view over the coin).
Now add water to the bowl - the coin will mysteriously float up into view due to the refraction of light as it emerges from the water into the air.

Age range: 11 – 13   Apparatus required: •Coin •Bowl •Cardboard tube and stand •TV camera

37. Mirror in tank – refraction and total internal reflection
The following experiment is a good method of demonstrating both refraction and total internal reflection. You will need a rectangular tank with water in it to which some fluorescein has been added to make the light beams visible. Have a mirror held by a thread mounted under water in one end of a rectangular tank.

A second mirror fixed above the tank enables you to direct a ray down onto the immersed mirror. The angle at which the ray of light hits the underneath of the water surface can easily be altered by pulling on the thread.

Refraction at the air-water surface can be shown by using only the second mirror while both are required for total internal reflection.

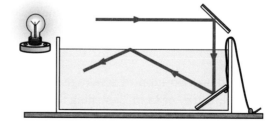

Age range: 11-13
Apparatus required: •Rectangular plastic tank •Two plane mirrors •Fluorescein •Fine beam of light from a high intensity light source or a laser •Thread •Water •Plasticine

DIFFRACTION

General theory for this section

Diffraction is the bending of radiation around obstacles or through apertures. Diffraction can also occur when waves reflect from an uneven surface. The greater the wavelength, or the smaller the obstacle or aperture, the greater the diffraction.

1. CD and DVD diffraction
2. Fingers and diffraction
3. Diffraction through fork prongs
4. Acoustic diffraction grating
5. Diffraction with sound (1)
6. Diffraction with sound (2)

7. Diffraction
8. Reflection grating
9. Diffraction through tights
10. Resolving power
11. Scattering of light in 'wet' and dry 'smoke'

1. CD and DVD diffraction

(a) A CD will give a lovely diffraction pattern due to the tracks on it acting as a reflection diffraction grating. The same effects may be obtained from a peacock's wing, a dragonfly's wing and iridescent beetles. There is no colour at all - the peacock feathers split up white light to make the brilliant colours!

(b) If you use a DVD the width of the diffraction pattern is increased. This occurs because the narrower tracks on the higher density DVD act as smaller obstacles and so give broader diffraction patterns. Take a piece of DVD or CD and use it to observe the spectral lines in the light from a fluorescent tube or the absorption lines in sunlight.

(c) An extension of experiment 1(b) is to use a laser with the CD placed on the bench. Direct the laser so that it hits the CD at grazing incidence. Take special care of beams that may be reflected in various directions.

Theory:
λ = dsinθ, for a smaller grating spacing (d) the greater the value of the angle of diffraction θ for a given wavelength (λ)

Age range: 14-18 depending on treatment
Apparatus required:
•CD or DVD •White light source such as the laboratory lights
•Gas discharge tube •Laser

Pupils should be told not to look along the line of the laser beam and care should be taken to ensure that beams cannot be reflected into the eye. Wearing 'laser goggles' with most current school lasers is hazardous because vision is so restricted.

2. Fingers and diffraction

Diffraction can be observed using nothing more than your fingers! Put two fingers together, hold them upright in front of your eyes and look at a light source through the small gap between them. Fine dark diffraction lines can be seen because of the light spreading due to diffraction in the narrow slit. It works best using a straight fluorescent tube.

Age range: 14-18 depending on treatment
Apparatus required: •Light source

3. Diffraction through fork prongs

This is another very simple demonstration of diffraction, using the same principle as that described in experiment 2. Hold up a fork and look at a light through the prongs - dark diffraction lines can be seen in the spaces between the prongs. Rotate the fork parallel to the prongs to give an effectively smaller gap and so wider fringes.

Age range: 15-18   Apparatus required: •Fork

4. Acoustic diffraction grating

An acoustic diffraction grating will show diffraction of sound. One of these can be made using a large cardboard tube with a row of 1 cm diameter holes running from end to end. Put a small loudspeaker at one end and adjust it to give a frequency of say 500 Hz. Now move a microphone along parallel to the tube and observe the rise and fall in sound intensity by looking at the microphone output on an oscilloscope.

Age range: 16-18
Apparatus required: •Cardboard tube •Loudspeaker and amplifier •Microphone and oscilloscope

5. Diffraction with sound (1)

Diffraction with sound waves can be shown easily by using a loudspeaker to produce a sound wave and then getting one of the students to align himself or herself behind another's head. The diffraction effects can then be observed by moving their own head from side to side. The sound waves spread round the obstacle (the pupil's head) and maxima and minima can be detected. Using a wavelength of about 10 cm (a frequency of 3 kHz) shows the diffraction round the head really well.

Age range: 15-18   Apparatus required: •Pupils •Signal generator •Loudspeaker

6. Diffraction with sound (2)

The diffraction of sound can also be shown by using the single slit technique. The slit is an aperture about 10 cm wide between two boards. Sound of frequency about 10 kHz is emitted by a loudspeaker placed behind the gap, and the diffraction can be observed by moving a microphone across in front of the gap. Feeding the output to an oscilloscope or meter can give a measure of intensity against position.

Age range: 16-18   Apparatus required: •Two boards •Loudspeaker •Signal generator •Oscilloscope

7. Diffraction

Misted-up glasses give good diffraction effects! I discovered this while trying to read a book in the bath with a cold pair of glasses. Viewing a light bulb through the fine mist of water vapour on the glasses showed coloured diffraction rings.

The physics of condensation is also demonstrated here! Hot air can contain more moisture than cold air and so when someone puts on a pair of cold glasses in a hot bath the air near the glasses is cooled and some of the water vapour it contained condenses on the glasses. I have also noticed the effect in my car, which was left outside on a cold night after being used the previous day with the heater on. The air in the car had been warm and so could contain a reasonable amount of water vapour, but overnight it cooled, and this water condensed out onto the inside of the windscreen.

Age range: 16-18   Apparatus required: •Glasses •Kettle

8. Reflection diffraction grating

This simple experiment was suggested by a Physics degree practical examination. Students were given a lamp, a filter and slit, a metal ruler graduated in half millimetres and a metre rule and asked to make an estimate of the wavelength of light. The idea is to lay the metal ruler on the bench and use it as a reflection diffraction grating. The effective size of the rulings can be calculated by knowing the angle at which the light hit the ruler. Diffraction images can be produced that rise vertically on the wall of the lab. Using a pen pointer laser here makes the experiment simpler.

 Pupils should be told not to look along the line of the laser beam and care should be taken to ensure that beams cannot be reflected into the eye.

Age range: 16-18
Apparatus required: •Sodium lamp •30 cm Metal ruler •Metre ruler •Pen pointer laser (optional)

9. Diffraction through tights

This is a very good example of diffraction from an irregular obstacle giving circular diffraction rings. Take a section of the tights, stretch it between your hands and then view a small torch bulb through them. Lovely coloured diffraction rings can be observed due to the diffraction from the irregular weave of the tights of the light from a white light torch bulb. Moving the tights towards and away from your eyes helps to make the coloured rings more easily visible.

Compare the effect with the regular diffraction pattern that you get from a clean, finely woven handkerchief. You can produce your own obstacles for this experiment by photographing a set of irregular dots (drawing shading film is ideal) and a set of regular dots.

The negatives are then used with the light. The initial size of the pattern can be altered using a computer or a photocopier to scale the image.

Age range: 14-18 depending on treatment
Apparatus required: •Small torch bulb •Tights •Handkerchief

10. Resolving power

To show the resolving power of the human eye draw two dots about 2 mm apart on a sheet of paper stuck to the board. View them from various distances, calculate the angle subtended by them at the eye when they appear to merge into one, and also study the effect of dim light on the ability to resolve fine detail.

In theory, as long as the light level is not too low you should do better in dim light because the resolving power of a circular aperture (your pupil) depends on its diameter, and in dim light the diameter of your pupil will be larger.

Theory:
The smallest angle (ϕ) that can be resolved in light of wavelength λ by a circular aperture of diameter a is given by $\phi = 1.22\lambda/a$

Age range: 13-18   Apparatus required: •Two small dots drawn close together on a piece of paper

11. Scattering of light in 'wet' and 'dry' smoke

This shows interesting scattering effects. The effect of moisture on the scattering of light in smoke can be simulated by introducing water vapour into a bell jar containing smoke. The smoke is blue in the dry air but white after introduction in the bell jar. The droplet size has been increased due to water vapour and so the scattering has been reduced.

| Cigarette smoking is now prohibited in schools so actual cigarette smoke should not be used in this experiment. |

Theory
The scattering of light by particles is inversely proportional to the particle size - smaller size gives greater scattering.

12. Diffraction and a fan

A normal household fan can be used to demonstrate that sound is a wave motion. Set up a signal generator and a loudspeaker behind a household fan and turn on both the fan and the sound source.

Put your head on the other side of the fan from the loudspeaker and listen to the sound.

If the frequency of the sound source is varied, diffraction may be heard as the sound waves pass between the rotating blades of the fan. Depending on the speed of rotation of the fan there will more or less diffraction. When there is little diffraction the sound will be 'chopped up' into pulses, and you will hear a warbling sound. However, if there is considerable diffraction around the blades of the fan the sound that you hear will be almost continuous.

| Do not use a fan without a wire cage around it unless it is very small and has plastic blades. |

Age range: 16-18   Apparatus required: •Signal generator •Loudspeaker •Fan

INTERFERENCE

General theory for this section:
When two groups of waves (called wave trains) meet and overlap they interfere with each other. The resulting amplitude will depend on the amplitudes of both the waves at that point. The photograph shows some waves overlapping in a fountain.

To make things simple let's just consider two waves overlapping and assume that both the waves have the same amplitude.

If the crest of one wave meets the crest of the other the waves are said to be in step (or in phase). The two sets of waves 'add together' and the resulting intensity will be large. This is known as **constructive interference**.

If the crest of one wave meets the trough of the other they are said to be out of step (or out of phase). The two sets of waves cancel each other out and the resulting intensity will be zero. This is known as **destructive interference**.

A phase change of π occurs at a reflection with an optically more dense boundary, e.g. air to glass.

1. Hologram
2. Interference and distance measurement

3. Interference with sound
4. Interference and butterflies' wings

1. Hologram
Every Physics department should have at least one white light hologram for demonstration. I have collected a number of simple ones from cereal packets. Good ones can also be bought on their own.

2. Interference and distance measurement
Use a pair of glass plates illuminated by sodium light to show the interference patterns due to the gap between the plates. Place the plates on top of each other on the bench and illuminate them from above with light from a sodium lamp. Irregular interference fringes can be seen due to the changing separation between the plates. Pressing on the top plate will alter these patterns, especially if the two plates are separated at one end by a piece of tissue paper. A tiny piece of grit between the plates will show circular interference rings. A TV camera is especially useful here to show the experiment to the whole class.

Theory:
The path difference between light reflected at the lower surface of the upper plate and the upper surface of the lower plate is 2dn where d is the separation of the plates and n is the refractive index of the air.

Age range: 16-18   Apparatus required: •Sodium lamp •Two glass plates •Tissue paper

3. Interference with sound

Interference with sound can be demonstrated by setting up two loud speakers connected to the same signal generator. Get the pupils to walk round the lab passing the speakers as they do so - a good interference pattern will be observed. They will notice that there are some places where the sound is loud and others where it is relatively soft. A wavelength of about 0.75 m (frequency 440 Hz) is quite good. Smaller wavelengths give good effects if you simply sit still and move your head from side to side. The experiment would be better outside, where the results would not be affected by reflection from the lab walls.

An alternative is to detect the maxima and minima using a microphone that can be moved in front of the speakers on a long rod such as a metre rule. The output of the microphone can be fed through an amplifier to a CRO and the amplitude of the resulting trace measured.

As an extension of this take two stereo speakers, reverse the phase of one and point them towards each other – the bass tends to cancel.

Theory:
If the path difference between the speakers and the student's ear is a whole number of wavelengths the waves will add up and the student will hear a maximum. If it is an odd number of half wavelengths destructive interference will take place and the sound will be much quieter.

Age range: 14-18
Apparatus required: •Signal generator •Two loud speakers •Microphone •Oscilloscope •Amplifier

4. Interference and butterflies' wings

The beautiful colours on a butterfly's wings are due to the interference of light reflected from their surface. That these colours really are due to this effect can be shown by placing a few drops of a clear liquid such as acetone onto the wing surface. The liquid will fill up the gaps between the ridges on the scales and so change the colour. Viewing the wings with different colours of light also shows some interesting effects.

The Christmas tree structure in the morpho group of butterfly wings is especially spectacular – iridescent blue colours being formed. Do not kill a butterfly deliberately to use in this experiment.

You might also try similar experiments using feathers - peacock's tail feathers are particularly good.

 Propanone (acetone) is highly flammable, irritating when in contact with both the eyes and skin. Propanone vapour inhalation should be avoided. Eye protection should be worn.

Age range: 16-18   Apparatus required: •Butterfly wing   •Acetone and dropper •White light source •Filters

POLARISATION

General theory for this section:

A polarised wave is one where the vibrations are in one direction only. The human eye cannot distinguish between polarised and unpolarised light.

Malus' Law: This is an equation that gives the intensity of light (I) transmitted by a piece of Polaroid:

$I = I_o \cos^2 \theta$ where θ is the angle between the planes of polarisation of the polariser and analyser.

Brewster's Law: tan p = n where p is the polarising angle and n is the refractive index of the material. At this angle of incidence the reflected beam is completely plane polarised.

Polarisation is a way of distinguishing between longitudinal and transverse waves - transverse waves can be polarised while longitudinal waves cannot.

1. Polaroid and Photoelastic stress
2. Polarisation by reflection
3. Polarisation of a TV signal

4. Polarisation and a calculator
5. Rotation of the plane of polarisation
6. Sunset in milk in water

1. Polaroid and Photoelastic stress with the Overhead Projector

(a) To demonstrate the effect of polarisation two overlapping pieces of polaroid should be placed on the overhead projector. It only works using the type of projector where the light comes from underneath the transparency. Rotating one will show how the light intensity varies with angle and if this is measured with a light meter it is possible to get a verification of Malus' Law.

(b) A beautiful extension to this is to put a piece of plastic bag or a clear plastic ruler or protractor between the two crossed polaroids to shows photoelastic stress. One piece of polaroid should be placed on the glass of the projector with the plastic ruler on top of it, and with the second piece of polaroid put on top of the ruler.

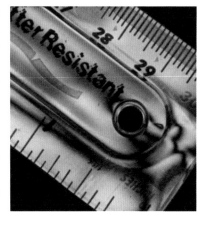

The plastic rotates the plane of polarisation of the light and different wavelengths are rotated different amounts by the stressed areas of the plastic, giving beautiful coloured areas. A small cut in the plastic also shows localised stress patterns.

Age range: 16-18
Apparatus required: •Overhead projector •Two pieces of polaroid •Plastic bag
•Protractor and/or clear plastic ruler

2. Polarisation by reflection

View the glare from desks or roads through either a piece of polaroid or a pair of polaroid sunglasses. Rotation of the polaroid will cut down the glare - hence the use of the polaroid glasses for driving. Reflection from a glass-fronted cupboard also shows the effect very well. The existence of a polarising angle (p) which for glass is about $57°$ is easy to show. Use a TV camera if possible to show the effect to the whole class at once.

Age range: 16-18
Apparatus required: •Polaroid sheets or polaroid sunglasses •Glass fronted cupboard
•TV camera if available

3. Polarisation of a TV signal

It is easy to show the plane of polarisation of a TV signal by simply rotating the aerial. The outdoor type is the best with the rod and a number of half wave bars mounted across it. Are all the TV stations in your area polarised the same way and what would happen if they weren't?

Age range: 14-18
Apparatus required: •TV set •TV aerial

4. Polarisation and a calculator

The liquid crystal display on a calculator (or lap top computer) is polarised. This fact leads to yet another very impressive, yet simple demonstration. Put a piece of polaroid in front of the calculator screen and just rotate it until the display disappears. Using the TV camera to show the effect to a class is especially helpful.

Age range: 14-18   Apparatus required: •Calculator •Piece of polaroid •TV camera if available

5. Rotation of the plane of polarisation

An extension of experiment 1 is to use a flat piece of plastic on which is stuck a number of small pieces of clear adhesive tape. Some areas can be just one piece thick while others have pieces stuck one on top of the other. Some really nice patterns are observed on the OHP reminiscent of the crystal structure of a metal.

Age range: 16-19   Apparatus required: •OHP •Clear adhesive tape •Two pieces of polaroid •Scissors •Flat piece of plastic

6. Sunset in milk in water

Sunsets, the scattering of light by small particles and the polarisation of scattered light can all be demonstrated by the following two experiments.

(a) Get a rectangular plastic tank and fill it about three-quarters full with water. Then add a few drops of milk. Mix the milk in, and then shine a light through it - a projector is ideal.

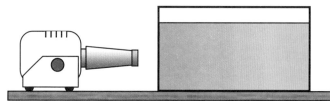

Viewed from the opposite end the lamp looks red like a sunset while when looked at from the side it looks blue - tending to green. This difference in colour is due to the tiny fat particles in the milk scattering the light - blue is scattered more than red, so as you look through the tank, most of the blue has been scattered out, leaving red light. Testing the light scattered from the sides will show that it is also polarised!

Don't add too much milk - a drop or two is enough to start with. This explains why the sky is blue (light scattered from the particles in the atmosphere and why the sunset is red - only the red is left after the light has passed through a large thickness of atmosphere, other colours having been scattered out). Superb sunsets have occurred after major volcanic eruptions.

Speculate what the colour of the sky would be on planets with denser atmospheres than that of the Earth.

(b) Drops of Dettol® (antiseptic liquid) also work well.

I gather that the colour of the iris in the eye is due to scattering. Babies are usually born with blue-grey eyes - the molecules are not linked into large chains. As they grow up the chains join and so the scattering is reduced and the iris colour often turns to brown.

Theory:
Scattering is proportional to the fourth power of the frequency.

Age range: 16-18
Apparatus required: •Rectangular plastic tank •Projector •Polaroid sheets •Milk •Dropper

Further information - The action of a polarizer and an analyser

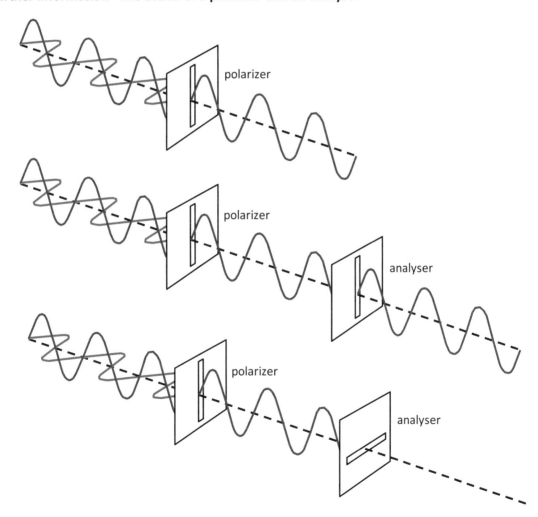

If the vibrations of a transverse wave are in one plane only then that wave is said to be plane-polarised. (Longitudinal waves cannot be plane-polarised.)

MISCELLANEOUS WAVES, SOUND & LIGHT

1. Coloured flames
2. Tape recorders in Physics
3. Cross and spot for the blind spot
4. Sodium lamp and Young's slits
5. Painting a corridor
6. Grease spot photometer
7. Persistence of vision
8. Absorption spectrum of sodium
9. Laser model - hand
10. Singing flames and beats
11. Colour discs in front of a projector
12. Laser light and the 60 W bulb
13. Binocular vision
14. A shadow photometer
15. Ribena and lime
16. Colour subtraction
17. Silhouette photographs
18. Chaotic systems
19. Phase angle
20. Ultraviolet experiments
21. P and S waves simulation
22. Sensitive flames
23. The eye
24. Aberration of light - rain
25. Coloured shadows
26. Corrugated cardboard and wave motion
27. Using a pinhole instead of glasses
28. Standing waves
29. Moiré, fringes in a net curtain or night dress
30. The television stroboscopic effect
31. A vibrating stick in a spectrum
32. Colour filters on the overhead projector
33. Path of the Sun with a pinhole camera
34. Periscope
35. Patterned glass and syrup
36. Mirror writing
37. Pepper's ghost
38. Silhouettes
39. The magic mirror
40. Diffraction through a night dress

1. Coloured flames

Burn pages of a colour magazine to give coloured flames.

 Cut samples from coloured pages and use tongs to hold these while they are burnt. Warn pupils not to inhale the smoke and/or fumes from the burning paper.

Age range: 11-13
Apparatus required: •Bunsen •Coloured magazine pages

2. Tape recorders in Physics

A variable speed reel-to-reel tape recorder is useful for the demonstration of the change of pitch when the tape speed is changed. Recording a note at one speed and then doubling the tape speed will increase the pitch of the note and musicians may realise that it has in fact gone up by one octave. The reverse is true of course if you slow the tape down.

Age range: 11-13   Apparatus required: •Variable speed tape recorder

3. Cross and spot for the blind spot

Draw a cross and a spot on a piece of paper 12 cm apart. Hold the paper up with the cross in front of your left eye and about half a metre away. Look at the cross with the right eye while closing the left. If the paper is moved backwards and forwards a place will be found where the spot will disappear as the image of it is falling on the blind spot of the right eye.

Age range: 11-14   Apparatus required: •Copy of the cross and dot – retain the same separation

4. Sodium lamp and Young's slits

The classical double slits experiment may be performed using a set of double slits and a spectrometer. Mount a pair of double slits (separation about 0.8 mm and width about 0.2 mm) in a holder on the spectrometer table. Point the collimator at a sodium discharge lamp, remove the objective lens of the telescope and adjust the eyepiece. Good interference fringes should result. Compare this result with the experiment with a laser which shows large interference fringes across the lab! The laser fringes are sharper due to the monochromatic nature of the laser light and its greater coherence.

 Pupils should be told not to look along the line of the laser beam, and care should be taken to ensure that beams cannot be reflected into the eye.

Theory

Width of the fringes = $\lambda d/D$ where d is the distance between the slits, D is the distance of the slits from the fringes and λ the wavelength of the light.

Age range: 16-18 Apparatus required: •Spectrometer • Sodium lamp • Laser

5. Painting a corridor

The most reflective colour for painting a room/corridor can be investigated by using an LDR and various coloured sheets of paper. Light is simply shone on the paper and the intensity of the reflected (scattered) light measured using an LDR. For a more detailed investigation include the data sheets from RS components on the ORP12 which give the variation of resistance of the LDR with illumination measured in lux.

Age range: 14-18 depending on treatment
Apparatus required: •LDR •Coloured paper •Ohm meter •Power supply •Lamp •Leads

6. Grease spot photometer

It is simple to measure the brightness of a lamp, or indeed the Sun, using the old-fashioned grease spot photometer. This is simply a spot of molten candle wax (or oil) dropped on to a piece of paper. If the illumination of the spot is the same on both sides then the spot virtually disappears. However, if it is not and you view the spot from the side where the illumination is greater the spot will look darker than the surrounding paper. Compare a candle with a 12 V bulb, varying the brightness of the bulb, and plot a graph of power against brightness. This traditional method avoids the calibration curve of the ORP12 LDR.

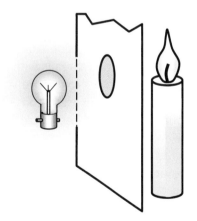

An extension of this experiment is to write a message on a large sheet of paper using melting wax. Mount the paper vertically with a light behind it. As the intensity of the light on one side is increased or decreased the writing will appear and disappear.

Age range: 14-18
Apparatus required: •Prepared grease spot on a sheet of white paper in a support •Light bulb •Candle •Power supply •Voltmeter and ammeter •Leads

7. Persistence of vision

In a TV set the screen is scanned 25 times per second. The human eye is unable to detect any variation much faster than this due to persistence of vision. This can be demonstrated by using a card with a double thread fixed to each end and with a jumping horse on one side and a gate on the other. As the card is spun by tightening and slackening the threads it looks as if the horse is jumping the gate!

Age range: 7-13   Apparatus required: •Card with horse on one side and gate on the other •Thread

8. Absorption spectrum of sodium

Set up a sodium discharge lamp in line with a Bunsen burner and a white screen. Light the Bunsen and shine light from the discharge lamp onto the Bunsen flame (blue). On the screen you can see some convection shadows but little else. Now hold a stick of sodium chloride in the flame.

A superb black shadow should be seen on the screen. Holding a wooden splint in the flame until it burns shows no shadow. The dark shadow produced when the sodium chloride stick is held in the flame is due to the sodium within it absorbing the photons of just the right energy from the light emitted by the sodium lamp. The bright flame is due to the emission of photons and the re-emission of the absorbed photons in all directions.

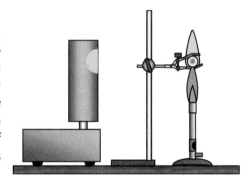

Age range: 16-18
Apparatus required: •Sodium lamp •Stick of sodium chloride •Bunsen and board •Retort stand, boss and clamp

9. Laser model - hand

The stimulated emission from a laser can be simulated as follows. Suspend a piece of card from a rod by two threads with a pendulum bob on the end. Get an electric fan and blow a jet of air at the card. Now move your other hand up and down in the air stream. If you get the frequency right the oscillations of the card will build up in just the same way as a beam of light along the axis of a laser increases in intensity as it reflects backwards and forwards between the ends of the tube.

Age range: 14-18
Apparatus required: •Card •Small electric fan with plastic blades a hair dryer set to cool

10. Singing flames and beats

Draw out a 1 cm glass tube to give a bore with a diameter of 0.5 mm. Connect it to a gas supply, light the gas emerging from the fine end of the tube, and put it in a glass tube of diameter 3.5 cm and 83 cm long. A loud noise results. Now try another with a length of tube one or two cm shorter. When both flames are lit, beats are produced between the different pitched notes.

Age range: 16-18   Apparatus required: •Glass tube •Bunsen

11. Appearance of objects in different coloured light

Coloured objects appear different colours when viewed with light of different wavelengths. This can be demonstrated by sticking three discs of coloured paper onto a board and then illuminating them with light from a projector. (Alternatively print out coloured words like those below). First use white light, and then green, red or blue filters.

This can be done either by using prepared coloured slides or by simply holding pieces of acetate colour filters in front of the projector. Relate this effect to the difficulty of buying of clothes under artificial light. (If you have large pieces of film they can be mounted in card frames and placed on the overhead projector.)

View the coloured writing prepared below through different coloured filters and see what colours you can see.

RED BLUE GREEN

Age range: 9-14

Apparatus required: •Coloured filters •Projector •Sheet of paper with a disc of red, green and blue paper fixed to it

12. Laser light and the 60 W bulb

It is instructive to compare the intensity of illumination of these two lights as a source of potential danger to the eye. Consider the 60W light bulb. Assuming that all the electrical energy is converted to light and that it is all radiated uniformly then at a distance of 1 m from the bulb the power density is 4.8 Wm^{-2}. Compare this with the laser. Although the power of a laser of the type used in schools is only 1 mw the area of the laser beam is some 2 mm^2, remaining fairly constant with increasing distance and so giving a power density of 500 Wm^{-2}, over a hundred times greater.

13. Binocular vision

The slightly different appearance of a view from your two eyes that gives us the perception of depth can be shown by this simple experiment. Put your two index fingers together and look past them into the distance. The ends seem to join together to make a finger sausage!

Age: 10-14

14. A shadow photometer

This is a method of comparing the brightness of two sources of light by using the "density" of the shadows that they give. A board marker pen is stood in front of a white screen and a lamp is set up to cast a shadow of the marker on the screen. A second lamp is placed by the first, so giving another shadow. The two lamps are equally bright when the two shadows are of equal depth and the two lamps are the same distance from the screen.

Age range: 16-18

Apparatus required: •Board marker or pencil •Two lamps •Power supplies and meters •Leads

15. Ribena and lime

Partly fill a clear straight-sided glass with a blackcurrant drink. Then gently pour a 1 cm thick layer of limejuice on to the top. After some time the green colour of the lime will have diffused into the red of the blackcurrant drink giving a spectrum effect from green to red.

Age range: 7-14   Apparatus required: •Straight sided glass •Blackcurrant drink •Lime juice

16. Colour subtraction

Three filters, one red, one green and one blue placed on an overhead projector and overlapped is an easy way to show the subtraction of colours.

Age range: 11-13   Apparatus required: •Overhead projector •Colour filters

17. Silhouette photographs

This is an interesting introduction to photography. You will need a dark room, some photographic paper and chemicals (developer and fixer) and a series of interestingly shaped objects such as leaves, cogs, protractors and jewellery. Place the object (or objects) on the paper using only the red safe light. Switch on the main light for two or three seconds. An invisible latent image will be produced on the paper, which can then be developed. All the examples suggested make excellent shadow pictures.

 Dilute quinal/hydroquinine solutions are used for developing. Eye protection is required and contact with the skin should be avoided.

Age range: 11-14 Apparatus required: •Dark room •Objects •Photographic paper, fixer and developer

18. Chaotic systems

(a) Chaotic systems have a number of stable states and this can be shown by using a long flexible strip of metal rather like a giant hacksaw blade. This is mounted vertically and held at the base by a clamp. If the strip is pulled sideways it oscillates but always comes to rest in the vertical position. If a lump of plasticine is fixed to the top it now has three stable states - one vertical as before but now two more, one on either side of the vertical. You can never be sure in which of these states it will finally come to rest if disturbed from its original position. (Bristol University demonstration)

(b) A further demonstration of chaos and the sensitive dependence of the outcome on the initial conditions is to suspend a steel ball bearing over two magnets. When it is swung the ball bearing exhibits a chaotic path and the point where it finally comes to rest depends critically on its point of release. Doing this experiment on an overhead projector makes the motion clearly visible to a class.

Age range: 16-18
Apparatus required:
•Long whippy piece of steel with a holder fixed to the top •Ball bearings •Thread •Overhead projector

19. Phase angle

Mount a ball on a rotating table, and use a lamp to cast a shadow of the ball on a screen. (The lamp should be a long way from the table and the table relatively close to the screen.) Rotate the table and record the position of the ball and the angle through which the table has turned - the zero could be taken when the shadow of the ball is either in the centre of its traverse or at one end. Plot a graph of the displacement of the shadow against the sine (or cosine) of the angle turned by the table.

20. Ultraviolet experiments - safety considerations vital here

Some very nice effects can be shown with ultraviolet light as long as the correct safety precautions are followed. Clean hair shows a greenish hue, teeth gleam, and fluorescein glows green. I have collected a set of other objects, mostly from gift shops - fluorescent T-shirts, silly putty, rocks (the correct wavelength of UV light is needed here), a star chart, security markers, an advent calendar and so on.

 Lamps emitting short-wave ultraviolet have clear quartz envelopes and must only be used when the eyes are screened by a sheet of glass. Lamps with dark glass envelopes pose a minimal hazard to the eyes, but exposure to all ultraviolet must be minimised because of the risk of melanoma.

21. P and S waves simulation

In an earthquake two forms of wave are transmitted through earth - the Primary or P wave (a longitudinal or push vibration) and the Secondary or S wave (a transverse or shaking vibration). The differing properties of these two types of vibration can be shown by the following experiment. Use a plastic beaker with tracing paper stuck round it and with a small bulb fixed on one side. Place a beaker of water inside, and observe the passage of light through the system.

A bulb on one side represents the epicentre of the earthquake and the paths of light through the double beaker represent the paths of the P and S waves.

22. Sensitive flames

The effect of sound waves on a fine flame can be shown by this experiment. Draw a glass tube out from a diameter of 1 cm to a diameter of 1 mm. Connect it to the gas supply, and light the end of the tube - a long fine flame should be produced. This can now be used to investigate sound levels such as nodes and antinodes in standing waves. Modern versions use a sound level meter but are perhaps not so visually impressive.

Age range: 11-18
Apparatus required: •Glass tube •Gas supply

23. The eye

The following series of simple experiments can be performed to study the physics of the eye.
(a) The ability to resolve fine detail. Draw two dots about a millimetre apart on a piece of paper. Fix this to a wall, and see how far away pupils have to stand until they can only see it as one dot.
(b) Look at newspaper pictures and actual photographs using a lens and compare the two. This book has been printed using dots but they are so fine that you can't separate them with a lens.
(c) Help with a lens. See how the use of a lens enables you to read print very close up.
(d) Optical illusions. Show some of these just for interest.

24. Aberration of light - rain

An analogy of the aberration of light can easily be demonstrated by walking through vertically falling rain under an umbrella. You are dry when you are standing still but you get wet when you move!

25. Coloured shadows

The addition of colours can be seen clearly if light from three ray boxes each containing a different coloured filter (red, blue or green) is shone on to a white sheet of paper. Varying the intensity of each will give any colour of the spectrum. Standing three board markers in the way gives three superb coloured shadows. Each individual shadow is the sum of the colours from only two of the ray boxes.

Age range: 11-13
Apparatus required: •Three board writers •Three ray boxes and power supplies •Three coloured filters

26. Corrugated cardboard and wave motion

Using a square of corrugated cardboard or plastic, which has been cut at an angle to the corrugations, gives two axes of sine waves. This can be used as an aid when teaching the wave equation
$y = A\sin 2\pi(ft - x/\lambda)$

The wave like corrugated edge on one side of the square gives the x variation and the other right angles to it the t variation while the height at any point represents the y value or displacement of the wave.

Theory:
$y = A\sin 2\pi(ft - x/\lambda)$ one side gives varying t for fixed x (say x = 0) $y = A\sin 2\pi ft$
and the other varying x for fixed t (say t = 0) $y = A\sin 2\pi x/\lambda$

Age range: 16-18
Apparatus required: •Sheet of corrugated plastic or cardboard (plastic is better - the corrugations can be bigger)

27. Using a pinhole to help you read without glasses

An amazingly simple experiment but of great help to anyone who forgets their glasses! Make a pinhole, and look through it at print - you can read it without glasses! This works for both long and short-sighted people. An alternative version is to look through the small hole made between the tips of your first and second finger and the side of your thumb. The advantages of this method are that you always carry your fingers with you and that the size of the hole is variable.

The phenomenon is explained by understanding that as the aperture is reduced the depth of focus is increased.

Age range: 7-19
Apparatus required: •Fingers

28. Standing waves

The effect of the length of a cord, rather than its tension, on the standing waves that can be produced on it can be shown very simply by this experiment. Fix the end of a string to an off centre hole in a wheel on an electric motor (or the top of a vibration generator). Hold the other end, but have it passing through a short length of plastic tube or bung to allow it to rotate freely. Switch on and move, your hand towards and away from the motor. Large standing waves result.

Theory:
Frequency of the fundamental standing wave on a cord of length L, tension T and mass per unit length m is given by the equation $f = 1/2L(T/m)^{1/2}$ so the frequency is inversely proportional to the length of the cord.

Age range: 16-18
Apparatus required: •Cord •Motor and power supply or vibration generator and signal generator.

29. Moiré fringes in a net curtain or night dress

The overlapping of the fine weave of two net curtains or two layers of a fine night dress show good Moiré fringes. Interference can also be simulated by two transparent plastic discs with circles drawn on them placed on the overhead projector. (See also page 171).

Age range: 16-18   Apparatus required: •Net curtain or night dress •Overhead projector useful

30. Stroboscopic effect with a television

A wonderful example of both the stroboscopic effect and the motion of waves on a stretched string can be obtained using a television and a rubber band. Switch on the television and if possible tune to static clear screen, or else connect a TV camera to the television and point the camera to a blank board. Now stretch the rubber band in front of the screen and pluck it. You will see waves travelling slowly along the band – the scanning property of the television acts like a stroboscope. By suitable experimenting with the length and tension of the band the waves can be made almost stationary.

I have tried both suspending a weight from the band and also using a screw thread to vary the tension.

Age range: 14-18
Apparatus required: •Television •Rubber band •Set of slotted masses •Retort stand •TV camera if possible

31. Apparent bending of a vibrating stick in a spectrum

You can show the apparent bending of a stick (a pencil will do) when it is oscillated across a spectrum. As the stick is vibrated it appears to be bent. The effect only appears when the stick is illuminated by the coloured light. It is due to the persistence of vision of the eye in different regions of the spectrum. The cones take different times to reset when illuminated by different colours.

Age range: 14 – 19
Apparatus required: •Device for producing a spectrum •Stick or pencil

32. Colour filters on the overhead projector

Show disappearing writing by shining light through a filter on the overhead projector which is overlapping a transparency with writing on it. For example if a red filter is used beneath some red writing the writing should disappear if a suitable colour of red is used.

33. Path of the Sun with a pinhole camera

Set up a cylindrical pinhole camera with a piece of photographic paper taped inside it opposite the pinhole. Take the camera outside on a sunny day with the pinhole covered. Uncover the pinhole and leave the camera for a few hours. When the paper is developed a dark line will be seen showing the path of the Sun during the day.

Age range: 11-14
Apparatus required: •Pinhole camera •Photographic paper •Access to a dark room and chemicals

34. Periscope

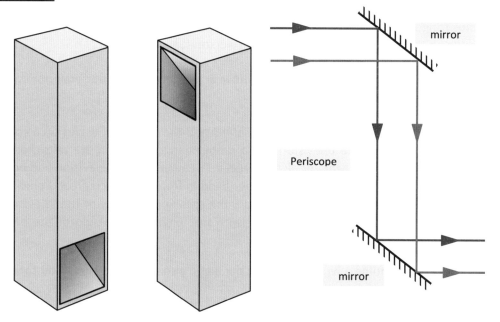

Make a rectangular cardboard tube, and then cut a hole in opposite sides of the tube at the top and bottom.

Fix a mirror at the top and another at the bottom – both at 45° to the tube. The shaded sides of the mirrors in the diagram show the back of each mirror.

You can buy ready-made periscopes but I think that it would be instructive for the pupils to make their own or at least to watch one being made.

Age range: 7-14
Apparatus required: •Cardboard •Two plane mirrors •Tape or two triangular blocks of wood for mounting the mirrors

35. Patterned glass and syrup

Get a piece of patterned glass and mount it horizontally about 5 cm above some printed material such as a newspaper. When you look down the print will be distorted and you won't be able to read it. Now pour some golden syrup onto the top of the glass (I used a teaspoonful for the photo).

Now you will able to read the text through the part of glass covered in syrup but still not through the glass on its own. The refractive index of syrup is similar to that of glass, so you are effectively ending up with a roughly parallel-sided block. Corn oil works as well, but it is rather runny.

Age range: 11-18 depending on treatment
Apparatus required:
•Two strips of wood for mounting glass
•Piece of patterned glass (off-cut, say 10 cm square)
•Sheet of newspaper
•A little golden syrup

36. Mirror writing

Test the skill of the pupils at drawing a line between the two lines of the double triangle, double rectangle and then the double star when you can only see them by reflection in a mirror.

Arrangement of the apparatus.

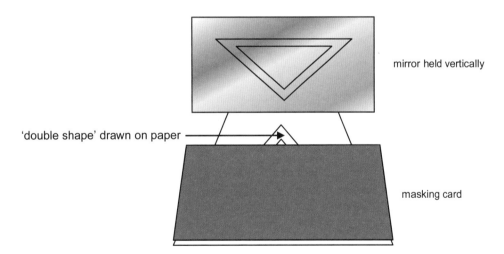

mirror held vertically

'double shape' drawn on paper

masking card

The idea is to draw a line between the lines of the two shapes on a sheet of paper. The masking card is held in the way so that you can only see the point of your pencil and the two shapes by reflection in the mirror. The rectangle is difficult, the triangle is harder still and the star is really hard!

Age range: 5-14
Apparatus required: •Prepared shapes drawn on paper as shown •Pencil •Masking card •Plane mirror

37. Pepper's Ghost

This is a very old experiment but great fun to do. It used to be used on stage to make a ghostly figure appear, but we can construct a modern 'school' version by making a candle appear to be burning inside a glass of water. In fact it is simply that the virtual image of the candle flame is at the same position as the water-filled beaker. The cleaner and bigger the glass sheet available for this the better. A suitably edged piece of window glass is ideal.

If you do not show the children how it is made until afterwards, it is a very good experiment for asking them to try and explain why they see what they do.

A wonderful example of this effect could be seen in the production of the stage show "Phantom of the Opera" where lighted candles appeared to rise from the stage. It was purely an illusion. I was told that the whole image was just a reflection from a mirror set off stage!

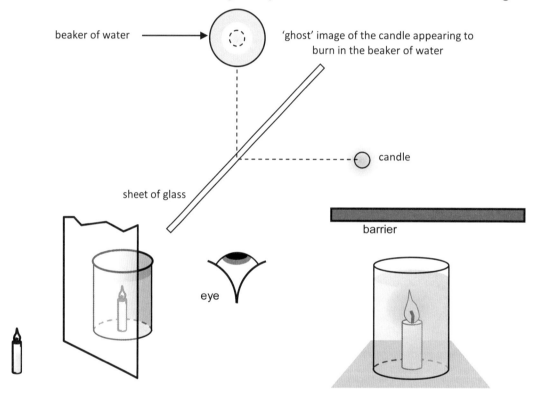

Age range: 7-14
Apparatus required: •Glass sheet (with rounded edges) •Candle •Beaker of water

38. Silhouettes

Use a large sheet of lining paper and a projector or OHP to make silhouette pictures of members of the class. Draw round the shadow of their heads. Then have an 'identification parade' to try and guess who the people are. Once again, although the science is just the formation of shadows, there are all kinds of other skills involved in producing the silhouettes and then identifying them.

Age range: 7-14   Apparatus required: •Cardboard •Scissors •Light source

39. The magic mirror

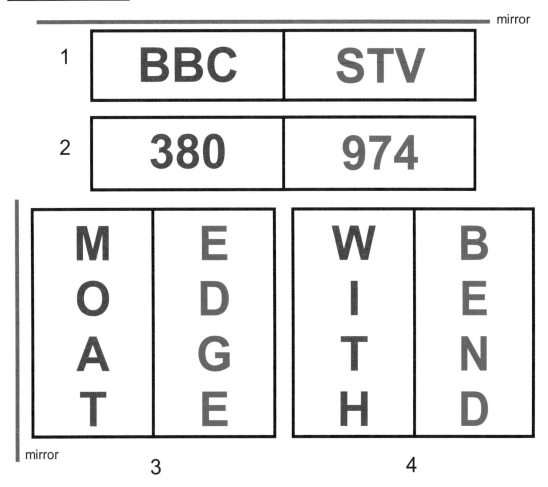

This is a mirror that seems to be able to tell the difference between red and blue!

Put cards one and two in front of the mirror and look at the reflection of the cards in the mirror. Now put the mirror alongside cards three and four, and see what they look like in the mirror. (See diagrams.)

Can you work out what is happening? Think about the axes of symmetry of the different letters and numbers.

(Many thanks to Colin for the idea for this experiment)

Age range: 5-14
Apparatus required: •Prepared cards as shown •Plane mirror

40. Diffraction through a night dress
A lovely example of diffraction can be seen through a night dress or a fine net curtain like the one shown in the photograph. (See also page 167)

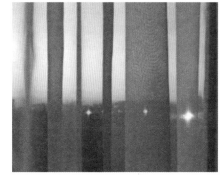

Age range: 16-18

EXPANSION OF SOLIDS AND LIQUIDS

General theory for this section

When a material gets hot it expands - this is because the molecules in it are moving about more vigorously and so need more room.

As a solid is heated the molecules vibrate more violently and the solid expands in all directions. The longer it was to start with and the greater the temperature rise the more the solid expands. Different materials expand by different amounts for the same rise in temperature.

The amount of expansion depends on:

(a) what material it is

(b) how big the temperature rise is

(c) how long it was to start with

All liquids expand more than all solids. The volume of the liquid gets greater as it is heated. The greater the rise in temperature the more it expands. The actual change in shape of the liquid depends on the shape of the container that it is in.

1. Expansion of metal	5. Expansion and contraction of glass
2. Jumping metal discs	6. Expansion of a solid rod
3. Iron rod in projector - expansion of metals	7. Bi-metallic strip
4. Expansion of a liquid	8. Interesting temperatures

1. Expansion of metal

Hold a long strip of aluminium cooking foil horizontally and tightly between two clamps. Heat it from beneath with some candles - significant sag can be produced. (Compare this with the hot wire ammeter.)

A thought-provoking question is the washer problem. If you take a metal washer and heat it, does the hole in the centre get bigger or smaller? It gets larger, since all parts of the metal expand, but those parts nearest the centre expand least.

Uses and effects of the expansion of solids:
rivets, telephone wires, railway lines, buildings, bridges, clock pendulums, tarmac-filled gaps in concrete motorways.

Age range: 11-13
Apparatus required:
•Two retort stands, bosses and clamps •Candles or Bunsens •Strips of aluminium foil

2. Jumping metal discs

Bimetallic discs can be purchased from a number of firms advertising on the internet. If you press the silvery back convex face it clicks so that this face becomes the inner or concave face. This configuration is unstable and it returns to the original shape. However, if the disc is warmed by rubbing it between your fingers or putting it in hot water it will remain stable in the new shape for a while. If it is now left on a flat surface it flexes and jumps in the air as it cooled down. The discs are bimetallic in structure – one face being nickel and the other stainless steel.

Age range: 11-18   Apparatus required: Bimetallic discs

3. Iron rod in projector - expansion of metals

A very simple way to demonstrate the expansion of metals is to put a steel rod in a projector beam (brass or copper will do as well, of course). A rod of about 50 cm in length and with a diameter of about 0.75 cm works well although the size is not critical. You will need the old type of projector, and the end of the rod should be placed where the slide carrier was. The projector is switched on so that it projects a magnified shadow of the rod on to a screen a few metres away. Make a mark on the screen at the end of the shadow. Heat the rod, and watch it expand by observing the movement of the end of the shadow.

 Ensure that the end of the rod being heated in the Bunsen flame is to one side of the slide carrier to avoid damaging the projector body or shattering of the lenses.

This can be used as a simple demonstration or, if more detail is needed, measurements can be made of the magnification of the projector (width of shadow/width of rod) and a guess made at the average temperature rise of the rod to give the coefficient of linear expansion of the metal. Also show that when the rod cools down it will return to its original length - make sure nobody knocks into the bench!

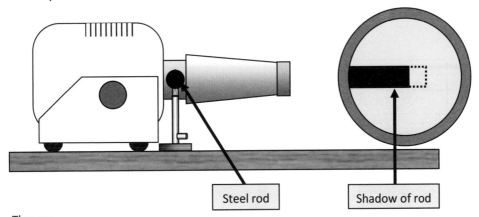

Steel rod | Shadow of rod

Theory:
Expansion of a metal bar of length L heated by θ °C = $L\alpha\theta$ where α is the coefficient of linear expansion of the metal (about $10^{-5}\,°C^{-1}$ for most metals)

Age range: 11-13 or 16 with measurements and calculations
Apparatus required: •Projector •Metal rod •Retort stand and clamp •Ruler •Bunsen

4. Expansion of a liquid

Take a round-bottomed flask and fill it to the brim with coloured water. Take a 1-2 m long piece of capillary tubing, push one end into a rubber bung and push the bung into the top of the flask. Observe the expansion of the liquid when the flask is heated. If you watch carefully it is interesting to see that initially the level of the liquid falls. The glass expands first, but since it is a bad conductor of heat it takes a while for the heat to pass through to the liquid, raise its temperature and so cause it to expand.

Age range: 11-13
Apparatus required: •Round-bottomed flask and bung with hole •Capillary tubing •Bung •Bunsen •Tripod •Retort stand, boss and clamp •Heat-resistant mat

5. The expansion and contraction of glass

In a desert the temperature at night falls rapidly as the sun goes down – the outside of the rocks cool, and since the inside is still warm (and large) the outer layers attempt to contract but are prevented from doing so by the inner part of the rock beneath them and so flake off. This can be shown by experiments with hot glass and cold water.

(a) Heat a glass rod in a Bunsen flame, and then plunge it into a beaker of cold water – the glass shatters

(b) Heat a glass marble in a Bunsen flame using a pair of tongs and then drop it into a beaker of cold water – the marble shatters. It falls below the water surface before shattering!

 Use safety screens to protect both teacher and pupils. The teacher should also wear goggles, and use a leather glove to hold the glass rod. The shattered glass should be disposed of carefully.

Age range: 11-14
Apparatus: •Glass rod •Beaker of cold water •Safety screen and goggles •Marbles •Tongs •Bunsen

6. Expansion of a solid rod

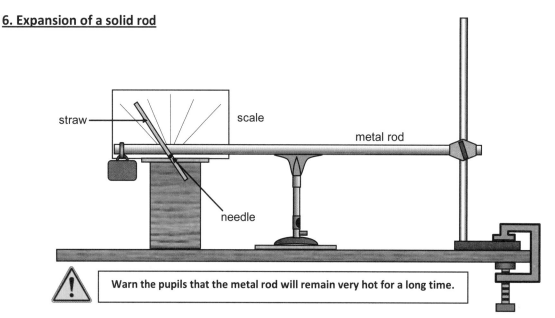

 Warn the pupils that the metal rod will remain very hot for a long time.

Use half a drinking straw to make a pointer. Set up the apparatus as shown above with the scale behind the pointer. Record the position of the end of the straw pointer against the scale. Heat the rod with the Bunsen burner and observe what happens to the pointer. Record the position of the pointer on your scale after a few minutes heating.

By the movement of the pointer you can see that the rod has expanded.

To get a rough idea of how much it has expanded you will need to find out the circumference of your needle and measure the amount of rotation. The diameter of the needle will probably be about 3mm, but you will have to measure it.

Age range: 11-14
Apparatus required: •Metal rod (one from a retort stand would be suitable) •Scissors •1kg mass •Bunsen burner and two heat-resistant mats •Retort stand, boss and clamp •G clamp •Needle •Straw •Wood block •Piece of card for making a scale •Protractor •Micrometer screw gauge

7. Bi-metallic strip - heating and cooling

A bi-metallic strip made of two metals welded together is an excellent way of demonstrating the different coefficients of thermal expansion of different metals. It will bend when heated with the metal that expands the most (brass in the case of a brass-iron strip) on the outside of the curve. An alternative demonstration with the bi-metallic strip is to put it in a fridge (or in a cooling mixture of ice and water). The strip will bend with the brass layer on the inside, showing that brass also contracts more than iron. Point out that it is the **change** of temperature that matters.

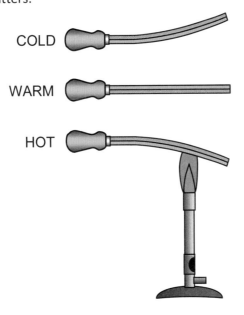

COLD

WARM

HOT

Age range: 11-13
Apparatus required: •Bi-metallic strip in holder or a pair of tongs •Bunsen

8. Interesting temperatures

The diagram shows some interesting temperatures from absolute zero at -273 °C to 6000 °C – the temperature of the surface of the Sun.

A useful exercise with younger pupils would be to make a large map of the world and mark on the hottest and coldest temperatures at different places.

Theory note:
Absolute zero is −273.15°C. This is the coldest that it is possible to get. It is the temperature at which all molecular motion stops – the entropy reaches its minimum value. The temperature scale starting at absolute zero is called the Kelvin scale of temperature. 0°C = 273 K, 100°C = 373 K.

Age range: 7-18

Temperature in °C	
6000	Surface of the Sun
1500	Iron melts
360	Mercury boils
260	Nylon melts
200	Solder sets
100	Water boils
37	Normal body temperature
20	Normal room temperature
0	Water freezes
-44	Mercury freezes
-72	Carbon dioxide "freezes"
−112	Alcohol freezes
-192	Nitrogen boils
-200	Surface of Jupiter
-270	Deep space
-273	Absolute zero

EXPANSION OF GASES

General theory for this section:

When a gas is compressed or expanded without its temperature changing (isothermal) the product of its pressure (P) and volume (V) is constant i.e. $P_1V_1 = P_2V_2$. This is Boyle's Law.

To keep the temperature constant, heat energy must be added during expansion and removed during compression.

The equation that describes the behaviour of a gas under any change is the ideal gas equation:

PV = nRT where n is the number of moles of the gas, R the gas constant and T the absolute temperature (T = 273 + temperature in centigrade)

If the volume is kept constant the pressure of the gas is directly proportional to the absolute temperature, and if the pressure is kept constant the volume is directly proportional to the absolute temperature.

1. The expansion of air	5. Tin can above a Bunsen
2. Exploding balloon - heat	6. Expansion cooling
3. Soap film - expansion of air	7. The bicycle pump
4. Pop corn and expansion of a gas	8. Wine bottle and coin

1. Expansion of gases - actually air, a mixture of gases

The expansion of air can be used to make a simple yet accurate air thermometer. Take a large round-bottomed flask, and fill it about one third full with coloured water. Next fit a long (at least 1.5 m) glass tube into a rubber bung, so that the bung is about ten centimetres from one end. Push the bung firmly into the flask, making sure that the end dips into the water in the flask so that about two thirds of the flask is trapped air. Heat the flask either by using your hands or heating very gently with a Bunsen. The expansion of the air in the flask forces the coloured water up the tube.

The heat of your hands is usually sufficient to show a large expansion, and it makes an interesting and sensitive comparison between the temperatures of various pupils' hands. Calibrating the apparatus enables it to be used as an actual thermometer.

Age range: 11-13

Apparatus required: •Large round bottomed flask •Bunsen burner
•Large bore capillary tube (to make the expansion easily visible)

2. Exploding balloon – heat

Blow up a balloon, close the open end by tying it up, and then heat it gently above a Bunsen flame. Holding it well above the flame will prevent the rubber simply melting. The expanding air in the balloon will demonstrate the expansion of gases by bursting the balloon.

⚠️ **Wear eye protection and have the pupils sitting at least 2 m away. The balloon has to be held so high that a safety screen will not offer protection.**

Age range: 11-13   Apparatus required: •Balloon •Bunsen •Eye protection

3. Soap film – expansion of air

An alternative method for demonstrating the expansion of air uses some delightfully simple apparatus. Use a large round-bottomed flask and make a soap film over the neck by dipping the neck into some strong soap solution.

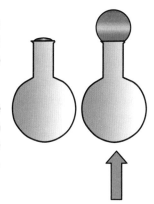

Warm the flask with your hands - the expansion of the air in the flask will give a good bubble on the end. Warming it over a Bunsen flame will make it happen quicker but it is then quite easy to pop the bubble. As the air cools, the bubble collapses back to a flat film. It helps to keep the flask in a fridge before starting the experiment.

Age range: 11-13
Apparatus required: •Large round-bottomed flask •Soap solution

4. Popcorn and expansion of a gas

Use the expansion of popcorn to demonstrate the increase in the volume of air when it is heated. I usually make it in a tall one litre beaker covered by a saucer so that the children can see what is going on. Put enough oil in to just cover the base of the beaker, sprinkle in a layer of popcorn and then heat it gently over a Bunsen. The popcorn expands in a few minutes after reaching a sufficiently high temperature.

 | **Any food prepared in the laboratory should not be eaten. If done in a food-technology room with cooking utensils the popcorn may be eaten.**

Age range: 11-13
Apparatus required: •Popcorn (uncooked) •Tall 1 litre beaker •Saucer to cover the beaker •Cooking oil •Bunsen •Tripod •Gauze •Heat-resistant mat

5. Tin can above a Bunsen.

The expansion of a gas as its temperature rises can be shown quite impressively by the following experiment. Get a small metal tin with a tightly fitting metal lid. Put it on a tripod behind a safety screen, and heat the tin. After a few moments the expansion of the air in the tin should blow the lid off.

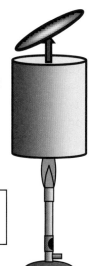

Tip - a little water in the tin will help things along and ensure a good explosion, although some pupils may notice the steam!

 | **Don't put the lid on too tightly, and don't go to check if it hasn't worked – turn off the gas and wait for it to cool down. Use safety screens and insist that everyone in the laboratory wears eye protection.**

Age range: 11-13
Apparatus required: •Metal tin with a tight fitting lid •Bunsen •Safety screen •Tripod •Heat-resistant mat •Eye protection

6. Expansion cooling

The formation of ice round a gas cylinder when the gas escapes is a very good demonstration of cooling on expansion. A very impressive demonstration of this effect is to show the formation of dry ice as gas expands from a high-pressure carbon dioxide cylinder. Even the small carbon dioxide filled bulbs used in soda siphons will show this. They can be punctured with care using a compass point and show a marked cooling as the gas emerges. Some idea of the energy transfer on expansion can be gained by holding the bulb in a beaker of water, using a pair of wooden test tube tongs.

 | **Dry ice should only be made using a 'siphon' type carbon dioxide cylinder with a 'Jebfreezer' attachment or a thick cloth bag. Eye protection is needed and leather gloves should be worn. Pupils must not handle dry ice.**

Age range: 11-16
Apparatus required: •Carbon dioxide cylinder and cloth •Soda siphon bulb •Sharp point to puncture the bulb (a pair of compasses or dividers is ideal)

7. Bicycle pump - adiabatic and isothermal changes

The rapid compression (or expansion with the valve reversed) of the air in a bicycle pump shows adiabatic changes. Normal pumping heats up the air in the pump, while a rapid expansion shows cooling. A slow change allows heat transfer, and so there is no change of temperature - an isothermal change.

Age range: 11-18 depending on treatment
Apparatus required: •Bicycle pump •Thermometer or thermistor

8. Wine bottle and coin

Get an empty wine bottle and put it in the fridge. When it is really cold remove it and put a coin on the top so that the hole is covered. (Moisten the coin first to get a good seal.)

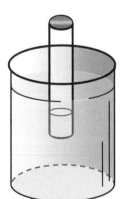

As the air in the bottle warms up it expands, so pushing the coin upwards – a little air comes out, and the coin falls back on to the neck of the bottle. This process is then repeated, and you should hear a clicking noise as the coin rises and falls.

An alternative is to put the bottle containing air at room temperature, with the coin on top, into a bowl of hot water. The same effect occurs.

Age range: 11-14
Apparatus required: •Wine bottle •Coin •Fridge, freezer or a bowl of hot water

9. Expansion and compression of air – soap bubble indicator

Make a soap film across the end of a glass tube. Lower the tube into a beaker of water and watch the soap film expand so that it is curved. The further down you push the tube the more curved the film becomes, showing the increase in pressure at greater depths.

Age range: 11-14
Apparatus required: •Soap solution •Water •Beaker •Glass tube

CONDUCTION OF HEAT

General theory for this section:
Conduction occurs by the transfer of energy through a material by the collisions of molecules. In metals conduction is further increased by the free electrons carrying energy from places of high temperature to those at a lower temperature.

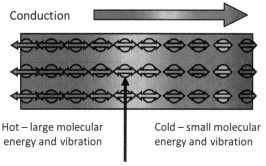

Conduction

Hot – large molecular energy and vibration

Cold – small molecular energy and vibration

Atom (or molecule)

1. Espresso coffee/or beer
2. Sweaters and anoraks
3. Thermal conductivity of water
4. Baked Alaska
5. Thermochromic paint for conductivity
6. Line of pupils - conduction
7. Conductivity of air
8. Lifting up a flame and copper gauze
9. Insulation
10. Wooden rod and copper tube
11. Good and bad conductors
12. Melting ice cubes

1. Espresso coffee/or beer - conduction in foam

My wife and I were sitting on Waterloo station about to drink a cup of really frothy espresso coffee when she looked at the foam on the top and said, "I suppose that helps to keep it hot!"

Indeed, the thick layer of foam on a cup of espresso coffee helps to insulate the liquid below it! There is a considerable amount of air in the foam, which makes an insulating blanket.

An extension of this would be to investigate the cooling of the same mass of frothy coffee and non-frothy coffee - both starting from the same initial temperature in the same sized beakers.

Age range: 11-13
Apparatus required: •Frothy coffee •Non-frothy coffee! •Beakers •Thermometers

2. Sweaters and anoraks - the thermal conductivity of air

As a demonstration of the poor thermal conductivity of air get a small child to put on as many layers of clothing as they can: sweaters, anoraks, pullovers, jackets and a lab coat. (Small children are better - they can wear more layers of adult clothes!)

You could use a thermometer probe to investigate the temperature beneath the layers of clothing.

Age range: 11-13
Apparatus required: •Lots of large thick clothing

 Do not let them wear multiple layers of clothing for too long. It gets very hot inside!

3. Thermal conductivity of water

The poor thermal conductivity of water can be shown by putting a piece of ice in the bottom of a test tube and holding it in place with a piece of copper gauze wedged above it in the tube. Fill the rest of the test tube with water and heat it at the top until it boils. Due to the poor conductivity of water the ice at the bottom remains solid even though the water is boiling at the top.

Age range: 11-13
Apparatus required: •Piece of ice •Test tube •Water •Bunsen •Tongs •Heat resistant mat •Metal gauze

 Wear eye protection. Do not use soda glass test tubes, the glass will shatter. Use Pyrex, or similar, tubes.

4. Baked Alaska

This tasty dessert shows the insulation effects of the air within the meringue. As the meringue cooks the air pockets within it form an insulating blanket and the ice cream within it does not get hot enough to melt as long as the cooking is fairly rapid.

5. Thermochromic paint for conductivity

This specialist paint can be used to paint different metal rods in a variation of the simple conductivity experiment. In the simple experiment two rods of different metals are held in a Bunsen flame and their conductivity is compared by the pupils seeing which one they have to put down first before it gets too hot. This one has the highest thermal conductivity. To avoid burns simply paint the rods with the thermochromic paint, hold them in a non-conducting (wooden) clamp, and watch the change in colour of the paint.

 Show pupils how to deal with minor burns by using running cold water for a few minutes.

Another version is to use heat sensitive paper. The paper will turn blue as it gets hot. Place a piece of the heat sensitive paper on a tripod; the rods from the earlier experiment can then simply be rested on it while their other ends are heated with a roaring Bunsen flame. The rate at which the paper in contact with the rods turns blue gives a good comparison of their thermal conductivity.

Age range: 11-13
Apparatus required: •Conductivity rods kit (rods of brass, aluminium, copper, iron, zinc and glass) •Bunsen •Tripod •Heat-resistant mats (2) •Thermochromic paint •Heat sensitive paper

6. Line of pupils - conduction

This analogy shows conduction along a solid rod. The transfer of energy occurs by the vibration of molecules. Each molecule stays where it is and simply vibrates - it is the energy that is transferred down the rod. Ask the pupils to stand in a line and link arms. Then shake the line at one end. The vibration of the pupil at the end is transmitted along the line until the one at the other end is moving. Don't shake them so hard that they fall over! This simple demonstration refers to a non-metal solid. The ingenious teacher might be able to devise a way of showing conduction in a metal where much of the energy transfer is due to free electrons. If you are really brave take the group of pupils to the gym or sports hall and get them to kick a large number of footballs about – not recommended in the Physics laboratory!

7. Conductivity of air

Hold your hands carefully on either side of a roaring Bunsen flame - you feel virtually no heat since the transfer of heat from the flame to your hands in this position is only due to the conduction of heat through the air. This demonstrates very simply that air is a very poor conductor of heat. It feels much hotter if they are held above the flame, showing the principles of convection - air expands when it is heated, its density goes down and so the hot air rises!

 Candle flames may be less hazardous. Show pupils how to deal with minor burns by using running cold water for a few minutes.

Age range: 11-13   Apparatus required: •Bunsen or candle •Heat resistant mat

8. Lifting up a flame and copper gauze on chip pan - conduction in gauze

This experiment clearly shows the high thermal conductivity of copper and also the need for gas to be at a sufficiently high temperature before it will burn. Light a Bunsen and hold a piece of copper gauze over the outlet and resting on top of the Bunsen tube - the flame burns through it. Then gently lift the gauze - the flame comes up with it, burning above the gauze and leaving an area of un-burnt cooler gases below it. The heat is conducted away from the gauze and into your hands, leaving the gases below the gauze too cold to catch fire. As long as you don't hold on too long you can support the gauze with your hands.

It is a very good demonstration of how the traditional Davy Safety lamp works. It is possible to lift the flame right off, so putting it out. Don't forget to turn the gas off afterwards!

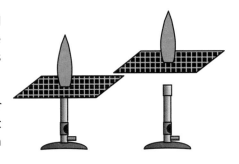

As a practical application of this a sheet of copper gauze can be placed over a chip pan to prevent the fat catching fire. It is another example of the conduction in metals.

 This should only be done by the teacher as a demonstration experiment.

Age range: 11-13
Apparatus required: •Bunsen or candle •Piece of copper gauze •Heat resistant mat

9. Insulation

The insulating properties of asbestos are described in a nineteenth-century Physics textbook written in French by Ganot in 1850. Apparently, by using a layer of asbestos in their hands men could "lift red-hot iron balls without inconvenience"! Clearly they did not know of the dangers of asbestos then.

Heat resistant tiles – Apollo 10

10. Wooden rod and copper tube

This is a very good demonstration of differing thermal conductivities. The apparatus consists of a copper tube, one end of which fits tightly round a wooden rod. A piece of paper is wrapped tightly around the join of the wood and the copper, and the paper over the join is heated gently in a Bunsen using a clear blue flame. The rod should be rotated during heating to stop the paper catching fire. The paper will blacken over the poorly conducting wood while staying undamaged over the better conducting copper.

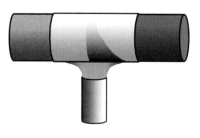

A very good comparison between the conductivities of two materials can be made by walking in bare feet on a carpet and then on a tiled floor. Although both are at the same temperature it feels colder on the tiled floor since the tiles are a better conductor than the carpet and so heat energy is transferred from your feet to the floor.

Age range: 11-13   Apparatus required: •Bunsen •Heat resistant mat •Composite wood/copper rod

11. Good and bad conductors of heat energy

Good conductors:

Copper	Heating appliances, boilers, fire tubes in steam engines, tip of soldering iron
Aluminium	Cooking utensils
Iron/Steel	Shaped into fins to give a large surface area for cooling in air-cooled engines

Bad conductors:

Felt, glass fibre	Lining of roofs, lagging to pipes and boilers (i.e. heat insulation)
Paper	Wrapping hot food such as fish and chips
Plastic	Handles to cooking utensils
Wood	Handles to cooking utensils, wooden spoons, table mats
Cork	Table mats
Straw	Roofing (thatch), hay-box used in camping
Glass, porcelain	Crockery (little heat transfer to hands and lips)
Fat	In the skin and around organs of animals and humans
Bricks, plaster	Housing
Air	Woollen clothing, feathers, fur, eiderdowns, string vests, cellular blankets, cavity walls, double glazing

12. Melting ice cubes

Take two tiles of identical dimensions, one metal and one wood, both painted matt black to look the same and both at room temperature. Get a student to come out and touch both tiles and say which feels colder (the metal one). Don't let them hold the tile. Now take two ice cubes of the same size, and put one on each tile, inside a rubber ring to catch the drips. Ask the students which will melt more rapidly. The ice cube on the metal tile melts extraordinarily fast - almost all gone in about a minute.

Theory:
The metal is the better conductor; hence it feels colder but conducts heat from the surroundings to the ice cube, so melting it faster.

Age range: 11-16   Apparatus required: • Two matt black painted tiles •Two ice cubes

CONVECTION

General theory for this section

This section deals with convection currents in fluid. These may be either liquids or gases.

Most people remember the phrase 'Hot air rises', but why does it?

Convection currents occur because a fluid expands when it is heated. This expansion reduces its density so the low-density fluid will rise through that of higher density. Convection is therefore caused by the movement of the more energetic molecules from one place to another.

1. Christmas table decoration
2. Convection: a cardboard serpent
3. Heat loss from young animals
4. Convection in a flame
5. Convection currents
6. Falling candle

7. Convection in chimneys
8. Convection in the home
9. Convection and a tea bag
10. Lava lamp
11. Three candles

1. Christmas table decoration

This uses a lovely wooden table decoration that is widely available. Around the base is a set of candles and at the top is a wooden rotor with a series of large angled blades. The rotor is fixed to a rotor to which figures and animals are attached. Hot air rising from the set of candles turns the rotor that rotates the whole display. Would it work in a gravity-free environment?

Age range: 11 – 14
Apparatus required: •Table decoration and candles •Matches

2. Convection: a cardboard serpent

Cut a paper, card or foil snake-like coil and suspend it by a thread above a light bulb. The rising hot air will rotate the coil giving a simple but effective demonstration of convection in a gas. Heat energy expands the air, thus lowering its density; this lower density air then rises.

Age range: 11 -14
Apparatus required: •Paper serpent •Thread •Stand •Light bulb in a holder •Card.
(I have found that a circle of card about 5 cm across cut into a spiral works well if you cut it into a spiral with arms about 1.5 wide leaving a disc In the middle to attach the thread.)

3. Heat loss from young animals: the effect of surface area

We used to estimate the surface area of a small mammal by wrapping it in a paper tube maybe not suitable these days but we can still compare the surface area to mass ratio for young and old animals. You can extend this to the calculation of surface area to mass ratio. For example a sphere has the smallest surface area to mass ratio for a given volume.

A set of wooden blocks can be made into a tall thin person or a short fat one - the tall thin one has the greatest surface area and would therefore lose heat most rapidly from the surface. The surface area of a pupil can be found approximately by wrapping them in sheets of newspaper.

Try boiling some potatoes and measuring how rapidly they cool, some being cut into small pieces. The smaller ones have the greatest surface mass ratio and so cool the quickest.

Age range: 11-14   Apparatus required: •Wooden blocks •Saucepan •Potatoes •Newspapers.

4. Convection in a flame

The convection currents in a flame can be seen by casting a shadow of it on a screen. Candles and a Bunsen with a blue non-roaring flame work well if you use a projector to show the movement of the low density air above the flame.

Age range: 11-16
Apparatus required: •Bunsen •Heat-resistant mat •Projector.

5. Convection currents

Convection currents in liquids can be easily shown with potassium permanganate crystals in water. You can do this in a beaker of water or use the special rectangular test tube available from the manufacturers.

Simply drop some crystals into the water near to one side of the beaker, They will fall to the bottom, but if the beaker is now heated at the base on the opposite side the colour will be drawn across and rise up that side.

If you use the rectangular tube, drop a few crystals in the top and then heat one bottom corner. The crystals dissolve and the colour moves round the tube, showing the convection currents in the water. 'Catching' the moving colour by moving the Bunsen enables you to change its direction.

A suspension of aluminium paint in water is an alternative technique and more long-lasting, because with the potassium permanganate the water simply turns pink after a while and no convection can be observed.

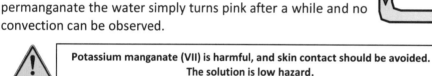

> ⚠ **Potassium manganate (VII) is harmful, and skin contact should be avoided. The solution is low hazard.**

Age range: 11 -14
Apparatus required: •Beaker or rectangular test tube •Bunsen •Potassium permanganate crystals •Heat-resistant mat.

6. Falling candle

This intriguing demonstration shows what happens when the effects of convection are 'cancelled out'. A candle is fitted to the inside base of a tin; the candle is now lit, and the tin is dropped. The tin should be big enough to provide enough oxygen, but the flame still goes out.

Theory: Since the can and candle are in free fall, one of the conditions for convection does not apply - that is, although the hot waste gases in the candle flame have expanded they do not rise away from the flame since they and the flame are both falling. This means that there is no convection in the can. The candle therefore tries to burn in its own waste products and fails. Helen Sharman tells of how she had to sleep in a draught from a fan in the Russian spacecraft so that she didn't suffocate in her own exhaled breath. Michael Foale had a similar experience in Mir.

Age range: 11-14
Apparatus required: •Tin can •Candle •Matches •Protection for the floor (a piece of old carpet)

7. Convection in the high chimney and the double chimney

(a) This experiment shows the effect of convection in a high chimney. Use a tall metal tube to show the convection currents in a chimney. (I use a piece of metal pipe about 1.5 m long and some 10 cm in diameter.) A Bunsen burner (or a candle) should be placed at the bottom of the chimney and if small pieces of paper are introduced into the flame they will be shot out of the top of the chimney by the rising air currents. It always reminds me of when I put our first Christmas tree on to the fire in our flat at the bottom of a four storey block! The convection currents were enormous, and it 'went up like a torch' - not to be recommended!

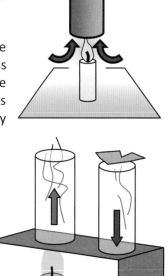

(b) Another nice demonstration uses the commercially available double chimney - simply a glass-fronted box with two glass chimneys in the top with a candle below one of them. If the candle is lit convection is created; hot air rises out of one side and draws cold air in at the other. A smouldering taper held over the chimney without the candle will show the smoke being drawn down into that side and ejected at the other by the hot air currents.

A further variation of this is to put a candle on the bench, light it and lower a large glass tube (0.5 m long and at least 5 cm in diameter) down over the candle so that it touches the bench. The candle soon goes out due to lack of oxygen. Repeat the experiment, but this time lower a metal plate down the centre of the tube so that it hangs over the candle flame. The flame stays alight; hot gases escape up one side of the plate and fresh air is drawn down the other.

Age range: 11-14
Apparatus required: •Metal chimney •Retort stand, boss and clamp •Double chimney apparatus •Candles •Bunsen •Matches.

8. Convection in the home

The following list gives you some idea of where convection is important in the home:
Cooking in hot water
Christmas decorations – a candle under a mobile
Convector heater – hot air rises through the heater
Central heating boiler
Immersion heater at the bottom of a hot water tank
Kettle with the element at the bottom
Cold air convecting off the outside of windows
Air movement in cavity walls before putting foam insulation in
Radiators – they work by air convection and not by radiation
Chimney to an open fire or a boiler
Chest freezer – it does not matter too much if you open the top for a little while because the colder air will sink to the bottom of the freezer.

9. Convection and a tea bag

This is a fun experiment to demonstrate convection especially if you use the £10 note!

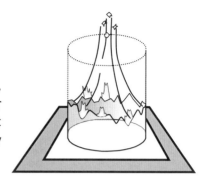

Take a rectangular tea bag, cut off the end with the string, unfold it, and remove the tea. Shape the bag into a cylinder and stand it on a sheet of paper on the bench (a heat resistant mat underneath the paper is not really necessary but might be a good idea the first time you try this).

Set light to the top of the bag and wait.

The flame will burn downwards, sending a fine stream of ash into the air. As the flame nears the paper the tea bag continues burning, but by this time the upward convection current is sufficient to draw the last remnants of the bag upwards and they simply float away, leaving the paper untouched.

Replacing the sheet of paper with a £10 note makes the demonstration even more exciting but if you do so it is at your own risk!

Age range: 11- Adult
Apparatus needed: •Tea bag •Matches •Heat resistant mat •Sheet of paper •£10 note – OPTIONAL!

10. A lava lamp

This is a commercial lamp. As it warms up the material in the liquid rises and falls, showing beautiful convection currents as its density changes. Thus is rather like Galileo's thermometer in some ways. (See Density, Upthrust and Archimedes, experiment 9.)

Age range: 11-14
Apparatus required: •Lava lamp

11. Three candles

Set up the three candles on a beehive shelf over water. The candles should be of significantly different lengths.

Light all three candles, cover them with a large beaker, and wait to see which goes out first.

Surprisingly, perhaps, it is the long one.

Theory
Although the emitted carbon dioxide is heavier than air when it is at the same temperature it is also hotter in this experiment and so convection currents take it to the top of the beaker so putting out the tallest candle first.

Age range: 11-14
Apparatus required: •Three candles •Beehive shelf •Dish •Large beaker •Matches

HEAT RADIATION

General theory for this section:

The range of infra-red radiation is from roughly 750 nm to 10 000 nm (7.5×10^{-7} m to 10^{-5} m or one hundredth of a millimetre). Long wave heat radiation will not pass through glass. Hot metal objects will start to glow when they reach a temperature of around 500 $^{\circ}$C.

Black surfaces emit and absorb heat radiation better than shiny white ones. Shiny surfaces are the best reflectors.

Distribution of energy $\quad E_{\lambda}$

1. Radiation - aluminium tape
2. TV and stereo remote controller
3. Greenhouse effect
4. Crookes' Radiometer
5. Thermoscope - radiation detector
6. Radiation and thermometers
7. Absorption of radiation
8. Heat radiation

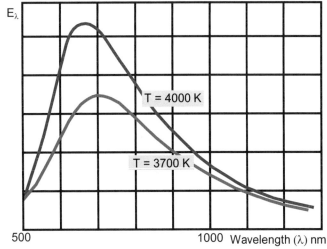

T = 4000 K

T = 3700 K

500   1000   Wavelength (λ) nm

1. Radiation - aluminium tape

Take a 1 m length of aluminium tape, a strip of aluminium foil will do, and blacken both sides of it except for a length of 5 cm in the centre. Pass a current through it - you will probably need up to 8A. Although initially the blackened sections will give off some smoke this is just due to the soot. Eventually the shiny section will become red hot and melt - showing that it does not radiate so well and so its temperature rises.

 | **Demonstration only. Do not allow the pupils to do this.**

Age range: 11-13   Apparatus required: •Low voltage power supply •Clamps and crocodile clips •Long strip of aluminium foil blackened with soot

2. Infra-red radiation - the TV/stereo remote controller

In the TV remote control device we have an ideal focused beam of infra red radiation. This can be used to study:

(a) the absorption of infra red by glass and plastic

(b) the reflection of infra red from flat and rough surfaces

(c) the diffraction of infra red through a narrow slit – it is left for the reader to decide what would be a "narrow slit" for infra red radiation!

The best detector that I know for infr-red is a small TV camera. Connect the camera to a colour TV receiver and point the TV remote controller towards it, focussing the camera to give a clear image on the screen. Now press any of the buttons on the remote controller. Although you cannot see any radiation emitted by the controller the camera will pick up the infrared and a bright flash will appear on the TV screen! My eighteen-year-old students have queried the colour of this light!

Age range: 15-18
Apparatus required:
•TV remote controller •Glass •Plastic •Metal sheet •Narrow slit •TV camera and television

3. Greenhouse effect

For this simulation you need a clear plastic sandwich box, two thermometers and a sunny day. Place one thermometer in the box and the other in the sun on the ground outside it, preferably sheltered from draughts. Leave them for an hour and observe the effects on the thermometers. (The rise in temperature is partly due to the inability of the trapped air to escape by convection.)

Theory:

The greenhouse effect occurs because the radiation emitted by the Sun (with a surface temperature of 6000 °C) has a spread of wavelengths which peak in intensity at around 500 nm, and this radiation can penetrate clouds of methane, water vapour, carbon dioxide, nitrous oxide and CFCs in the atmosphere. However, when the solar radiation falls on the ground it only raises its temperature to around 20 °C. The radiation emitted from an object at this temperature has a peak of around 12 mm (12000 nm) and this longer wavelength cannot penetrate the gaseous clouds, or in this case the plastic. The air below therefore heats up!

Age range: 10-16
Apparatus required: •Sandwich box •Two thermometers.
(You might need a radiant heater if there is no Sun)

4. Crookes' Radiometer

This is an excellent piece of apparatus for demonstrating that dull black surfaces absorb heat radiation better than shiny ones. The glass bulb is filled with low pressure air and as radiation falls on the vanes the black surfaces absorb more radiation than the silvered ones, the air near them heats up - expands and so pushes the vanes round.

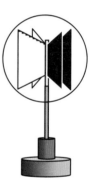

Try placing a sheet of glass or a beaker of water between the heat source (a small electric fire, candle, light bulb or Bunsen burner) and the radiometer and investigate the effect of these materials on the transmitted infra-red radiation.

Age range: 11-13
Apparatus required: •Crookes' radiometer •Heat source •Glass •Beaker of water

5. Thermoscope - radiation detector

This is made from two glass bulbs - round flasks will do - joined by glass and rubber tubing and partly filled with water. One flask is blackened, the other is silvered with aluminium paint, and a lamp is placed in between them. Due to the different amounts of absorption of radiation by the two flasks one gains more heat energy than the other, the vapour pressure inside the black one increases more rapidly and water moves along the glass tube from the black to the shiny bulb. You used to be able to buy them with ether inside, and this works much better because of the volatile nature of ether, but it is not safe to make one up in the lab because thexethylene (ether) is extremely flammable, its heavy vapour spreads rapidly and may be ignited by a flame or spark some distance away.

6. Radiation and thermometers

The different amount of absorption of heat radiation by different surfaces can be studied using the following simple experiment. Take two thermometers, blacken the bulb of one of them with soot or black paint and then place them both in boiling water. When the temperatures of both has reached 100 °C (or as near as possible depending on the boiling point of water that day) take them out quickly and fix them in clamps in the air. Observe the rate of cooling. The blackened one will cool much more rapidly, showing that black surfaces emit heat better than shiny ones.

The absorption of heat by black surfaces is very obvious when walking round a swimming pool on tiles. The darker coloured ones absorb more heat energy from the Sun and so get hotter - they can be too hot to step on in bare feet!

Age range: 11-16
Apparatus required:
•Two thermometers - one blackened with soot or black paint •Retort stands, bosses and clamps
•Boiling water

7. Absorption of radiation

This experiment shows that different coloured surfaces absorb heat radiation at different rates.
Take four equal sized plastic beakers, and fill them with the same amount of coffee (liquid) but of different concentrations from very strong to very weak. Allow them to reach room temperature and then put them out in the Sun. (Use an infra red heater if it is a cloudy day!)

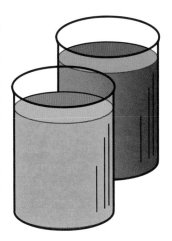

Use a thermometer to record the rise in temperature of each beaker as time passes. The very concentrated (darker) solution should rise in temperature faster than the weaker one.

Age range: 11-16
Apparatus required: •Coffee •Plastic beakers •Thermometer Infra red lamp (optional)

8. Heat radiation – things to talk about

1. Radiators in houses are actually convector heaters. They do not actually radiate very well; but they ought to be painted black.
   Car radiators usually are a dark colour so that they can get rid of the heat efficiently.
2. Aluminium foil is sometimes put behind radiators to reflect the heat out into the room.
3. A vacuum flask has shiny surfaces on the vacuum side to prevent heat loss.
4. White clothes are worn in summer as they reflect the heat better than dark ones.
5. The reflector behind an electric fire should be kept clean so that it will reflect the heat well.
6. Spacecraft have shiny surfaces to reflect the radiation from the Sun.
7. Highly polished teapots will keep hot longer as their surfaces do not give out heat so well.
8. White-washed buildings will keep cooler in hot weather than darker ones.

HEAT ENERGY

General theory for this section:
When heat energy is applied to an object its temperature rises.
Heat energy = mass (m) x specific heat capacity (c) x change in temperature (θ)
(Energy is in joules, mass is in kg, temperature in $^{\circ}$C and specific heat capacity in $Jkg^{-1}\,^{\circ}C^{-1}$)
When a substance changes its state, energy is needed to do this.
Specific latent heat of vaporisation (heat needed to change 1 kg of the liquid into vapour)
Specific latent heat of fusion is the heat energy needed to change the state of 1 kg of solid into a liquid
Using an electrical heater: Energy input = Power x time = $VIt = (V^2/R)t$

SPECIFIC HEAT CAPACITY

1. Power of a Bunsen burner
2. When do you add the milk?
3. The most effective immersion heater

4. Heat energy in a flame
5. Energy in a candle
6. Steamed pudding & specific heat capacity

MELTING, BOILING AND EVAPORATING

7. Latent heat – kettle
8. Milk bottle top in cold weather
9. Floating ice cube
10. Evaporation
11. Regelation and the ice block
12. Boiling water under reduced pressure
13. Boiling under reduced pressure (2)

14. The freezing mixture
15. Volume change solid to gas
16. Change of volume of melting ice
17. Change of volume of melting ice - burette
18. A home-made air-cooling system
19. Fish in a freezing pond
20. Lagging and heat loss

SPECIFIC HEAT CAPACITY

1. Power of a Bunsen burner

This experiment acts as a useful introduction to work on specific heat capacity. Heat a known amount of water (say about 1.5 kg) in an aluminium saucepan for a known time (three to five minutes), and measure the temperature rise. Knowing the amount of energy delivered in a certain time, you can then work out the power of the Bunsen burner. Assume that the specific heat capacities of the water and material of the container are known.

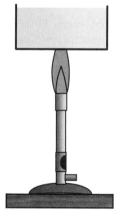

The powers that my pupils obtained ranged from 0.3 to 0.5 kW depending on the type of Bunsen and the time of heating, since they did not allow for heat loss.

Theory:
Energy supplied by Bunsen = Power x time = [(mass of water x specific heat capacity of water) + (mass of container x specific heat capacity of container)] x temperature rise

Age range: 13-16
Apparatus required: •Bunsen •Aluminium saucepan •Stop clock •Balance

 Eye protection required. Make sure that the container being heated is small enough to remain stable on the tripod.

2. When do you add the milk?

This is the classic cooling experiment. You have a hot cup of coffee and a given amount of cool milk. The problem is to decide when to add the milk so that the resulting mixture will reach a given lower temperature the quickest.

Theory

According to Newton's law of cooling the rate of loss of heat from an object is directly proportional to the temperature difference between it and its surroundings, so the higher the temperature the faster the coffee will cool. Adding milk will immediately reduce the temperature so it is better to allow the coffee to stand for a little while before adding the milk, thus utilising the rapid rate of cooling when the temperature difference is high.

Age range: 11 - 18 depending on treatment
Apparatus required: •Beaker of hot water •Beaker of cold water •Thermometer •Stop clock

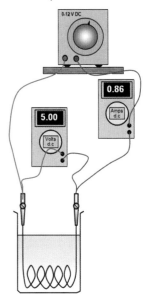

3. The most effective immersion heater

Use different types and dimensions of wire to heat up about 75 g of water in a 100 ml beaker of water. Using a constant voltage, you can show that the low resistance wires, i.e. wires that are short and thick, are the best heaters. This makes a very good piece of investigative practical work.

Theory:

Power of heater = $VI = V^2/R$ so for a given voltage the output power is directly proportional to the current, and so inversely proportional to the resistance, wires with low resistance giving more power than those of high resistance. Resistivity (ρ) = RA/L and so Power = $V^2A/L\rho$. So the energy output in a time t is $V^2At/L\rho$. This is equal to $mc\theta$ and so the rise in temperature (θ) is $V^2At/L\rho mc$, where m is the mass of water, ρ the resistivity of the wire and c the specific heat capacity of water.

Age range: 14-16   Apparatus required: •Ammeter •Voltmeter •Wires of different types and diameters •Beaker •Leads •12V Power supply

4. Heat energy in a flame

Students often have difficulty separating the ideas of heat energy and temperature and this experiment is designed to help! Compare the energy in a candle flame with the energy in a hot bath. Put out a match flame with wet fingers, and then try putting your hand into a bucket of hot water. Although the flame is much hotter than the bucket of water (its temperature is about 800°C compared with the 60°C of the water in the bucket) the energy content is much less. Your hand warms up a little and the flame cools, and since your hand is so much more massive than the flame there is little temperature rise.

 Extinguish the flame quickly with wet fingers. Do not allow the pupils to try it.

Theory:

Assume the flame has a mass of a milligram, a specific heat capacity of 2000 $Jkg^{-1}K^{-1}$ and a temperature of 820 °C the heat energy emitted when it cools to room temperature is just less than 2 J. A bucket of 4 kg of hot water initially at 60°C will release 672 kJ when it cools to room temperature!

Age range: 11-16   Apparatus required: •Candle •Bucket of hot water (60°C) •Stop clock

5. Energy in a candle

An estimate of the heat energy given off by a candle can be made by the following experiment. Use the candle to heat about 250 g of water in an aluminium can, measure the rise in temperature, and hence work out the energy given off by the length of candle burned. Then by measuring the length of a whole candle work out the energy produced by a whole candle, and finally the comparative cost of a kWh of energy produced by using either the candle or the mains electricity to drive a heater. The mains electricity is cheaper, by a factor of up to ten! Specific heat of water is 4200 Jkg^{-1} $^{\circ}C^{-1}$ and that of aluminium 1000 Jkg^{-1} $^{\circ}C^{-1}$.

Age range: 14-16   Apparatus required: •Candle •Calorimeter •Aluminium foil •Balance

6. Steamed pudding and specific heat capacity

This experiment is designed to test the statement that the jam in a steamed pudding is always hotter than the pudding. Actually cook a steamed pudding in its tin by heating it in a saucepan of boiling water in the lab. Use thermometers to measure the temperature of the pudding and jam. They both start off at the same temperature (roughly 100 $^{\circ}$C) when heating ceases but after a minute there could be as much as a 10 $^{\circ}$C difference between their temperatures. In fact in one experiment after getting the pudding out onto a plate and putting the thermometers in place the jam registered 70 $^{\circ}$C and the centre of the pudding 55 $^{\circ}$C. The difference in temperature is due to the much higher specific heat capacity of jam which therefore cools much more slowly. Opening the can at the wrong end can be disastrous and demonstrates the pressure effect of gases - blowing out scalding jam across the lab! An extension of this experiment could be to measure the specific heat of jam by heating a known mass of jam with an immersion heater. Note - jam puddings are better than syrup ones.

 Follow the instructions on the can. Do not allow the pupils to eat the pudding.

Age range: 14-16   Apparatus required: •Tinned steamed pudding •Two thermometers •Saucepan •Tripod •Bunsen burner •Heat resistant mat

MELTING, BOILING AND EVAPORATION

7. Latent heat - kettle

The specific latent heat of water can be measured very simply using a shiny electric kettle standing on a top pan balance. Fill the kettle with water, stand it on the balance, and bring it to the boil. When it is boiling vigorously take the reading of the balance - continue boiling for a measured time (say 3 minutes) and record the new balance reading at the end of that time (remove or open the lid to disable the cut-out). The difference between the two readings is the mass of water turned to steam in that time. Knowing the power of your kettle enables you to calculate the specific latent heat of vaporisation of water. A shiny kettle reduces heat loss, and good results have been gained by this method. A 1.5 kW kettle turns about 40 g of water into steam at 100 $^{\circ}$C per minute.

 Make sure the kettle is stable. With the lid off there will be a lot of steam.

Age range: 14-16   Apparatus required: •Shiny kettle of known wattage •Stop clock •Top pan balance

8. Milk bottle top in cold weather

A bottle of milk left out on the doorstep on a freezing cold morning soon freezes - the frozen milk pushing up the cap. You can simulate this by tightly fitting a piece of aluminium foil over a milk bottle full of water and putting it in the freezer. (A rubber band helps to keep it in place). The piece of foil will bulge upwards on freezing.

Age range: 11-13
Apparatus required: •Milk bottle •Aluminium foil •Rubber band or electrical tape •Access to a freezer

9. Floating ice cube

Float a pure water ice cube in a beaker of water with a paper scale fixed to the outside. Allow the ice to melt, and see if the water level goes down when the ice melts. There should be no change in level - the ice displaces its own weight of water, and so when it melts the water it forms should take up exactly the same volume as the water it displaced. Try it in brine (salty water). What would you expect to happen now? What about the change in sea levels when the polar ice caps melt? Is there a difference between the effect of the Arctic and the Antarctic? There is, since the Arctic ice is floating while the Antarctic ice is on a land mass.

Age range: 11-18 depending on treatment
Apparatus required: •Ice block •Beaker of water (parallel-sided plastic container if possible) •Ruler •TV camera (optional)

10. Evaporation

This experiment is a simple demonstration of cooling by evaporation. Put a small drop of perfume or surgical spirit BP on the skin. As the liquid evaporates, it takes heat energy from the hand and so you feel cold. This would also work by putting the liquid on a thermometer or a thermometer probe, but is perhaps not so memorable.

 | **Do not use it on any pupil who has a skin condition such as eczema.**

Age range: 11-15   Apparatus required: •Perfume •Surgical spirit BP •Thermometer (optional)

11. Regelation and the ice block

Make a shoebox sized ice block. Rest it between two stools on a couple of paper towels. Hang two 1 kg masses over it on a copper wire. The wire cuts into the block, but the ice then re-freezes over the top of it. This clearly demonstrates the lowering of the melting point of water when the pressure on it is increased. If the experiment is repeated with the two masses hanging on a string instead of the copper wire it won't work - the conductivity of the string is not great enough to carry away the latent heat of fusion of the ice. Refer this to the ice skater skating on water, not on ice, and the motion of glaciers – the melt water between the ice and the rock.

Age range: 13-15
Apparatus required: •Block of ice •Two 1kg masses •Copper wire •Tray to catch the melted water •Two lab stools as supports

12. Boiling water under reduced pressure

Boil some water in a round flask in the neck of which is a thermometer and a glass tube fixed to a rubber tube that can be sealed with a tube clamp. When it is boiling vigorously, close the clamp, and turn off the Bunsen immediately. Then invert the flask, and pour cold water over it. Water condenses in the flask, thus reducing the pressure, and boiling recommences. Further cooling gives a further reduction in pressure, and boiling can be obtained down to 40 °C. I have even once had water boiling in a flask in the lab at "body temperature" (37°C).

Dependence of the saturated vapour pressure of water on its temperature: 37°C 0.06x10^5 Pa, 60°C 0.19x10^5 Pa, 75°C 0.38x10^5 Pa, 85°C 0.57x10^5 Pa, 100°C 10^5 Pa

 All present should wear eye protection and safety screens should be used to protect both the teacher and the pupils.

Age range: 13-15
Apparatus required: •Water •Bunsen •Retort stand and clamp •Safety screen •Tray •Round-bottomed flask with bung, tube and thermometer fitted

13. Boiling under reduced pressure - an alternative method

A simpler method of demonstrating the boiling of water at low temperature is to draw some water at a temperature of about 50 - 60 ° C into a syringe so that about 20% of the volume of the syringe is filled. Then when the syringe is expanded rapidly the water boils under reduced pressure.

Age range: 13-15   Apparatus required: •Syringe •Hot water

14. The freezing mixture

Really low temperatures can be obtained by adding salt to ice, since the freezing point of the ice/salt mixture is lower than that of ice, and so the mixture will be a liquid at the normal freezing point of water. (Temperatures of -10°C are easy to obtain.) Refer to the use of salt on pavements in cold weather. The salt lowers the temperature at which the water/salt mixture freezes, and so at the temperature of the surrounding air the water still remains a liquid.

Age range: 11-15   Apparatus required: •Beaker •Ice •Salt

15. Volume change solid to gas

The change of volume when a solid turns into a gas can be shown by using a small plastic film holder. Put some solid carbon dioxide into the holder, put the lid on, and place the holder upside down on the bench. Put a transparent plastic sheet around it for safety, and wait. The solid sublimes (turns directly from a solid to a gas). The increase in volume of the carbon dioxide increases the pressure within the film holder. This blows the lid off the holder, shooting the holder into the air.

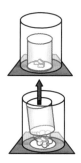

 Dry ice should only be made using a 'siphon' type carbon dioxide cylinder with a 'Jebfreezer' attachment or a thick cloth bag. Eye protection is needed and leather gloves should be worn. Pupils must not handle dry ice.

Age range: 14-16 Apparatus required: •Plastic film holder •Cylindrical plastic sheet screen •Solid carbon dioxide (dry ice)   These holders may be difficult to obtain – any small plastic pot with a lid will do.

16. Change of volume of freezing water - cast iron flask

A cast iron flask is filled with cold water and the lid screwed on tightly. The flask should then be put in a **plastic** beaker filled with a freezing mixture (alternate layers of crushed ice and salt) (see experiment 14). After a while (some minutes) a crack should be heard. The flask has broken due to the increase in volume of the water as it freezes - hence the need for a plastic beaker. Relate this to the problem of burst pipes in the winter.

This is also worth doing using a small plastic bottle which has been filled to the brim with water. It could be left in the freezer from one lesson to the next if you can't get one that will fit in the freezing mixture in a beaker.

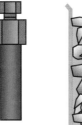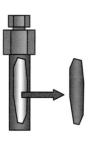

Age range: 11-13   Apparatus required: •Plastic beaker •Cast iron flask •Freezing mixture

17. Change of volume of melting ice - burette

Fill a conical flask with melting ice. Put a bung in the top with a burette in it. The burette should be partly filled with light oil. As all the ice melts and a decrease in volume occurs, the level of the oil in the burette should fall. Alternatively the flask could initially be filled with pure water and then placed in a freezing mixture, and the resulting expansion measured as the water freezes. Plastic bottles full of milk expand when they are kept in a freezer.

Age range: 11-18 depending on treatment
Apparatus required: •Burette •Oil •Freezing mixture •Conical flask •Bung

18. A home made air cooling system

This is simply a way of cooling down the air in a room during very hot weather. Take two or three large plastic drinks bottles, and fill them about nine tenths full with water. Put the tops on, and put the bottles in the freezer until the water has frozen and the ice formed has reached the temperature of the freezer (about −10°C).

Remove the bottles, and put them in front of an ordinary air fan. Turn on the fan, and you will get a stream of really cold air so cooling the room. The ice takes a surprisingly long time to melt even on a hot day.

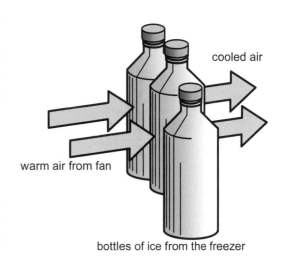

cooled air

warm air from fan

bottles of ice from the freezer

Age range: 11-18
Apparatus required: •3 large plastic bottles •Access to a freezer •Air fan blower

19. Fish in a freezing pond

Diagrams of the fate of fish due to the freezing of ice emphasise the importance of the relative densities of ice and water. Since ice is less dense than water at 0°C the ice floats; the water with the greatest density - that at 4°C - will sink to the bottom. It's a good job, otherwise the oceans would freeze up from the bottom upwards, seriously reducing the amount of sea water!

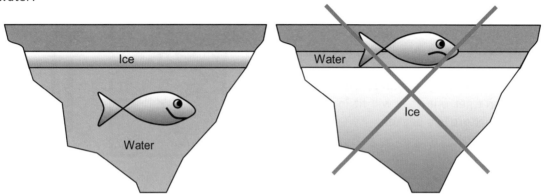

20. Lagging and heat loss

In all the problems that we have looked at so far we have assumed that no heat is lost to the surroundings, but this is not true. There will always be some heat loss, and the heat energy that we put into the water that we are heating is always going to be a bit less than we think, and so the rise in temperature in a certain time will also be less. Lagging the object will help, and the following graph shows the effect of doing this. The graph also shows how the graph levels off when the water boils.

(A similar graph for heating a metal block with a heater also levels off but in this case it would show the block melting and not boiling).

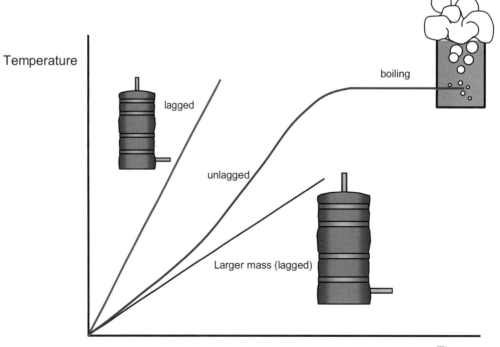

THERMAL EFFECTS AND MOLECULES

General theory for this section:

The temperature of a gas depends on the kinetic energy of its molecules.

$PV = [1/3]mNc_{rms}^2 = nRT$ (n is the number of moles, N is the number of molecules)

Kinetic energy of a molecule = $[3/2]kT$ where R is the molar gas constant = 8.3 $mol^{-1}K^{-1}$ and k is Boltzmann's constant = 1.38×10^{23} JK^{-1}.

1. Brownian motion - a luminous elephant
2. Diffusion in a jelly
3. Random walk
4. Porous pot and diffusion
5. Kinetic theory directly

6. Silent kinetic theory
7. Mixing alcohol and water
8. Diffusion in gases
9. A simulated damp proof course

1. Brownian motion and the luminous elephant

The smoke cell experiment where particles of smoke are seen to exhibit a juddering motion when viewed under a microscope is an excellent way of showing the random motion of air molecules. The kinetic theory model containing ball bearings in a cylinder that can be vibrated is a useful simulation of this behaviour. Increased vibration simulates an increase in temperature as the ball bearings move faster. There are also various analogies that can be used to demonstrate this effect. Here is one!

Imagine an elephant (representing a smoke particle) painted with luminous paint in a darkened sports hall. Also in the hall are a large number of children (representing the air molecules). They are dressed in black so that they are invisible when an observer looks into the sports hall through a skylight in the roof. The children are now told to run around; they do so, colliding with each other, the walls and the luminous elephant.

What does the observer see? Simply a luminous elephant juddering about as it is being knocked from side to side by some invisible force.

2. Diffusion in a jelly

Make a yellow jelly in a dish, and allow it to set. Very carefully pour on another jelly - this time a red one. Set the second jelly quickly in the fridge before it has time to melt the first one. Observe the join between the two jellies after some days. A flow of colour should be seen around the join, showing a diffusion of the particles of each jelly.

Age range: 11-13
Apparatus required: •Jellies •Crystallising dish

3. Random walk

The random nature of gas molecule motion can be shown by using isometric graph paper and a dice. The six-sided dice represents the six possible directions of motion in a three dimensional world. The isometric paper has six possible directions from any intersection on its surface and can be used to represent random walk. Rather like the motion of a drunk in the crowd!

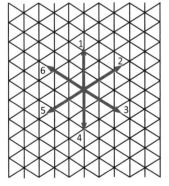

Age range: 14-16   Apparatus required: •Isometric graph paper •Dice

4. Porous pot and diffusion

The different rates of diffusion of gas and air can be shown by using a porous pot. Put a bung into the top of the pot with a tube in it, and fill the pot with gas from the gas tap. Upturn the pot so that the tube goes into water in a beaker. The gas diffuses out through the pot quicker than the heavier air diffuses in, and water rises up the tube.

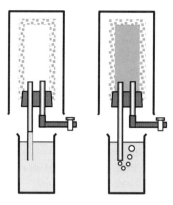

Alternatively hold a glass beaker over the porous pot and fill the beaker with gas. Bubbles of gas now come out through the water.

Theory:
Graham's Law states that the rate of diffusion of a gas is inversely proportional to the square root of its density. Heavier gases will diffuse more slowly than light ones.

Age range: 11-13   Apparatus required: •Porous pot •Beaker •Bung and tube •Beaker of water •Retort stand, boss and clamp •Gas supply

5. Kinetic theory directly

This can be shown directly by the oscillation of a small mirror made of aluminium foil suspended by a fine thread in a bell jar. Observe the collisions of the molecules of air with the mirror by using a light beam directed across the lab - it works better at low pressures <10 mm of mercury (<10^3 Pa or less than 1/100 of normal atmospheric pressure).

Eye protection required. Only bell jars designed to be evacuated should be used. Ensure that there are no cracks or chips in the glass which could cause the jar to implode when evacuated. Safety screens should be used to protect those present. Laser goggles are not required with low power laser pointers or school lasers.

Age range: 11-18
Apparatus required: •Bell jar •Vacuum pump •Small mirror or piece of rigid aluminium foil •Fine thread •Light beam (laser pin pointer)

6. Silent kinetic theory

Simply sprinkling some camphor particles on to the surface of some water in a glass dish resting on an overhead projector can simulate the random motion of particles in a gas. The camphor dissolves irregularly, and the result is that the particles rush around randomly - just like the molecules in a gas. As more dissolves, the motion slows down, giving a fair simulation of a gas cooling.

Age range: 11-13   Apparatus required: •Overhead projector •Camphor crystals •Dish of water

7. Mixing alcohol and water

This simple experiment gives an idea of the gaps between molecules. Take 100 ml of water in a 250 ml measuring cylinder and add exactly 100 ml of alcohol to it. The resulting volume is only about 195 ml. The molecules have intermingled, filling up the gaps between each other. Adding sugar to water is another example.

Age range: 11 – 13 Apparatus required: •200 ml measuring cylinder •100 ml measuring cylinder •Alcohol •Water

8. Diffusion in gases

Three possible demonstrations

    (a)   Open a bottle of perfume at the front of the lab and ask the class to record when they begin to smell it!

    (b)   There is also the classic experiment with concentrated ammonia and hydrochloric acid placed on plugs of cotton wool at opposite ends of a glass tube. After a while a white ring forms in the tube due to the interaction of the two chemicals. The differing masses of the molecules means that they diffuse through the air in the tube at different rates, and so the white ring formed in a tube when they meet will not be in the centre.

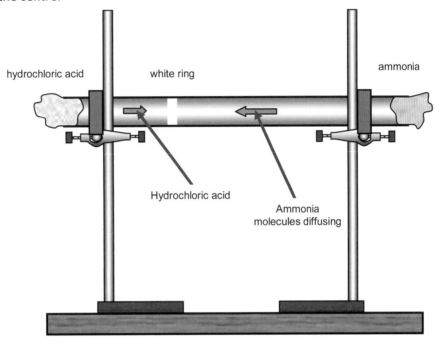

hydrochloric acid   white ring   ammonia

Hydrochloric acid

Ammonia
molecules diffusing

 Concentrated ammonia is corrosive, and the gas is toxic. Eye protection is needed, skin contact should be avoided, and the gas should not be inhaled. Concentrated hydrochloric acid should be treated in a similar way.

(c) Simply opening the two bottles close to each other will show the diffusion, "smoke" coming from the bottle of ammonia after a while.

Age range: 11-13
Apparatus required: •Bottle of perfume •Concentrated solutions of ammonia and hydrochloric acid •Metre-long glass tube •Cotton wool •Two retort stands, bosses and clamps •Dropping pipettes •Two protective saucers

9. A simulated damp proof course

Many of us know how important a damp proof course is in preventing water entering our houses. You can make a simple simulation of this by building two walls of sugar cubes in a tray with a piece of plastic in one wall between the first and second layers of cubes. Now pour some coloured water into the tray and watch the diffusion of coloured liquid up the two walls and the effect of the plastic layer "damp proof course".

Age range: 11 -1 3   Apparatus required: •Sugar cubes •Coloured water •Tray

MISCELLANEOUS HEAT

1. At what temperature does paper burn
2. Galileo's thermometer
3. Galileo's thermometer again
4. Heat end vibrations – solid carbon dioxide
5. Boiling water in a paper bag
6. Effect of heat on a rubber band
7. Clouds in a bell jar
8. Red noses - thermal effects
9. Stretching a cooled elastic band
10. Silt meter

11. Elephants' ears and cooling
12. Polystyrene
13. Entropy increase
14. Absolute zero
15. A good huddle
16. Mechanical energy to Heat energy
17. Hot air balloon - candle
18. Floating bubbles
19. Dipping bird
20. Heat sensitive mat - liquid crystals

1. At what temperature does paper burn

Using a suitable thermocouple temperature probe, try and repeat the idea of the old film "Fahrenheit 451" to find out at what temperature paper burns. This is best done outside the lab or in a fume cupboard!

 Demonstration only.

Age range: 11-14   Apparatus needed: •Temperature probe •Paper •Metal plate

2. Galileo's thermometer

This is a rather expensive (some £40 upwards) but beautiful use and demonstration of the effect of temperature on liquid density and flotation. A series of glass spheres are immersed in a liquid of density very similar to that of the spheres. They each contain different amounts of air and have small metal tags of differing mass hanging from the bottom and so rise and fall as the temperature changes. More spheres are at the top of the cylinder when it is cold - the density of the liquid is high and gives more upthrust. As the liquid heats up so the upthrust on the spheres decreases, and they begin to sink to the bottom.

3. Galileo's thermometer again

It is possible to produce a home-made version of Galileo's thermometer with Christmas tree balls loaded with plasticine. Balls about 1 cm in diameter work best for this.

Age range: 11-14   Apparatus required: •Tall beaker •Christmas tree balls •Plasticine •Bunsen burner •Heat-resistant mat •Tripod and gauze

4. Heat end vibrations – iron rod on solid carbon dioxide

Rest one end of an iron rod on a piece of dry ice (solid carbon dioxide), the other end on a table. Jar it a little - the rod emits a high-pitched vibration. I have seen a similar effect in a baking tray with gravy in it placed on a cooker ring, although in this case the frequency of vibration was too low to hear.

5. Boiling water in a paper bag

Water can be boiled in a paper bag - but why doesn't the paper burn? This is also easy to demonstrate using a paper cup – the water in the cup keeps the temperature of the paper below that required for ignition.

Age range: 11 – 13 Apparatus required: •Bunsen burner •Paper cup and paper bag •Heat resistant mat

6. Effect of heat on a rubber band

A long rubber band with a mass on the end is hung in a tall beaker of water. The taller the beaker, the longer the rubber band or piece of elastic, and the more of it immersed in the water the better. The water is then heated, and the change in length of the band (it shrinks) is measured. A way of getting the longest piece of rubber under the water is to use a large glass tube with a rubber bung in the lower end heated in a water bath - the water bath being a tall one-litre beaker. The temperature of the water near the rubber band is found by hanging a thermometer down the large glass tube.

Age range: 16-18
Apparatus required: •Long thin rubber band •Glass tube (diameter 5 cm length 0.5 m) •Tall beaker •Bung •Bunsen burner •Tripod •Heat-resistant mat

7. Clouds in a bell jar

Clouds can be formed in a bell jar if the air inside it is allowed to expand adiabatically. Take a bell jar and put 1 cm of water in the bottom and then blow into the bell jar. The air inside is compressed, and as it expands you might expect to see clouds due to the adiabatic expansion and subsequent cooling - but none form. To get the cloud, you need a little pollution to give nuclei on which the water can condense. This can be provided in the form of smoke. If a little is puffed into the jar, clouds immediately form. (You can warm the jar to encourage evaporation.)

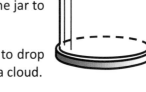

Another way of getting the clouds after blowing into a flask is to drop a smouldering match in to give the nuclei and thence produce a cloud.

Age range: 11-18 depending on treatment
Apparatus required: •Bell jar •Rubber tube •Smoke generator

8. Red noses - thermal effects

The plastic red noses from various years of Comic Relief in England show wonderful thermal effects, the plastic changing from red to yellow or red to pink when they are put in hot water. You can also get various plastic animals that will do the same. I have some model dinosaurs that change from brown to green when heated and even a couple of small plastic dogs that have a red poorly paw when put in a beaker of icy water. Rubbing the paw with your finger to "make it better" warms the paw, and the red mark disappears!

9. Stretching a cooled elastic band

The effect of a change of temperature of a rubber band can also be investigated using a cooling experiment. Hang up a rubber band, and then stretch it using slotted masses suspended from the lower end. Cool sections of the band using a freezer spray, and observe the widths of the warm and cool sections. I have been told that when your lips are compressed in a kiss they actually cool, but I leave it to your ingenuity to devise an experiment to show this!

Age range: 15-18
Apparatus required: •Rubber band •Slotted masses •Freezer spray •Retort stand, boss and clamp

10. Silt meter

This experiment is a simulation of river pollution. Each group has a large beaker of water to which they add drops of milk. They place a low voltage bulb on one side of the beaker and observe the transmission of light through the liquid - detecting the intensity with a Light Dependent Resistor (LDR). As more milk is added, and it doesn't need much, the intensity of the transmitted light falls, simulating the effect of a polluted river. The milk is less messy than mud. This has been found to be a good assessed practical investigation and could be extended by asking the pupils to estimate the concentration of milk in an unknown sample, using their calibration graph from the first part of the experiment.

Age range: 14-16
Apparatus required: •Light dependent resistor and ohm meter •Calibration graph •Beaker of water •Milk and dropper •Low voltage power supply •Bulb •Leads

11. Elephants' ears and cooling

A good example of the effect of area on the cooling of a body can be shown by using three cups: one with no ears, one with ears and the third with the ears folded down. Make the ears out of aluminium foil. Fill them all with boiling water, and measure the rate of cooling. The fins on an air-cooled engine are a good example of area cooling in practice. Painting the 'ears' black makes the experiment even more effective.

A dinosaur known as a dimetrodon had a sail on its back and used to stand facing north-south in the early morning so that the rising sun would warm up the blood in the sail, enabling it to get going for the day.

An Arctic fox has small ears while a desert fox has much larger ears. Apart from being good for hearing, the large ears will lose heat effectively.

Age range: 10-13
Apparatus required: •Three cups or mugs •Aluminium foil •Thermometers •Hot water

12. Polystyrene

This material is yet another example of the effect of a poor thermal conductor like a carpet. If you walk on a carpet in bare feet it feels warm, but if you step off on to a tiled floor it feels much colder, although the temperature of the floor and carpet are the same. Similarly a piece of polystyrene feels warm to the touch although being at the same temperature as other objects in the lab. However, a large piece of metal initially at the same temperature as the polystyrene will feel colder to the touch.

Theory:
Both these facts can be explained by realising that the tiles and the metal conduct heat energy away from your body, leaving your hands or feet cooler. A quantitative experiment to demonstrate this can be done by placing identical beakers of water on a slab of polystyrene and metal and measuring their rate of cooling.

Age range: 11-13
Apparatus required: •Slab of polystyrene foam •Large slab of metal the same size as the polystyrene if possible •Thermometers •Beakers •Stopclock

13. Entropy increase

Entropy or disorder must always increase! This can be shown by running a video of a pile of falling blocks backwards. Since entropy always increases, you can tell if the film is running forwards or not by the increase of disorder that results if no external human influences act. You can refer this to the ultimate fate of the Universe - a smeared out warmth is the likely final state rather than discrete hot spots.

14. Absolute zero

You may know that one of the laws of thermodynamics is that absolute zero (-273.15 °C) can never be reached. In fact it gets more and more difficult to remove energy as the temperature gets lower - the energy steps become smaller and smaller. It is rather like going down a never-ending escalator - the steps on the escalator also get smaller and smaller towards the bottom, and in the case of the reducing temperature they go on doing this for ever.

15. A good huddle

To show the effect of groups of animals keeping warm, prepare seven or eight test tubes - all containing the same amount of water. Place them in a water bath (this could be just a large beaker of water), heat them to the same temperature, and then remove them, leaving one on its own and the others in a group. Record the temperature of each test tube with time - the one on its own will cool down much quicker than those in the huddle since it has a much greater surface area to volume ratio.

An interesting extension of this experiment is to investigate the effect of mass and surface area on the rate of cooling using balloons filled with hot water. Measure their temperature with a thermometer probe placed inside them, and experiment with:

(a) different sized spherical balloons
(b) spherical balloons and sausage shaped balloons of the same mass
(c) spherical balloons of the same size and mass, but one suspended in air and the other suspended in a bucket of water at room temperature

Age range: 11-13
Apparatus required: •Test tubes with little or no flange at the top •Water bath •Thermometers •Suitable method of holding a group of test tubes •Various balloons •Bucket •Thermometer probe

16. Mechanical energy - Heat energy conversion

A couple of suggestions to show the conversion of mechanical energy to heat energy are:
(a) Saw through an insulated bolt, and let the pieces fall into a plastic beaker of water - of course the hacksaw gets hot as well!
(b) Hammer a piece of lead and then measure the temperature rise with a thermistor

Age range: 14-16   Apparatus required: •Lead •Hammer •Hacksaw •Plastic beaker of water •Bolt

17. Hot air balloon - candle

Try making a hot air balloon from a large plastic bag such as a bin liner and then try "flying" it by putting it over a hair dryer. The hair dryer has no naked flame and the experiment is therefore safer and easier to control. Keep the lower end open with a ring of wire.

 It is better to launch this in the lab or sports hall rather than in the open air.

Age: 7-14   Apparatus required: •Large plastic bag (bin liner) •Wire •Hair dryer

18. Floating bubbles

The following experiment is a fascinating demonstration of the insulating properties of a gas (in this case steam). Place a metal plate about 10 cm in diameter and 0.5 cm thick on a gas burner (better than a Bunsen, as the whole plate gets heated). Heat the plate strongly, and then drop a small droplet of water onto it. The water evaporates immediately. However, when the plate reaches about 200°C, the water evaporates so rapidly from the lower surface that the resulting steam insulates the upper part of the droplet and it does not evaporate. When this state is reached more water can be added, so increasing the size of the droplet, which now "floats" on the insulating layer of steam. Discs of water up to 2 cm in diameter can be produced.

 Eye protection is required. Take care that nobody gets too near the hot metal plate.

Age range: 11-1 8
Apparatus required: •Gas burner •Dropper •Metal plate •TV camera if available

19. Dipping bird

This wonderful old toy can still be bought. It rests on the side of a glass and dips its head into the cold water. As the liquid inside its body evaporates it forces liquid up the neck, altering the balance of the bird, which then dips its head into the water.

If the head is not wetted then a very instructive version of the experiment occurs. The bird tends not to drink but placing a saucer of hot water beneath its bottom will heat up the liquid sufficiently to increase the rate of evaporation and make it start rocking. Energy is provided by the hot water – you don't get something for nothing!

Also try it with meths in the glass instead of water.

Age range: 11-18 depending on treatment
Apparatus required: •Dipping bird •Wine glass
•Water •Saucer •Meths

20. Heat-sensitive mat - liquid crystals

This mat with a layer of liquid crystals below a transparent top is available from gift shops. Some lovely coloured effects are produced when a mug of hot drink is put on it, or when you just lay your hand on it. The colours that you get when they put their hands on the mat can give some idea of the temperature of various pupils' hands.

CURRENT ELECTRICITY

General theory for this section:

Electric charge in a solid is carried by particles called electrons. One electron has a very tiny charge and so for practical measurement of electric charge we use units called COULOMBS.

A coulomb (C) is an AMOUNT of electric charge in just the same way that a litre is an AMOUNT of water. One coulomb is the charge of roughly six million million million electrons!
The movement of this charge round a circuit is called the **electric current**. Electric current is the rate of flow of charge round a circuit. The current at a point in the circuit is the amount of charge that passes that point in one second.

Electric current is measured in AMPERES (AMPS, symbol A).

A piece of wire is made of millions of atoms, and each one of these has its own cloud of electrons. However, in a metal there is a large number of electrons that are not held around particular nuclei but are free to move at high speed and in a random way through the metal. These are known as **free electrons,** and in a metal there are always large numbers of these. It is when these free electrons are all made to move in a certain direction by the application of a voltage across the metal that we have an electric current.

The difference between a metal (a large and constant number of free electrons), a semiconductor (a few free electrons, the number of which varies with temperature) and an insulator (no free electrons) is shown in the following diagram.

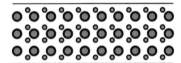
semiconductor

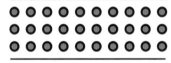
insulator

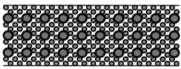
conductor

Resistance = Voltage/Current   Resistance = Resistivity x Length/Cross sectional area

For a metal
Resistance = Resistance at 0°C[1 + temp. coefficient of resistance x temperature change]

Average Effects of Continuous ac or dc Electrical Currents on Healthy Adults

Electrical Current	Biological Effect
1 mA	threshold for feeling
10-20 mA	voluntary let-go of circuit impossible
25 mA	onset of muscular contractions
50-200 mA	ventricular fibrillation or cardiac arrest

The figures given above depend on the path of the current through the body. The current that flows will also depend on the resistance and the voltage. Thus, in schools, adopting a large safety factor using voltages below 40V (dc or peak ac) are regarded as safe.

If you are outside in a thunderstorm it is important to give a possible path for a lightning strike between the highest part of your body and the ground that would not pass through your brain or your heart. This can be done by kneeling down with your 'bottom in the air'!

1. The electron steeplechase
2. Fusing currents in wires
3. The human battery
4. Surge of current in a light bulb
5. Hot wire ammeter
6. Birds on high voltage wires
7. Conductivity of glass
8. Parallel circuits
9. Wolf whistling beaver
10. Lie Detector
11. Resistance - conducting putty
12. Repulsion of aluminium strips
13. Making d.c and a.c visible
14. Flow of charge
15. Chicken and a closed circuit
16. Parallel circuit - the bath analogy
17. Bulbs in series
18. A carbon resistor and heat
19. The transistor switch
20. Conduction in liquids
21. The lemon battery
22. Series circuit puzzle

1. The electron steeplechase

This analogy is designed to explain energy losses in a series circuit. Imagine that the electrons are running round a steeplechase course. As they go round they lose energy - on the track it would be by going over a barrier, in a circuit it might be by passing through a bulb. When they reach the end of the track, or circuit, they have low energy and must be given a further input of energy - say by a battery - before they can make another circuit.

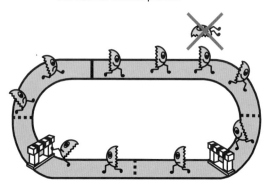

Two important rules about them - (i) they are not allowed to give up the race - the same number of electrons that leave the start must reach the finish (this emphasises the constancy of current at all points in a series circuit) and (ii) the velocity of the electrons remains unaltered. We assume that they do not lose much, if any, energy on the flat - this is analogous to the low energy loss in the connecting wires of a circuit due to their low resistance.

2. Fusing currents in wires

Find the current at which a wire will fuse, either by a steady increase or by the sudden application of a large current. Wire wool works quite well for this, although a piece of resistance wire stretched between two retort stands glowing bright yellow before it fuses is quite spectacular. For older students a consideration of the radiation emitted by the wire will lead to a study of Stefan's Law (Energy emitted by a "black body" at absolute temperature T = σAT^4 where A is the surface area and σ is Stefan's constant). Factors such as the surface area of the wire and the ratio of fusing current to wire diameter could be investigated.

Age range: 11-16 or above for an individual investigation
Apparatus required: •Wire wool •Resistance wire •Ammeter •12V dc power supply (8A)
•Heat-resistant mat •Crocodile clips •Leads

3. The human battery

Place one hand on a copper sheet and the other hand on a zinc sheet and measure the potential difference between them. Voltages of about 0.7 V can be produced due to the electrochemical reaction between the two dissimilar metals and the moisture of your hands. As with the lie detector, try the effects of stress on the "volunteer"!

Age range: 14 –18   Apparatus required: •Voltmeter •Zinc sheet •Copper sheet •Leads •Crocodile clips

4. Surge of current in a light bulb

(a) Investigate the surge of current when a filament light bulb is switched on. It is worth mentioning that switching on is the time when it is most likely that the bulb will blow. The filament has a low resistance when cold, and therefore a large current flows, heating occurs rapidly, there is a large thermal expansion and the resulting thermal shock can break the filament.

(b) The change of resistance of the filament of a bulb with temperature can be seen very easily as an extension to experiment 17. If the supply is adjusted to around 12 V and then switched on, the small bulb lights brilliantly. The current is large, since the 12V 36W bulb is still cold and its resistance is low. As it warms up - this takes a little less than a second - the resistance rises, the current falls and the small bulb's brightness decreases.

Theory:
Resistance of a metal conductor increases with increasing temperature. As the temperature rises the thermal motion of the atoms within the metal impedes the motion of electrons through it, and so the resistance rises.

Age range: 16-18
Apparatus required: •12 V bulb in suitable holder •Small torch bulb •12 V power supply

5. Hot wire ammeter

Suspend a taut piece of copper wire between two retort stands with its ends fixed to insulated terminals. Hang a 50 g mass from the centre to keep it in tension. Pass a current through it, and measure the depression of the mass. Plot a graph of depression against current. Note that this will work for both a.c and d.c.

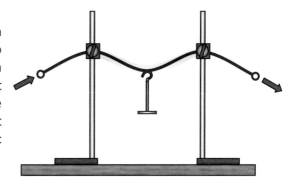

Theory:
As a current passes through the wire it will heat up and so expand. The weight hanging from its centre will cause it to sag.

 Warn pupils of the hazards of burns from the very hot wire as the current increases.

Age range: 13-16
Apparatus required: •Copper wire 28 SWG •Two retort stands, bosses and clamps •12V dc supply giving up to 8A •50g mass on metal hanger •30 cm ruler in bench clamp •TV camera if possible

6. Birds on high voltage wires

Why is it that birds can sit on high voltage cables without danger? Of course, it is fine if they do not touch the ground or have one foot on the live cable and one on the neutral. When they are standing on a single cable they are quite safe, because the potential difference between their two feet is far too low to be dangerous.

7. Conductivity of glass

This is a fascinating demonstration. Take two pieces of thick copper wire, wind one round each end of a soft glass rod, and connect the ends of the wires to a 240V mains power supply in series with a 100 W lamp. Switch on - nothing happens, since the glass is an electrical insulator. Now heat the glass strongly with a Bunsen. As the glass becomes molten conduction occurs, and the light comes on.

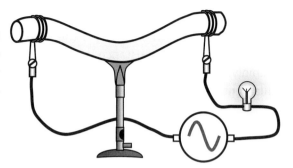

It is much more impressive with the mains where, once conduction has started, the heat of the current itself is often enough to maintain the current flow.

⚠️	**DEMONSTRATION ONLY! NOT TO BE ATTEMPTED BY ANY PUPIL** **This demonstration should only be done if the teacher has been trained by an experienced colleague so that it can be carried out with minimal risk and if it has been practised. The hazard of severe or fatal electric shock from the 230V ac supply is present no matter what precautions are taken.** **A special risk assessment and approved method must be followed, e.g. from CLEAPPS.**	

Age range: 14-16
Apparatus required:
•Variac transformer •Soft glass rod •Bunsen burner •Two lengths of bare copper wire •Wooden clamp •Crocodile clips •Heat-resistant mat •100 W lamp in holder •Three insulated in-line connectors

8. Parallel circuits

Pupils are taught that the addition of a resistor to a circuit will decrease the flow of current and are therefore puzzled when told that two resistors in parallel draw a greater current from the supply than one of the resistors on its own. You can use the traffic analogy to explain this. The addition of a bypass round a town will actually increase the traffic flow on the major road. Similarly, another resistor in parallel with the first will allow more current to flow from the supply. (See also the bath plug analogy shown in experiment 16 on page 211.)

9. Wolf whistling beaver

I have a soft toy beaver bought in France. When you walk in front of it the beaver wolf whistles, but why? In its chest there is a small light sensor, which activates a circuit if the light level changes.

What better way can there be to show the properties of such a sensor?

(•These used to be available in 2010 from Stock Foille, 16190 Montmoreau, Charente, France. Cost about £15 including postage)

10. Lie detector

This experiment is a fun extension of resistance and simulates a lie detector or embarrassment meter! Wrap pieces of aluminium foil round two toilet rolls, or tape two sheets of foil to the bench.

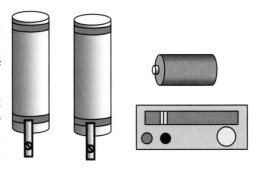

Connect a 1.5 V cell and a spot galvanometer in series with the foil, and then complete the circuit by getting one of the pupils to hold the toilet rolls. Now try and embarrass them. The conductivity of the skin changes, and as a result the reading on the spot galvanometer changes also. Quite often just sitting there can embarrass the volunteer - they know what secrets about them the rest of the class knows. Resistance between the two hands is of the order of 200 kΩ.

Be sensitive here - I never let anyone's private life get exposed to the others. The same effects occur if the volunteer is put under stress - try asking them some Physics questions!

> **Demonstration only. Never do this outside school supervision. Only use a 1.5 V cell and never connect it near to a pupil's head.**

Age range: 14-16
Apparatus required: •Two cardboard tubes •Electrical tape •Aluminium foil •Spot galvanometer •1.5 V cell •Crocodile clips •Leads

11. Resistance - conducting putty

Use this commercially available material to make different shaped specimens to demonstrate the effect of shape and size on the resistance of a specimen. Even series and parallel circuits can be moulded! Use a couple of metal discs (such as two coins) pressed on to either end of the specimen as a means of making electrical contact.

Age range: usually 16-18
Apparatus required:
•Conducting putty •12V dc power supply •Ammeter and voltmeter •Crocodile clips •Two metal discs •Leads •A high resistance digital ohmmeter can be used instead of the ammeter and voltmeter and power supply

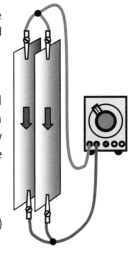

12. Repulsion of aluminium strips

Two slack aluminium strips mounted vertically side by side can be used to show the forces between currents. Make sure that they cannot touch when a current is passed through them. A single folded strip will show the repulsion of currents flowing in opposite directions - down one side and up the other.

Age range: 16-18
Apparatus required: •Two aluminium strips •Holders •Low voltage (12V) power supply •Ammeter •Leads

13. Making a.c and d.c visible

Take a piece of thick blotting paper, and soak it with some thinly running paste of starch (or flour) mixed with potassium iodide. Allow it to dry, and then mount it on a metal base. Connect the base to one terminal of the supply using a crocodile clip. Run a probe connected to the other terminal of the supply along the paper surface. First use a dc supply and then an ac supply. The dc supply will give a continuous line while the ac will give a series of dashes.

The action of the electricity releases iodine ions, which move towards the positive terminal where they react with the starch, giving a dark blue colour.

Age range: 14-18

Apparatus required: •Blotting paper •Starch or flour •Probe • Low voltage (12V) Power supply •Potassium iodide crystals •Crocodile clips •Metal sheet •Leads

14. Flow of charge

This experiment is designed to measure the drift velocity of ions in a liquid and gives you an idea of the drift velocity of electrons in a piece of metal when a potential difference is placed across its ends. Soak a rectangle of filter paper in ammonium hydroxide solution, and lay it on a microscope slide. Place an optical pin across each end and clip them in place with crocodile clips.

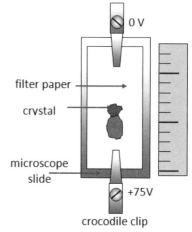

Connect an HT supply with its output current limited to 5 mA across the pins, and place a potassium permanganate crystal in the centre of the paper. Apply a potential difference of 75 V between the crocodile clips and measure the time it takes for the purple colour to travel 1 cm. Doing the whole experiment on a plastic strip with a half millimetre scale marked on it helps, and using a TV camera to view the whole slide on a screen helps even more.

 Demonstration only. Ammonia solution (ammonium hydroxide) is corrosive and releases ammonia gas which may cause respiratory disorders especially to asthmatics. HT units must be under careful control and the voltage limited to the maximum required to produce a result with their output current limited to 5 mA. Do not touch the exposed crocodile clips or pins.

Theory:

In a wire the current is given by the equation $I = nAve$ where v is the drift velocity of the electrons, A the cross sectional area of the wire, n the number of electrons per metre cubed and e the electron charge. Similar values to v can be obtained by this drift velocity experiment. Values of a few mm a minute are common for potential differences of 100V between electrodes some three or four cm apart.

Age range: 16-18

Apparatus required: •HT power supply (50-100V) output limited to 5 mA •Crocodile clips •Two optical pins •Microscope slide •Filter paper •Millimetre scale •Stop clock •Potassium permanganate crystals •Ammonium hydroxide

15. Chicken and a closed circuit

How do you use a toy chicken to show children that you must have a complete circuit for electric current to flow? Hold the chicken in your hand. With any luck it will chirrup, but why? There is a battery in the chicken and in the base there are two contacts. If your hand is slightly moist it completes the circuit.

16. Parallel circuit - the bath analogy

Imagine a bath full of water but with two plugs and plugholes. The plughole allows water to fall into a tank where a pump pumps it back to the tap. Now turn on the tap and pump, and pull out one of the plugs. Water circulates round - the level of the water in the bath stays the same.

Now pull out the other plug! To keep the water level in the bath the same the pump must work twice as hard - the rate of flow of water from the tap is doubled, but the rate of flow of water from the first plughole is unaltered. This is a good analogy with a parallel circuit - the two plugholes representing the branches of the circuit, the pump replacing the battery, and the tap the wires before they branch. The height of the water in the bath is analogous to the potential in the circuit.

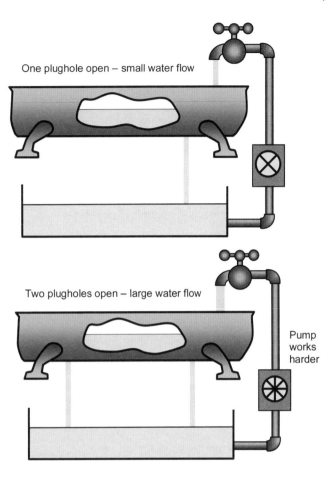

One plughole open – small water flow

Two plugholes open – large water flow

Pump works harder

17. Bulbs in series

I always introduce the idea of voltage by comparing the drop in potential round a circuit containing a number of bulbs with the drop in potential energy down a flight of stairs with each stair representing one of the bulbs. From there I go on to show two experiments to demonstrate this.

In the first one connect a 2.5 V torch bulb in series with a 12V 24W bulb. Steadily increase the potential difference across the circuit, and show that initially the small bulb does not blow. They both carry the same current but the greatest potential difference drop occurs across the large bulb.

In the second experiment fifteen 2.5V torch bulbs are connected in series to 40V 1A supply. They all light. The same current passes through each - the potential difference drop across each is roughly the same - about 2.5V.

Age range: 13-16
Apparatus required:
•Bulb 12V 24W •Fifteen torch bulbs 2.5V 0.25A •Ammeter 0-1A digital •Leads

18. A carbon resistor and heat - semiconductor or not?

The effect of raising the temperature of a carbon resistor can be investigated in the following way. Take a 10 MΩ resistor, connect it to a high resistance ohmmeter, and mount it in a holder. Use a hair dryer to heat the resistor, and measure the resistance as the temperature changes. The resistance is first seen to fall and then rise again.

Theory:
At first the semiconducting nature of carbon is more important - more free electrons are created and the resistance falls. As the temperature gets greater the increased thermal motion gives a greater rise in the resistance - a minimum of resistance is reached, and then it starts to rise.

Age range: 16-18
Apparatus required: •Hair dryer •10 MΩ resistor •Mount •High resistance ohmmeter •Leads

19. The transistor switch

In a transistor a large collector current is controlled by allowing a very small current to flow through the base of the transistor. Analogies for this could be:

   (a) A policeman directing a queue of cars or

   (b) an attendant controlling a large queue of people at a football match or

   (c) a school helper controlling a lunch queue.

20. Conduction in liquids – the need for ions

This experiment shows that ions are needed for electrical conduction in a liquid.

Set up the circuit as shown in the diagram, and fill the beaker with distilled water. The lack of ions in the water will mean that the bulb does not light.

Now slowly add the salt, stirring all the time. Eventually the bulb will light, and as more salt is added it will become brighter due to the higher concentration of sodium ions and chloride ions in the liquid.

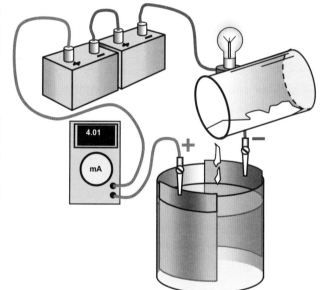

Age range: 11-14
Apparatus required: •Beaker (250 ml will do) •Distilled (deionised) water •Leads •Two crocodile clips •Two pieces of copper to act as electrodes •Battery or low voltage power supply •Suitable mounted light bulb •Salt (sodium chloride) •Glass rod as a stirrer

21. The lemon battery

Put two dissimilar metal electrodes (for example copper and zinc) into a lemon. A potential difference of about 1 V should be obtained between them. (Lemons usually give about 1.08 V and oranges 0.95 V.) This can either be detected by using a low voltage bulb (more impressive) or a digital voltmeter. I have not really been successful recently with lighting a bulb, but the voltmeter did show that there was something happening.

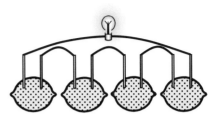

A way of making this experiment more impressive is to use a set of lemons in series to trickle charge a capacitor. Then discharge this through an LED to give a flash of light like a camera flash.

Age range: 10-18 in slightly different forms
Apparatus required: •Lemons •Electrodes of copper and zinc •Crocodile clips •Low voltage bulb LED RS 586 447 •Capacitor 220 mF 25 V •dc voltmeter •Leads

22. Series circuit puzzle

Copy and cut out the following pieces and use them to demonstrate the correct connection of components in a series circuit.

You will find that there is only one way in which they will fit together to produce a circuit with the two bulbs and two cells in series.

You could devise a parallel version of this game as well.

Age range: 7-14   Apparatus required: •Card copies of the circuit elements

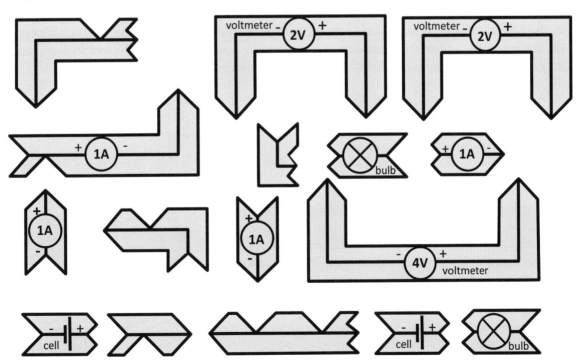

MAGNETISM

General theory for this section:

The Greeks discovered magnetism in about 600 BC. They noticed that a substance called lodestone had some strange properties. If a piece of lodestone is hung on a thread it will always point in the same direction. Lodestone - we now call it magnetite - is an oxide of iron, and it was the first known magnetic material. Lodestone will also attract other magnetic materials.

Like poles repel and unlike poles attract. The force decreases with increasing separation.
Common magnetic materials: iron, steel, cobalt, nickel.

1. Magnetic fields and tape recorders
2. Magnets and a top pan balance
3. Glass rods to hold floating magnets
4. Magnetic field patterns
5. Indian rope trick
6. Three dimensional magnetic fields
7. Magnetic fields and credit cards

8. Curie effect - iron
9. Magnetic force
10. Magnetic theatre
11. Magnetic fishing
12. Executive magnetic toys
13. Magnetic accelerator

1. Magnetic fields and tape recorders

(a) Sound is stored on a magnetic tape as a pattern of tiny magnetic domains within the tape. This can be demonstrated clearly by showing the effect of a magnet on a recorded tape. Record some speech on a cassette tape, and then pass the cassette between the poles of a strong magnet. Now replay the tape - the magnetic pattern will have been altered, and the sound will be badly distorted or even completely erased. The tape can be used again afterwards. If you have a video recorder try this using videotape - some interesting effects on the picture when it is replayed will result.

(b) For the second part of the experiment you will need a reel-to-reel tape recorder, some iron filings and a signal generator. Use the signal generator to record a 50 Hz sine wave signal on tape. Remove that section of tape from the tape recorder and sprinkle some fine iron filings on it. The filings will adhere to the tape - more strongly in places where the signal was strongest, i.e. at the troughs and peaks of the sine wave. Different wave shapes and different frequencies may be studied. Fast tape speeds will show the effects much more clearly, of course.

(c) A simulation of the effects of tape recording using magnetic tape can be achieved using adhesive tape coated with fine iron powder.

Age range: 11-18 depending on treatment
Apparatus required: •Reel to reel tape recorder •Microphone •Strong magnet •Blank tape •Iron filings •Signal generator or musical tube of variable pitch

2. Magnets and a top pan balance – Newton's Third Law

The forces between two magnets can easily be shown by mounting a magnet on a top pan balance and lowering another towards it - guided by glass rods. This is also a good example of Newton's Third Law.

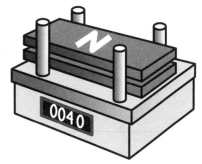

Age range: 11-14
Apparatus required: •Magnets •Suitable holder such as glass rods mounted vertically in a wooden block •Top pan balance

3. Glass rods to hold floating magnets

Glass rods mounted vertically in a wooden base are a good way of holding permanent magnets for magnetic levitation experiments. They are non-magnetic and there is little friction between them and the magnet.

4. Magnetic field patterns

The magnetic field of a permanent magnet can be demonstrated by one of the following experiments:

(a) Put a bar magnet on the glass of an overhead projector and cover it with a piece of acetate film. Sprinkle some iron filings on the film, and project the image on to a screen for class observation. The acetate sheet prevents the filings clinging to the magnet. Coils of wire mounted in plastic holders are commercially available to demonstrate electromagnetic fields.

(b) Another way of making a permanent record of the magnetic field of a magnet is to do a similar experiment on photographic paper in the dark room with just the safe light on. Put a piece of photographic paper over the magnet, and, after sprinkling the iron filings on the paper to get a good field pattern, turn the main light on for a few seconds. Then develop and print the paper, and use the silhouette photos of the magnetic field patterns to retain the image.

(c) This experiment is another way of producing a permanent record of the magnetic field of a magnet. Prepare some sheets of waxed paper by dipping them in molten wax. This is easy to do by having a tin of molten wax heated over a Bunsen. Lay the magnet on the bench and place a piece of waxed paper on it. Sprinkle some iron filings on to the paper until a good field pattern is seen. Now for the difficult part. Carefully lift the paper vertically off the magnet, keeping the paper horizontal, and melt the wax gently by passing it smoothly but quickly backwards and forwards through a clear blue Bunsen flame. Remove it from flame, and allow the wax to solidify, so giving a permanent field pattern. Finally fix it into a book using clear book covering film to preserve the pattern.

With all three of these experiments, tapping the edge of the paper slightly (before melting the wax in (c)) helps to move the iron filings and so improve the pattern.

Age range: 11-13
Apparatus required:
(a) •Magnet •Iron filings •Overhead projector •Acetate sheet
(b) •Magnet •Iron filings •Photographic paper •Access to a dark room •Photographic chemicals
(c) •Magnets •Iron filings •Waxed paper •Bunsen

5. Indian rope trick

Have a magnet concealed in a tube which is held in a clamp above a small steel screw that is fixed to the bench by a thread. The length of the thread should be a little more (a few centimetres) than the height of the magnet above the bench. The screw seems to rise into the air without support – it is actually held up by the invisible magnet. You can pass your hand through the gap between the screw and the magnet to show no support - of course your hand does not affect the magnetic field. Then try it with a metal plate, first aluminium and then steel.

Age range: 11-13
Apparatus required: •Screw •Thread •Magnet •Tube to hide the magnet •Retort stand, boss and clamp

6. Three dimensional magnetic fields

The three dimensional magnetic field of a magnet can be investigated by using a jelly. Make up the jelly in a clear mould, and then add the iron filings before it sets. Stir well, and then apply the field, or pour it into a mould which has a magnet in it, and allow the jelly to set! Various recipes are available! I am not really sure how long they keep without going mouldy! Maybe somebody could suggest an alternative material.

Age range: 11-13 Apparatus required: • Jelly •Magnet •Clear mould •Coil and power supply •Iron filings

7. Magnetic field and credit cards

It is important to keep all credit cards and other magnetic cards away from magnets. I was on holiday, staying in the hotel in the photograph, and was wearing a pair of trousers which had a small pair of magnets as a fastener on the back pocket.

I couldn't understand why the magnetic-card key to our room kept failing. My wife, she is not a physics teacher, then suggested it was because I was putting the card in my back pocket. I tested it with another card. She was right – the magnets were corrupting the information on the card. So be careful!

8. Curie effect - iron

The effect of heat on the ability of a bar to become magnetised can be studied using the Curie effect. Place a rod of iron on a tripod with a small magnet hanging from its end. Heat the rod strongly with a Bunsen flame - when the rod is hot enough the magnet will fall off. If you can spare the magnet, it is even better to heat the magnet itself. The motion of the magnetic domains is sufficient to destroy the overall magnetism of the magnet and prevent the rod being magnetised.

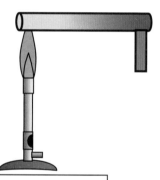

 Demonstration only. Take care not to touch the very hot metal rod.

Age range: 11-18 depending on treatment
Apparatus required: •Iron bar •Magnet •Bunsen •Tripod •Heat-resistant mat

9. Magnetic force

The forces between magnets can be demonstrated and indeed measured in the following way. Fix a ceramic magnet on the bench with one of its poles uppermost. Mount a hacksaw blade above this magnet, fixed down at one end and with a ceramic magnet fixed to the other so that it is above the magnet on the bench with like poles facing each other - the blade will curve upwards. Measurement of the amount of curvature, and a control experiment carried out by loading the blade with masses, can give you an idea of the forces between the magnets.

Age range: 11-13
Apparatus required: •Two ceramic magnets
•Hacksaw blade •Suitable clamp •Masses •Ruler

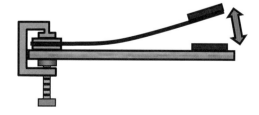

10. Magnetic theatre

A good way of introducing younger children to the uses of magnets is to make a 'magnetic theatre' similar to the one shown on the right. This is one where the characters are moved around the stage by a rod under the stage with a magnet fixed to it. The characters are mounted on bases containing a thin steel plate.

An investigation of the strength of magnet needed and the thickness and material of the 'stage' will give a good understanding of the properties of magnets. The pupils can also construct the stage and write the script.

Age range: 7-11
Apparatus required: •Small disc magnets •Steel plates (diameter about 1 cm) •Cardboard •Dowel rod

11. Magnetic fishing

This is a simple 'toy' that can be used to introduce younger pupils to magnetism. A series of cardboard fish should be cut out of cardboard and a steel paper clip fixed to each one.

Place the fish in a bucket, and try to 'catch' them using a small magnet on the end of a string tied to a length of dowel rod – the fishing rod. If each fish has a 'score' written on it, this makes a fun game. The photograph shows my wife taking part in a game where you had to fish for film stars to raise money for our village film club.

Age range: 5-11
Apparatus required: •Cardboard •Thread •Dowel rod •Paper clips •Bucket •Scissors
•Small magnets (not too strong)

12. Executive magnetic toys

These are just good to look at, but every school should have one or two. They stimulate much discussion about the magnetic effects, the balancing of the parts and the low friction at the points of contact.

Age range: 11-18 depending on treatment   Apparatus required: •Executive magnetic toys

13. Magnetic accelerator

A version of this fascinating 'device' can be made using ball bearings, disc magnets and plastic trunking. The first diagram shows a simple example of this. Enlarged views of the magnets and ball bearings alone are shown in the other four diagrams.

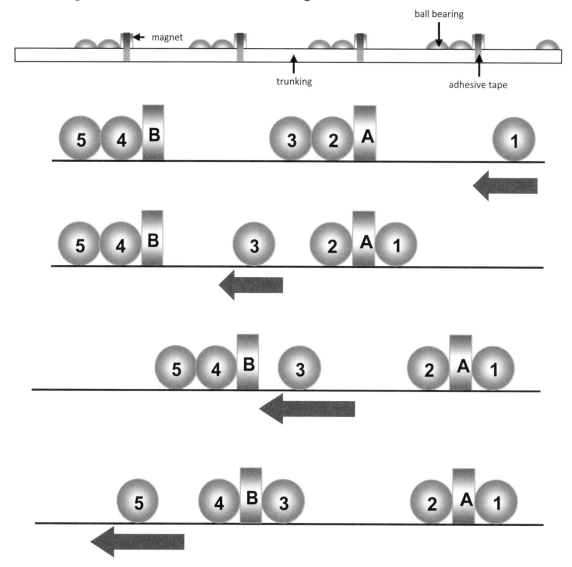

Ball bearing one is released and is attracted to magnet A. When it hits it its energy is transferred to ball bearing 3, which is free to move off, and so travels on at the same velocity as the impact velocity of ball bearing 1. This happens because it is further from the magnet than ball bearing 1 and so the attractive force on it is less than that on ball bearing 1. Ball bearing 3 is now attracted by magnet B and so accelerates, colliding with B with an increased velocity. The process now repeats itself with ball bearing 5 moving off to the left.

The final ball bearing on the left of the first diagram will move off at high speed, the actual speed depending on the number and strength of the magnets.

Age range: 11-18   Apparatus required: •Four neodymium disc magnets •Nine ball bearings •A piece of plastic trunking •Adhesive tape

ELECTROMAGNETISM

General theory for this section:
The strength (magnetic flux density) of an electromagnet in the form of a straight coil (solenoid) can be calculated from the formula $B = \mu NI/L$, where N is the number of coils, I is the current in amps passing through them and L is the length of the solenoid. μ is a constant depending on the material of the core. For an iron core this has a value of somewhere near 0.002 Hm^{-1}, while for air it is two thousand times smaller.

The strength of an electromagnet can be increased by increasing the number of coils per metre (for the same current), increasing the current flowing through it, or putting a piece of soft iron in its centre.

When a wire of length L is placed at right angles to a magnetic field of strength B it experiences a force BIL at right angles to itself and the field. The bigger the field, the current, or the length of the wire, the bigger the force.

1. Electromagnetic forces - suspended coil
2. Strength of an electromagnet
3. Faraday effect
4. Forces between currents
5. Model loudspeakers

6. Force on a current in a magnetic field
7. Magnetostriction
8. The catapult field
9. Filament oscillation
10. Simple electric motor

1. Electromagnetic forces - suspended coil

The magnetic field produced when a current flows in a coil may be detected by hanging a light coil of wire from its connecting leads near a magnet. When a current is passed through the coil the force between the coil and the magnet will either attract or repel the coil, making it swing towards or away from the magnet depending on the direction of the current in the coil.

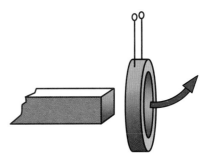

Age range: 13-16
Apparatus required: •Coil of fine wire •Low voltage (12V) power supply •Magnet in non-magnetic stand

2. Strength of an electromagnet

A very simple method of estimating the strength of an electromagnet is to see how many steel paper clips it will support. Connect up an electromagnet, switch it on, and support a string of paper clips from the lower end. Varying the current will change the strength of the electromagnet, and this can be measured by the number of paper clips that can be supported. Check that the clips are not magnetised before starting the experiment!

Age range: 11-13   Apparatus required: •Electromagnet •Power supply •Leads •Ammeter •Paper clips

3. Faraday effect

Shine a beam of light across the lab so that it passes through crossed polaroids at either end to cut off the light. Now put a strong permanent magnet (0.5 T) across the beam, and see if you can detect any change in the direction of polarisation. In other words, does any light now emerge from the second polaroid?

Age range: 16-18   Apparatus required: •Permanent magnet (0.5T) •Light source

4. Forces between currents

A way of demonstrating the force between currents is to use a small metal slinky spring. I have bought one that has a coil diameter of only 3 cm. Hang this up vertically with the lower end free, and pass a d.c current through it. The currents in adjacent loops of the spring are in the same direction and so the spring contracts - like currents attract. Placing a transparent plastic ruler in front of the coils enables the change in separation to be measured as the current in the coil is changed.

Using a.c. can give some interesting resonance effects if the tension of the spring is varied by adding small masses to the lower end.

Theory:
The force per unit length between two currents (I_1 and I_2) in two infinitely long parallel straight wires separated by a distance d is given by the formula $F = \mu_0 I_1 I_2 / 2\pi d$. I know that our spring is far from being a straight wire, but at least you can get an idea of the possible forces involved.

Age range: 16-18
Apparatus required: •Small slinky spring diameter of coils about 3 cm •Retort stand boss and clamp •Fine copper wire for leads •Low voltage power supply (ac and dc) •Transparent plastic ruler •TV camera if possible •Light slotted masses (<10g)

5. Model loudspeakers

An impressive model loudspeaker can easily be made from paper, some insulated wire and four strong bar magnets. Make a large paper cone, cut a piece off the bottom and fix a short cylinder of paper to the cone in its place. Wind a coil of thin enamelled wire (say 20 turns) round the cylindrical projecting part. Place the cylindrical part over four bar magnets taped together standing vertically on the bench and with the same direction of polarity. Suspend the cone by thin elastic from three or more retort stands, connect the coil to a signal generator, and switch on.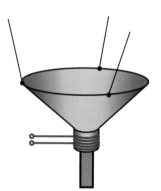

Using a low frequency voltage enables the oscillatory motion of the cone to be seen clearly.

Age range: 13-16 with further extension depending on treatment
Apparatus required: •Paper •Insulated wire •Four strong bar magnets (about 8 cm long) • Thread •Low voltage a.c power supply or signal generator •Three retort stands •Adhesive tape

6. Force on a current in a magnetic field

The following experiments are to demonstrate the force on a current in a magnetic field.
(a) Suspend a light rod from two thin copper wires so that the rod hangs horizontally between the poles of an eclipse major magnet (a large U shaped magnet with a flux density between the poles of about 0.5 T) and is free to swing. The field of the magnet acts vertically across the rod. Pass a current through the wires and rod, and the rod should swing in and out of the field.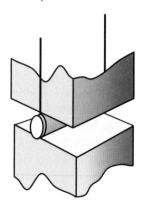

(b) In the second experiment a slack strip of aluminium foil is pinned to a cork mat with a large strong (0.5 T) magnet standing over it so that the strip lies between the poles. Passing a current through the strip in the correct direction makes it rise from the mat - a clear demonstration of the force on a current in a magnetic field.

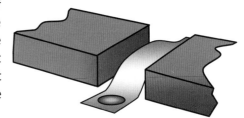

(c) In the third experiment the force is measured using a top pan balance. Clamp a metal rod horizontally above a top pan balance so that it passes between the poles of a horseshoe magnet that is resting on the balance. Pass a current through the rod, and use the change in the reading on the balance to demonstrate the force on the rod due to the field. Making measurements of the current in the rod and the change in reading on the balance will enable you either to calculate the strength of the magnetic field or to verify the law of force on the rod.

Theory:
Force on a current in a magnetic field = BIL where B is the magnetic flux density, I the current in the wire in amps and L the length of the conductor in the field.
The strength of the large magnet that I use is about 0.5 T and that of the small magnadur magnets about 0.05 T.

Age range: 14-18 depending on treatment
Apparatus required:
(a) •Light metal rod suspended by thin copper wires •Horseshoe magnet
(b) •Strong horseshoe magnet •Aluminium foil strip pinned to a cork mat •Crocodile clips •Low voltage power supply
(c) •Top pan balance •Stiff metal rod •Horseshoe magnet •Power supply

7. Magnetostriction
Wind a long coil of wire round a metre long rod of iron. Fix one end rigidly in a clamp, and mount the other in a projector beam or rest it on an L shaped glass roller to which is fixed a small mirror. Pass a current of about 0.5A through the coil, and observe the motion of the reflected light beam or the movement of the shadow.

Theory:
Magnetostriction is the dependence of the dimensions of a ferromagnetic specimen (iron rod) on the direction and intensity of its magnetisation.

Age range: 16-19
Apparatus required: •A metre-long rod of iron •Projector •Glass roller •Small mirror
•Low voltage power supply •Length of wire for making the coil

8. The catapult field

You can compare the force on a wire in a magnetic field to that of a stretched piece of elastic or the bed of a trampoline. For example, if you jump on to a trampoline there is a resultant vertical force that catapults you upwards – at right angles to the trampoline. Since a similar motion is observed when a wire carrying a current is placed at right angles to a magnetic field, the combined field produced by the wire and the magnet is often called the catapult field.

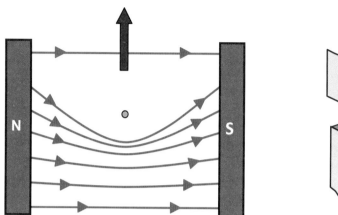 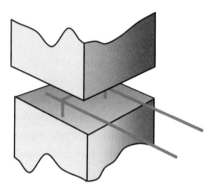

You can show this easily by mounting two lengths of thick (say 24 SWG) bare copper wire between the poles of a strong U shaped magnet so that they are horizontal and parallel. Then place a third wire across them so that it rests on the two straight wires. Passing a current through the wires will make the loose wire slide along - indeed if the current is big enough (a few amps) the wire will shoot off the end.

Age range: 13-16
Apparatus required:
•Two straight lengths (10 cm or so) of stiff, clean copper wire •One short length of thinner copper wire •A high current, low voltage power supply •U shaped magnet

9. Filament oscillation

This experiment demonstrates the force on a current in a magnetic field by showing the oscillation of a light bulb filament.

Set up the apparatus shown in the diagram, with the light bulb between the poles of the U shaped magnet. Use a convex lens to focus the image of the filament on the screen.

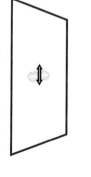 

Connect the bulb to a low voltage a.c. supply, and switch on. The image of the filament will oscillate, showing the change of direction of the force on it during the a.c. cycle.

Age range: 14-19
Apparatus required: •Filament light bulb in holder •Low voltage ac power supply •Leads •U shaped magnet •Convex lens and holder •Screen

10. Simple electric motors

This is a very simple and yet effective way of showing the force on a current in a magnetic field and for making a simple electric 'motor'. It is vital that the pupils are shown the diagram of the field (blue arrows), current (red arrow) and motion (black arrow) so that the effect can be properly explained.

The current flows across the screw head and magnet, and a force is exerted so that the magnet and screw rotate about a vertical axis. You can check this using Fleming's left hand rule.

(I am very grateful to Ian who first showed me this experiment)

Age range: 11-16
Apparatus required:
• Cylindrical neodymium magnet
• Screw
• AA cell
• Length of insulated wire (bared at the ends)

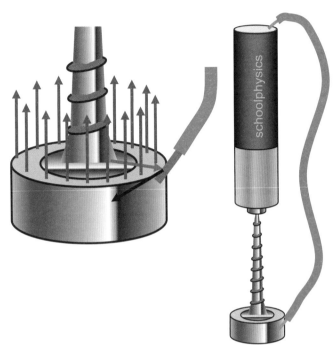

Electromagnets

A long straight coil of wire called a solenoid produces a magnetic field very much like that of a bar magnet. The shapes of some magnetic fields are shown in the diagrams below.

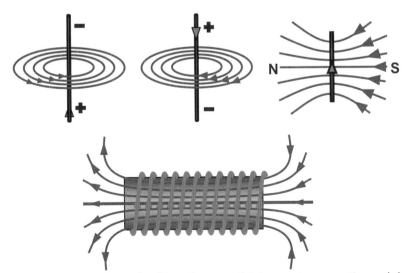

The core of an electromagnet is made of iron because this is easy to magnetise and demagnetise. Steel would not be suitable, because it stays magnetised for much longer, and so the electromagnet could not be switched on and off easily.

ELECTROMAGNETIC INDUCTION

General theory for this section:

When a changing current flows in a coil, a varying potential difference is induced in a nearby coil. The size of the induced potential difference depends on the number of turns of both coils and their linkage - whether there is a soft iron core joining them. It is formed because of the varying magnetic field produced by the primary current, and this variation can also be produced by moving a permanent magnet near a coil.

Currents are also induced in metal plates by moving a magnet near them - these are called eddy currents, and the magnetic field produced by them acts so as to reduce the original motion.

1. Eddy currents
2. Tape recorder simulation
3. Electromagnetic brake
4. Induction - light bulbs and coil a.c/d.c
5. Magnets oscillating in a coil
6. Jumping ring and solid carbon dioxide
7. Electromagnetic induction analogy
8. Thickness measurement - inductance
9. LED and coil - electromagnetic induction

10. Transformers - the action of a choke
11. Falling magnet in a tube
12. Aluminium plate under a swinging magnet
13. Detecting radiation
14. Electromagnetic separator
15. Audio loop
16. Frequency of the mains
17. Electromagnetic machine
18. Eddy currents and the linear air track

1. Eddy currents

This experiment is a very simple way of showing eddy current damping. Suspend a copper cylinder from a thread so that it hangs between the poles of a large permanent magnet (flux density about 0.5 T). Twist the thread so that it oscillates about a vertical axis when released. The motion of the cylinder shows considerable damping because of the eddy currents set up within it. Now repeat the experiment using a pile of small copper or brass coins taped together, the damping is now much less because the gaps between the coins only allow much reduced eddy currents to flow in the stack.

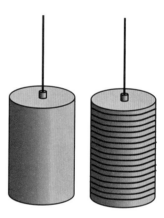

Age range: 16-18
Apparatus required: •Pile of small copper coins •Copper cylinder •Thread •Retort stand •Eclipse major magnet

2. Tape recorder simulation

Induced voltages can be shown in this simple simulation of the action of the playback head in a tape recorder. Move a 3600 turn coil over a row of ceramic magnadur magnets placed flat down on the bench, with their poles alternately N - S face up with the coil connected to an amplifier and speaker or to an oscilloscope. As the coil moves, a changing voltage will be induced in it, and this can be detected by the speaker or oscilloscope.

Age range: 13-16
Apparatus required: •3600 turn coil •At least ten magnadur magnets •Speaker or oscilloscope •Amplifier

3. Electromagnetic brake

Spinning a non-magnetic metal disc between a pair of magnadur magnets mounted vertically about 1 cm apart with opposite poles facing each other also shows eddy current damping. The disc can be made to spin in a vertical plane by tying a piece of cotton to the axle of the disc and passing it over a pulley to a weight that is free to fall. As the weight falls it accelerates continually without the magnets but reaches a terminal velocity when they are in place.

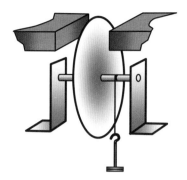

Compare this with the air damping experiment.

Age range: 16-18   Apparatus required: •Aluminium disc on horizontal axle •Cotton
                                             •Pair of magnadur magnets on steel yoke

4. Induction - light bulbs and coil a.c/d.c

The effect of self-induction of a coil in a circuit can be shown as follows:

(a) Connect two bulbs in parallel to a low voltage d.c supply. In one branch connect a resistor in series with the bulb, and in the other connect a coil with an iron core, the coil having an identical resistance to that of the resistor. Switch on. The bulb in series with the coil takes longer to come on, demonstrating the inductive effects of the coil.

(b) Put a bulb and a coil in series with first a low voltage d.c supply then a low voltage a.c supply. Notice the change in the brightness of the bulb due to the inductance effects of the coil with a.c.

Theory:

Inductance of a coil (L) = $\mu_o\mu_r N^2 A/L$ length L, cross sectional area A and of N turns.

A coil of length 5 cm, 2 cm square, with a steel core and of 1200 turns has a self-inductance of just under 30 Henrys. With an air core this reduces to 0.15 H. (150 mH). However, V = Ldi/dt, and so the time for the voltage across the 0.15H coil to rise to 0.2 A for a 2.5 V supply is 12 ms.

For the time to be a second or more, the inductance must be 12.5 H.

Age range: 16-18   Apparatus required: •Low voltage bulbs •Ammeter - both a.c and d.c •Coil
•Low voltage ac/dc power supply

5. Magnets oscillating in a coil

Suspend a magnet from a spring so that it hangs within a coil connected to an oscilloscope. Displace the magnet, and allow it to bob up and down. The resulting induced voltage can be studied. Notice the direction of the induced voltage compared with the direction of motion of the magnet.

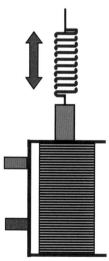

Ask the students whether or not they would expect to see eddy current damping in this demonstration.

Theory:

Since the magnet oscillates in the coil, induced voltages will be produced - the size of the induced voltage being proportional to the speed of the magnet and therefore giving a good demonstration of simple harmonic motion.

Age range: 16-18
Apparatus required: •Retort stand, boss and clamp •Magnet •Helical spring   •600 turn coil
•Oscilloscope •Leads

6. Jumping ring and solid carbon dioxide

(a) The repulsion between the magnetic fields produced by two electric currents can be shown by this experiment known as the jumping ring experiment. The core of a demountable transformer is opened, a mains coil (to be used as the primary) is connected to the a.c mains and an aluminium ring is used a secondary. The crosspiece is placed vertically on the arm round which the ring is slipped. Switching on the current shoots the ring into the air. As a problem for the older students, ask them what happens with a d.c supply.

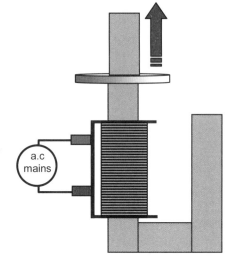

Theory:
Eddy currents induced in the ring form a magnetic field which is the same direction as that in the coil, and so the ring is repelled.

The ring can be cooled by placing it in solid carbon dioxide. This increases the height risen by lowering the resistance of the ring and so increasing the size of the induced current in it.

(b) An interesting extension to this experiment is to use a taller core round which to place the ring. The force on the ring acts for longer, and so the ring rises higher when the current is switched on. (A greater impulse Ft = mv).

 Staff should be competent, or trained, in the use of a demountable transformer. Coils and connections should be designed so as to minimise the risk of electric shock. Dry ice should only be made using a 'siphon' type carbon dioxide cylinder with a 'Jebfreezer' attachment or a thick cloth bag. Eye protection is needed and leather gloves should be worn. Pupils must not handle dry ice.

Age range: 15-18
Apparatus required: •Demountable transformer •Aluminium ring •Carbon dioxide cylinder •Mains coil •Mains power source •Additional laminated straight core section •Leather gloves

7. Electromagnetic induction analogy

I use the following analogy when attempting to explain the production of an e.m.f. by the cutting of magnetic field lines. Imagine a cornfield with the combine harvester cutting the corn stalks. The cutting is more effective when the cutting edge is at right angles to the corn stalks. This is an analogy with the cutting of magnetic flux by a wire - it is more effective, and so generates a greater potential when the wire is moving at right angles to the field direction.

Theory:
EMF generated = $BLv\sin\theta$ where θ is the angle between the wire and the field lines, L the length of the wire, v the velocity of the wire and B the magnetic flux density.

8. Thickness measurement - inductance

The loss of energy when two parts of the core of a transformer are separated can be used as a sensitive means of measuring thickness and also as a demonstration of this energy loss. Basically it is simply an a.c. electromagnet with two coils separated from its steel "keeper" by a number of sheets of paper. After calibration with paper of known thickness the voltage recorded in the secondary from a fixed primary voltage is used to measure the thickness of a sheet of paper. (Thanks to Kate for this idea from her A level coursework.)

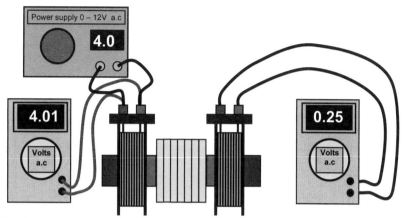

Age range: 16-18

Apparatus required: •Demountable low voltage transformer with removable core   •Sheets of paper •AC voltmeter •Low voltage ac power supply

9. LED and coil - electromagnetic induction

The basic experiment for demonstrating electromagnetic induction using a light bulb or a meter is very difficult to show as the current produced is usually too small to give a good effect.

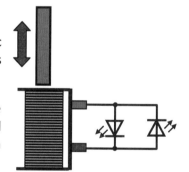

The following simple apparatus using two LEDs will make the effects much more obvious. Connect the two LEDs in parallel with each other but facing opposite directions and in series with the coil.

Move the magnet backwards and forwards in the coil, and observe that not only does one LED light up as the magnet is moved, but the LEDs light alternately when the direction of motion of the magnet is reversed. This needs a strong magnet, a large coil and low current LEDs.

Age range: 14-18   Apparatus required: •Two LEDs (one red one green) •Magnet •Coil •Leads

10. Transformers - the action of a choke

Set up a low voltage transformer with a laminated core and a step down ratio of 2:1. Put a low voltage a.c ammeter in the primary circuit. With the secondary circuit open the reading on the ammeter is almost zero, it is acting as a choke - induced currents in the primary reduce the p.d across it to almost zero. If a d.c supply is used the reading is high. Putting successively more bulbs (in parallel) in the secondary circuit will increase the current in the primary. Try using a soft iron yoke to complete the circuit of the core, and observe the effect on the brightness of the lamps.

Age range: 16-18

Apparatus required: •Low voltage transformer 2:1 •Low voltage a.c. ammeter • 2.5 V bulbs •Low voltage power supply a.c and d.c •Leads

11. Falling magnet in a tube

If you have never seen this one before then be prepared for a treat. It is a most impressive example of induced currents and relies on the magnetic field produced by a falling magnet in a tube acting so as to oppose the motion of the magnet so slowing down its rate of fall. Hold a 2 m long copper tube vertically, and drop a strong magnet down the tube. It takes over five seconds, compared with approximately 0.75 s when the same magnet is dropped down a plastic tube of the same dimensions. If the tube is cooled the resistance of the copper falls, the induced current is greater, and the magnet falls even more slowly.

Allowing the magnet to slide down the tube when it is inclined at an angle to the vertical is almost more impressive - it takes nearly thirty seconds to emerge depending on the angle of tilt of the tube!

(I have used the second version with the older pupils in a discussion of Galileo's diluted gravity experiment and the components of vectors.)

Theory:
Lenz's law: Induced emf (ε) = minus the rate of change of flux in the circuit or the flux acts so as to oppose the change producing it. $\varepsilon = -d\phi/dt$ Therefore the induced currents flowing round the tube produce a magnetic field along its axis, which slows down the rate of fall of the magnet.

Age range: 15-18
Apparatus required: •Cylindrical neodymium magnet •Copper tube 2m long if possible •Plastic tube 2 m long •Stop watch

12. Aluminium plate under a swinging magnet

Suspend a bar magnet by a thread so that it hangs horizontally above an aluminium plate, and start the magnet swinging. It will soon come to rest because of the induced currents in the plate. This is a simple example of eddy current damping.

Age range: 16-18   Apparatus required: •Magnet •Thread •Metal plate •Retort stand, boss and clamp

13. Detecting radiation

Use yourself as an aerial to detect mains frequency! Connect yourself to a cathode ray oscilloscope by holding a lead inserted into the Y INPUT socket. Put your other hand near to or around an insulated mains cable that has a current flowing through it. The cable connecting the CRO to the mains is an obvious choice. (Reaching up towards a fluorescent lamp also works). You will see an a.c trace of frequency 50 Hz on the oscilloscope screen.

 | **Ensure that the mains cable is undamaged, and avoid contact with the fluorescent lamp.** |

Age range: 15-18   Apparatus required: •Oscilloscope

14. Electromagnetic separator

A small-scale simulation of an electromagnetic separator used to separate non-ferrous metals from other non metallic scrap can be shown by the following experiment. Place a thin piece of card on the top of one arm of a U shaped core of a low voltage a.c. electromagnet. Put a few scraps of aluminium foil on the card. When the current is turned on they will be ejected from the field because of the eddy

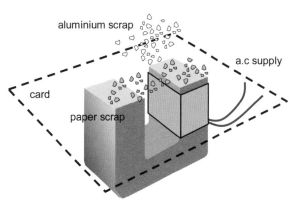

currents within them - see the jumping ring experiment.

Age range: 16-18
Apparatus required: •Electromagnet •Low voltage a.c. power supply •Aluminium scraps (foil) •Piece of thin card

15. Audio loop

A simulation of the audio systems provided in some theatres for the hard of hearing can be produced by connecting the output of a portable, battery-powered CD player to a wire which is placed round the walls of the lab. The resistance of the wire loop should be made similar to that of the recommended speakers for your tape recorder. If the tape recorder is then set running the sound output signal can be detected with a second small coil connected to an amplifier placed anywhere within the lab together with a pair of headphones.

 Do not interfere with the output from mains devices in this way. Using a battery-powered device prevents hazardous contact being made.

Age range: 16-18
Apparatus required: •Portable tape recorder or CD player •Coil •Headphones •Large length of wire

16. Electromagnetic machine

This is a lovely old type of device for treating various ailments. A full list of the ailments is supplied inside the lid. I would not like to put the probes where it is suggested in order to cure some of the ailments!

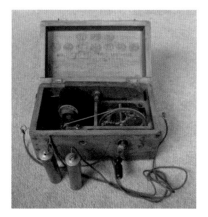

The machine consists of a coil rotating near the poles of a magnet and is provided with two brass electrodes. They have one in the History of Science Museum in Oxford - I have actually managed to buy a similar model but don't dare to hold the electrodes!

As the coil rotates a voltage is induced in the coil.

 If you have one of these machines DO NOT use it on the pupils

Age range: 15-19

17. Frequency of the mains

The induced current in a wire moving in a magnetic field can be used to make a measurement of the frequency of the mains. A wire is fixed to the bench at one end, and then over two glass prisms while the other end passes over a pulley and is attached to a set of slotted masses. (Values between 200g and 500g are needed for lengths of wire between about 30 cm and 50 cm.) A large U shaped magnet is placed so that the wire passes between its poles, the wire is connected to a low voltage 50 Hz supply, and a current of about 4A is passed through the wire. Adjusting the tension of the wire can set it into resonance when its fundamental frequency equals that of the supply.

 Limit the current to prevent the wire get hot enough to burn the skin especially when making adjustments.

Theory:
For a stretched wire the fundamental frequency (f) is given by the equation:
$f = 1/2L(T/m)^{1/2}$ where T is the tension in the wire and m is its mass per unit length

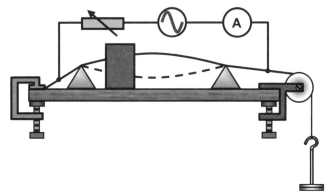

Age range: 16-18
Apparatus required:
• Large magnet (Field strength = 0.2 T)
• Wire • G clamp • Bench pulley
• Set of 100g slotted masses • Ruler • Two glass prisms • Low voltage ac Power supply

18. Eddy currents and the linear air track

An interesting variation on the theory of eddy currents can be carried out using the linear air track. Mount a large U shaped magnet over the track between two light gates so that a rider can pass beneath it. Mount one of the aluminium foil absorbers from the radioactivity kit on the rider so that the foil can pass between the poles of the magnet. Now accelerate the rider along the track with a constant force (by using a weight over a pulley). As the foil passes between the poles of the magnet, eddy currents will be induced in it and electromagnetic braking will result. Investigate the size of the eddy currents produced for different thicknesses of foil.

Theory:
Since the eddy currents act to oppose the motion, they reduce the acceleration of the rider.

The effect of different resistances, and therefore different eddy currents, can be found by changing the foil absorbers and measuring the resulting change in the velocity of the rider using the light gates.

Age range: 16-18
Apparatus required:
• Linear air track • Absorbers set • Pulley
• Weight • Thread • Blu tack ® • Light gate • Large U shaped magnet

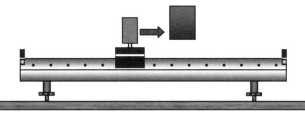

ELECTROSTATIC PHENOMENA

General theory for this section:

Radial electric field: Field intensity (E) at a distance r from a charge $Q = 1/4\pi\varepsilon_o[Q/r^2]$

Uniform field (i.e. that between two parallel plates, separation d and potential difference V):   Field intensity = V/d

Force between two charges (Q_1 and Q_2) = $1/4\pi\varepsilon_o[Q_1Q_2/r^2]$

Force on a charge (Q) in a uniform field = QE = QV/d

1. Induction and repulsion in electrostatics	18. Electrostatic fields
2. Plastic box smoke separator	19. Statics and covering film
3. Electric fields	20. Photocopier and electrostatics
4. The charge on your body	21. Electrostatics toys
5. Drawing pin on a Van de Graaff generator	22. Soap bubbles and Millikan
6. Some simple electrostatic demonstrations	23. Electrostatic repulsion - various versions
7. Bubbles and the Van de Graaff generator	24. Point discharge
8. A charged rod and water streams	25. Fluorescent tube and the plasma globe
9. Electric fields	26. Ions in a flame and a flame probe
10. Spark plug and the Van de Graaff generator	27. Cars and electrostatics
11. Van de Graaff generator and a radio	28. Pith ball on thread and the Van de Graaff
12. Electric fields	29. Paper and the Van de Graaff generator
13. More simple electrostatics	30. Field in a hollow charged conductor
14. Spark counter and ions from a flame	31. The phantom leg
15. Van de Graaff generator and cotton wool	32. Barbie doll and the Van de Graaff
16. Watch glass electrostatic repulsion	33. Van de Graaff generator and a paper sheet
17. Electrostatic forces - top pan balance	34. Cup cake cases and the Van de Graaff

1. Induction and repulsion in electrostatics

A charged polythene rod is brought up to a metal rod that is fixed horizontally on an insulating stand. Touching the other end is a light ball hanging from a thread. As the charged rod is brought closer, the ball will swing away from the metal rod.

Age range: 11-18
Apparatus required:
•EHT supply •Polythene rod and duster •Conducting ball on insulating thread •Metal rod

2. Plastic box smoke separator

Two metal plates are mounted parallel to each other in a transparent plastic sandwich box. Blow some smoke into the box and close the lid. Use a Van de Graaff generator to apply a potential across the plates, and the smoke will clear immediately since the charged plates attract the small particles of smoke towards them. The effect of different potentials can easily be studied.

 The EHT unit, with a current limit of 5 mA or less, and the Van de Graaff generator will both cause minor electric shocks which will be felt when the connections are handled. Staff should practice such demonstrations so that they know what to do and what to expect!

Age range: 14-18
Apparatus required: •Plastic box smoke separator •Van de Graaff generator or EHT supply •Smoke generator

3. Electric fields

Both the motion of a charge in an electric field and the forces between charges can be shown by mounting two metal plates vertically and some ten centimetres apart. Then suspend a table tennis ball (which has been coated with conducting paint) from a thread so that it hangs centrally between the plates. Apply a potential difference between the plates - something over 2 kV is needed. Pull the thread so that the ball touches one of the plates. The ball will then oscillate between the two charged plates, transferring charge from one plate to the other.

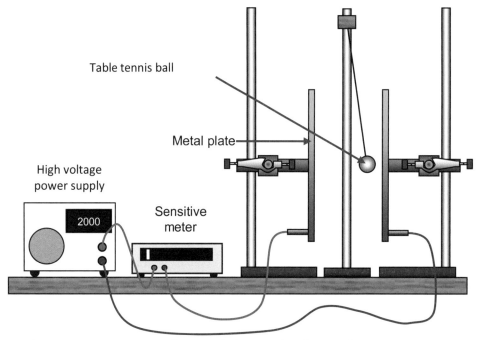

A moving charge means a current flow, and this can be detected using a spot galvanometer since the actual currents are very small (< 1 mA). A TV camera is a great help here to show the movement of the ball to the whole class - alternatively a shadow of the ball can be projected onto a screen.

This experiment has a simple and effective extension. Use the two vertical plates connected to 5 kV, and then drop a small piece of aluminium foil between them - it will oscillate backwards and forwards between them as it falls.

 The EHT supply with an output current of 5 mA or less will still produce small but non-hazardous electric shocks if the connections are not handled correctly.

Age range: 14-18
Apparatus required:
•Two metal plates with insulating handles •Two retort stands and bosses •Table tennis ball •Thread •EHT supply •Foil

4. The charge on your body

Use a d.c. amplifier or a pico coulomb meter to measure the charge of the human body! This demonstration is very dependent on what the students are wearing on their feet and what the floor is made of but it provokes some interesting discussion!

Age range: 16-18   Apparatus required: •Pico coulomb meter •Suitable output meter

5. Drawing pin on the Van de Graaff generator - dust/smoke collector

Fix a drawing pin with its point facing upwards in the bottom of a perspex can on top of the Van de Graaff generator, and blow some smoke into the can. Switch on the generator, and observe what happens. The discharge from the drawing pin point collects the smoke into a column. It is due to the concentration of charge at the point, and hence the large electric field there. This demonstration also works well without the can - simply using a pin mounted vertically on the dome.

 The Van de Graaff generator may give unexpected electric shocks. Staff should be prepared for this.

Age range: 11-13
Apparatus required: •Van de Graaff generator •Drawing pin in transparent perspex box •Smoke

6. Some simple electrostatic demonstrations

(a) Charged balloon sticking to the walls or ceiling
(b) Taking off a jumper over a nylon blouse or shirt
(c) Moving around under nylon sheets, wearing pyjamas or a night dress
(d) Rubbing your shoes on a synthetic carpet and then touching an earthed metal pole

Age range: 11-13
Apparatus required: •Balloon •Duster

7. Bubbles and the Van de Graaff generator

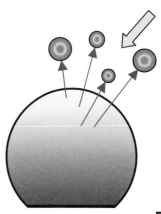

This experiment is a novel way of showing electrostatic induction and also the forces between like charges. Blow some soap bubbles near the dome of a Van de Graaff generator. Initially they are attracted to the dome but then spring away in the field if they gain the same charge as the dome.

 The Van de Graaff generator may give unexpected electric shocks. Staff should be prepared for this.

Age range: 14-18
Apparatus required: •Van de Graaff generator •Bubble liquid and blower

8. A charged rod and its effect on water streams

This next experiment is a beautiful, and to the pupils quite unexpected demonstration. Turn on a tap and let a slow but continuous dribble of water fall vertically from it. Bring up a charged polythene rod close to this dribble and the water will be deflected towards it. The deflection is due to the polar molecules (positive at one end and negative at the other) which orient themselves so that they are attracted by the charged rod. A charged plastic comb will also work well and showing this with a TV camera is a help to make it visible to a large group.

Age range: 11-18   Apparatus required: •Polythene rod •Duster •Tap with fine outlet

9. Electric fields

The apparatus shown in the diagram was home-made and has proved very useful for plotting electrostatic fields. A piece of conducting paper is placed over a piece of carbon paper on top of a sheet of white paper and is held in place by the two metal bars. A potential difference is placed across the two bars and using a probe made from an optical pin connected to a digital meter the shape of the field can be plotted. You can also trace the lines of equal potential. Screwing down the bolts in the centre of one or both of the bars enables the fields produced by point charges to be studied.

Age range: 16-18

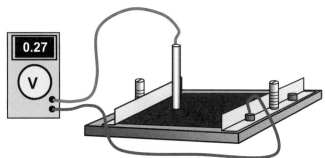

Apparatus required:
•Electric fields apparatus
•Optical pin •Carbon paper
•Conducting paper
•Digital high resistance voltmeter
•Low voltage dc power supply

10. Spark plug and the Van de Graaff generator

Use a Van de Graaff generator to demonstrate the action of a spark plug. Attach the top of the spark plug to the top of the generator using a lead and clip, and earth the other contact. The spark plug will operate when the generator is turned on.

 The Van de Graaff generator may give unexpected electric shocks. Staff should be prepared for this.

Age range: 14-18   Apparatus required: •Van de Graaff generator •Spark plug

11. Van de Graaff generator and a radio

Use a radio to detect the sparks from a Van de Graaff generator by the electromagnetic pulse of radiation that they produce. Refer to the effects of lightning on radio and TV transmission. You will need to check the correct wave band to use. Computers may be adversely affected by nearby sparks from a Van de Graaff generator.

 The Van de Graaff generator may give unexpected electric shocks. Staff should be prepared for this.

12. Electric fields - the school dinner experiment

(a) My rather unkind name for the electric field apparatus. You can make electric fields visible on an overhead projector by using a shallow, clear plastic dish of oil into which two electrodes are placed. Sprinkling semolina or fine grass seeds on the surface will show the field lines when the EHT supply (usually 5 kV and limited to 5 mA) is connected between the electrodes and switched on.

 The EHT supply should be limited to 5 mA or less

(b) Use the classic electric field apparatus on the overhead projector, but put a metal ring between the electrodes to demonstrate that there is no field inside a hollow conductor.

Age range: (a) 14-18 (b) 16-18
Apparatus required: •Electric fields apparatus •Overhead projector •EHT supply •Oil

13. More simple electrostatics

Make a paper flower with a metal foil cake case as its centre. Then charge it by touching it with a wire fixed to a plastic bottle that has been rubbed. The flow of charge between the bottle and the flower shows the connection between static and current electricity.

Age range: 11-13   Apparatus required: •Plastic bottle •Metal foil cake case •Wire

14. Spark counter and ions from a flame

Set up a spark counter with a p.d of 4 to 5 kV between the wire and the gauze so as to give a voltage not quite sufficient for sparking to take place. To demonstrate that a flame ionises the air, light a taper and blow the flame towards the gauze - sparking immediately results.

Age range: 14-18
Apparatus required:
•Spark counter •Taper
•EHT supply limited to 5 mA or less
•Insulated and protected leads

 The EHT supply should be limited to 5 mA or less

15. Van de Graaff and cotton wool to show field lines

The field lines from a charged dome can be seen by fixing some cotton wool on top of the dome. A long haired wig on the large dome also looks impressive! The strands of hair all acquire the same charge and so repel each other.

The Van de Graaff generator may give unexpected electric shocks. Staff should be prepared for this.

16. Watch glass electrostatic repulsion

The forces between two charged rods can be shown by the following simple experiment. Balance a charged polythene rod on an inverted watch glass. Then bring up another charged rod towards it – the first rod rotates on the watch glass, showing the repulsion between like charges. Attraction can be shown by bringing up a cellulose acetate rod.

Age range: 11-13
Apparatus required: •Watch glass •Two polythene rods •Cellulose acetate rod   •Duster

17. Electrostatic forces - balls and a top pan balance

Measure the electrostatic force between two charged balls (or rods) - one fixed to a clamp, the other to a top pan balance. Mount the retort stand on a laboratory jack so that the separation of the balls may be altered.

Age range: 14-18
Apparatus required: •Top pan balance reading to at least 0.01 g •Charged rods or balls •Laboratory jack

18. Electrostatic fields

A very good demonstration of electric fields uses the macro Millikan apparatus, a pair of aluminium plates some 30 cm square and about 5 cm apart which were used as a large scale demonstration of Millikan's oil drop experiment. I have used this with little aluminium foil figures to show electric fields. An even better demonstration is to use figures made from tissue paper, they do not have the problem of being conducting and will rise and fall in the field if it is adjusted carefully. The special apparatus does not have to be used - two aluminium sheets with a p.d. of up to 5 kV between them works perfectly.

This experiment will also work if pieces of puffed wheat are used in place of the pieces of paper in the space between two charged plates.

Yet another alternative is to sprinkle a small amount of sugar (or flour) on to the lower plate.

 | **The EHT supply should be limited to 5 mA or less.** |

Connect the plates to an EHT supply and switch on. The sugar oscillates between the plates showing induced charge, then attraction and then discharge. Some practice will be needed to get the correct potential difference and plate separation - i.e. the electric field intensity.

Age range: 14-18
Apparatus required: •Two metal plates mounted horizontally and separated by polythene spacers
•EHT supply limited to 5 mA or less •Paper •Sugar •Puffed wheat •Flour

19. Statics and covering film

The effects of static electricity can be demonstrated with cling film, book covering film or plastic document sleeves. Simply pulling the film off its backing paper will charge both the paper and the film. Testing the two parts with a gold leaf electroscope will show that they are oppositely charged. This can be an annoying property of some types of sticky tape.

Age range: 11-13
Apparatus required: •Plastic document sleeve •Roll of book covering film •Cling film

20. Photocopier and Electrostatics

This is a very simple demonstration of the behaviour of a photocopier. "Draw" a T shape on a polythene tile by rubbing along the shape with a duster to charge only that area. Now put the tile over a plate of semolina. The semolina will only be attracted to the charged T, shape in exactly the same way as carbon powder is attracted to the charged parts of the master drum in a photocopier. Use a coloured tile to make the semolina show up better, or use coloured spice powder on a white tile.

Age range: 11-16   Apparatus required: •Semolina •Polythene tile •Duster

21. Electrostatics toys

There are a number of lovely old electrostatics toys such as dancers on wires and the hunter with ducks. It is worth hunting round some antique shops to find examples of these.

As with all Physics toys, if you find one and can afford it then buy it – you never know if you will ever see one again!

22. Soap bubbles and Millikan

Set up a Van de Graaff generator with the high voltage dome connected to a metal tube held in an insulating clamp. To the lower end of this attach a length of rubber tubing. Cover the top of the tube with a soap film, and blow a soap bubble. Mount two metal plates horizontally and connect them either to an EHT supply, or to the Van de Graaff, and earth. Switch on the generator so that the bubble becomes charged. Switch off the generator. Now gently blow the bubble sideways into the gap between the charged plates. By adjusting the plates' separation or the potential difference between them (if connected to the EHT), or both, it should be possible to get the bubble to rise, fall or remain suspended in mid air - a useful demonstration of the Millikan experiment. In fact if the mass of the bubble is known we could actually measure the charge on it!

 The Van de Graaff generator may give unexpected electric shocks. Staff should be prepared for this.

Age range: 16-18
Apparatus required: •Two metal plates mounted horizontally and separated by polythene spacers •Soap bubble liquid •Metal tube •Rubber tubing
•Van de Graaff generator or EHT supply limited to 5 mA or less

23. Electrostatic repulsion - various versions

(a) Electrostatic repulsion can be shown by two strips of aluminium foil hanging from the same point and with the join connected to an EHT supply (or a Van de Graaff generator). They repel each other as the potential is increased, and they become more highly charged.

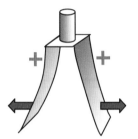

 The Van de Graaff generator may give unexpected electric shocks. Staff should be prepared for this. The EHT supply should be limited to 5 mA or less.

(b) Yet another version

Two charged plastic drinking straws are suspended with thread through them so that they hang horizontal and parallel. If they have opposite charge they will swing apart - a very simple demonstration of electrostatic repulsion. As an extension the forces between them can be worked out if you know the masses of the straws and the angle of the threads. A very approximate idea of the charges carried can then be found.

Age range: 14-18   Apparatus required: •Two strips of aluminium foil •EHT supply •Two drinking straws •Thread •Wooden or plastic clamp in stand

24. Point discharge

(a) Show the effects of charge discharge from a point by using a sensitive flame.
(b) The discharge from points can also be easily shown with the rotating windmill apparatus - either mounted on the top of the large dome itself or on a stand. It helps considerably if the stand is placed on a polythene tile to prevent leakage.

 The Van de Graaff generator may give unexpected electric shocks. Staff should be prepared for this. The EHT supply should be limited to 5 mA or less.

Age range: 11-13
Apparatus required: •Windmill of metal with pointed ends •EHT supply limited to 5 mA or less or Van de Graaff generator

25. Fluorescent tube and the plasma globe

This is a most impressive demonstration.

Take an ordinary fluorescent tube, and hold it near the plasma globe. This is a globe filled with low-pressure gas that has a ball electrode at a potential of some 20 kV at its centre. Switch on the globe. To most people's amazement the tube lights even though it is not touching the globe. I have found that if one end of the fluorescent tube is a little less than 10 cm from the globe, but not touching it, the demonstration works well. Moving your hand along the tube will "wipe off" the discharge, since you are earthing the tube at that point.

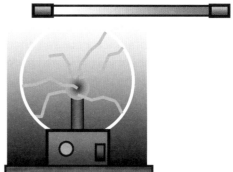

It shows the existence of an electric field round the globe - the potential difference between the two ends of the tube being sufficient to make it light.

Age range: 14-18   Apparatus required: •Plasma globe •Fluorescent tube

26. Ions in a flame and a flame probe for detecting electrostatic fields

(a) Set up two vertical plates, and put a candle between them. Connect the plates to an EHT supply and a spot galvanometer. When the supply is turned on, the reading of the meter stays at zero - no current flows. However, when you light the candle two things happen. The reading of the galvanometer shoots up and the flame is dragged towards one of the plates. The current is due to the ionisation of the air between the plates. The ions in the flame itself make it distort. A TV camera pointed between the plates helps to make this visible to the whole class. Alternatively use a light source such as a projector to give a shadow of the flame on a screen.

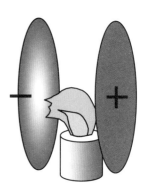

(b) A flame from a fine glass jet can be moved within the field. The deflection of the flame due to the movement of the ions within it shows the intensity of the field at that point.

 The EHT supply should be limited to 5 mA or less.

Age range: 14-18
Apparatus required: •Two metal plates mounted on insulating holders •EHT supply limited to 5 mA or less •Candle   •Glass flame jet

27. Cars and electrostatics

You may have noticed that you may get a shock when getting out of a car. Here are some (not so serious) suggestions as to how to prevent this happening!

(a) Driving in Wellington boots and a wet suit.   (c) Carrying a passenger to jump out first.

(b) Throwing out an anchor before you get out.   (d) Keeping the radio aerial up!

28. Pith ball on thread on a Van de Graaff generator

Fix a pith ball to a thread, and then stick the other end of the thread to the top of the large dome of a Van de Graaff generator. When the generator is switched on the ball and dome acquire the same charge, and the repulsion between the ball and the dome will make the thread stand up vertically.

 The Van de Graaff generator may give unexpected electric shocks. Staff should be prepared for this.

Age range: 11-13
Apparatus required: •Van de Graaff generator •Pith ball •Thread   •Sticky tape

29. Paper and the Van de Graaff generator

A very simple example of electrostatic repulsion is to tear up a sheet of paper into small pieces and put them on top on the large dome of a Van de Graaff generator. When the generator is turned on, the pieces of paper will fly off - they have all acquired the same charge as the dome and each other, and so will be repelled. On a good dry day they can fly almost a metre from the dome!

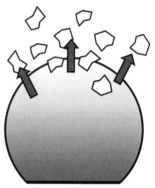

(Puffed wheat or popcorn also work well if placed in a small plastic container on the top of the dome!)

 The Van de Graaff generator may give unexpected electric shocks. Staff should be prepared for this.

Age range: 11-13   Apparatus required: •Van de Graaff generator •Paper

30. Field in a hollow charged conductor

Theory predicts that there is no field inside a hollow charged conductor.
This is easily demonstrated by taking a gold leaf electroscope, standing it on an insulating tile and connecting the cap to the case. Then charge the top plate. You will notice that the leaf does not rise – all the charge resides on the outside of the electroscope (plate and body), and there is no field within the case.

Theory:
Electric field (E) is the negative of the potential gradient (-dV/dx).
So if V is constant E = 0.

 The EHT supply should be limited to 5 mA or less.

Age range: 16-18
Apparatus required: •Gold leaf electroscope •Method of charging (charged rod or EHT supply limited to 5 mA or less)   •Insulating tile   •TV camera to make the experiment visible to a large group

31. The phantom leg

Take a fine-weave stocking and wedge a cardboard ring (cut from a storage tube) into the neck to keep it open. Charge the stocking by rubbing it with a balloon until the stocking expands as though it were filled by a "phantom leg". This is due to the like charges on all parts of the stocking repelling each other, so forcing the sides of the stocking apart.

Alternatively connect it to a Van de Graaff generator!

 The Van de Graaff generator may give unexpected electric shocks. Staff should be prepared for this.

Age range: 11 – 13   Apparatus required: •Stocking - fine texture - low denier •Balloon

32. Barbie doll on a Van de Graaff generator

If you are worried about the effects of static charge on your students and do not want to make their hair stand on end using a Van de Graaff generator, then try this experiment. Stand (or sit) a Barbie doll (or any other doll with long hair) on top of the Van de Graaff dome (you may need to fix it down). Turn on the machine, and watch the doll's hair rising!

Age range: 11-14
Apparatus required: •Van de Graaff generator
 •Barbie doll (or alternative)

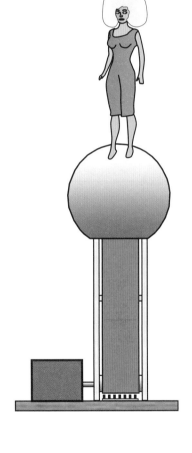

 The Van de Graaff generator may give unexpected electric shocks. Staff should be prepared for this.

33. The Van de Graaff generator and a sheet of paper

An interesting experiment using the Van de Graaff generator is to find out the maximum weight of a sheet of paper that it can support.

Measure the mass of a number of sheets of paper and then calculate the mass/m^2 of the paper (Δ). ('Normal' photocopy paper usually has a mass of 80 g/m^2.)

Cut a sample of known area, and place it on the Van de Graaff dome. Switch the machine on, and see if it rises. Experiment with larger and larger pieces until the sheet is just held above the dome.

 The Van de Graaff generator may give unexpected electric shocks. Staff should be prepared for this.

Age range: 16-18
Apparatus required: •Van de Graaff generator •Paper •Balance

34. Metal cup cake cases and the Van de Graaff generator

Foil cups

This is a lovely demonstration of the repulsive force between charges of the same sign. Put a pile of metal cup cake cases upside down on top of the large dome of a Van de Graaff generator and switch the machine on. As the charge builds up the top case will drift off – the repulsion is just bigger than the weight of the case. This is then followed by the next one down and so on, giving a "rain" of cases.

Alternatively a plastic bowl holding puffed wheat can be taped to the dome. The puffed wheat flies out when the machine is turned on!

The photograph shows an interesting extension. I made a small hole in each of the holders and threaded a length of cotton through them. The lower end of the cotton was fixed to the Van de Graaff dome and the upper end to the ceiling.

Age range: 11-18 depending on treatment
Apparatus required: • Van de Graaff generator
•About ten cup cake holders

 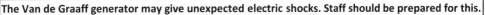 The Van de Graaff generator may give unexpected electric shocks. Staff should be prepared for this.

CAPACITORS

General theory for this section

Capacitance = Q/V

Energy stored in a capacitor of capacitance C charged to a potential V = ½ (QV) = ½ (CV^2)

1. Capacitor and bucket of water
2. Capacitor in a camera flash unit
3. Timing with a capacitor
4. The smoothing action of a capacitor

1. Capacitor and bucket of water

This is a useful comparison between a charged capacitor and a bucket full of water. A hole at the bottom allows water to run out and represents the current in the circuit as the capacitor discharges, the size of the hole representing the resistance of the circuit.

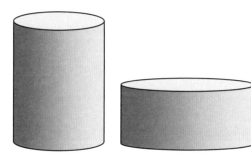

The depth of water represents the p.d. (V) across the capacitor and the volume of the bucket represents the maximum charge (Q) that can be stored by the capacitor when fully charged. You can see that in the same way that a certain volume of water can be stored in a low but wide bucket, a given amount of charge may be stored at high or low potential in two different size capacitors.

The greater the height of the cylinder the greater the water pressure at the base.

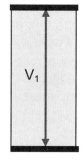
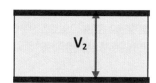

Theory:
 Q = CV so for a fixed charge a large V means a small C, whereas a small V means a large C.

Age range: 14-18

The shaded area represents the charge. The same charge is carried by two difference capacitors with different potential differences across their terminals.

2. Capacitor in a camera flash unit

Refer to this as a practical use of capacitors. The energy stored in the capacitor due to the small charging current from the battery over a few tens of seconds is released as one large burst in a fraction of a second.

Age range: 16-18

3. Timing with a capacitor

Connect a capacitor and a resistor in parallel with a low voltage d.c. supply. Switch on the dc supply and current will flow through the resistor continually but also charge the capacitor. In the supply circuit and the resistor circuit are two thin strips of aluminium foil.

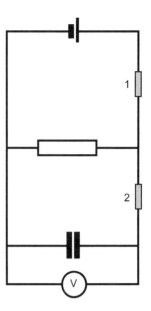

When the one in the supply circuit (1) is broken, the capacitor stops charging, and when the one in the resistor branch (2) is broken the capacitor stops discharging. Therefore the capacitor only discharges in the time between the breaking of the two strips. If this time is short then the current from the capacitor is roughly constant and so Q = It = CΔE where ΔE is the drop in potential across the capacitor. But E = IR and so t = CΔE.R/E. Useful for timing a bullet and falling objects as long as t is small. The validity of this could be checked by the pupils. The p.d across the capacitor should be measured with a digital voltmeter with a resistance of some MΩ.

Age range: 16-18   Apparatus required: •Capacitor •Aluminium foil •Low voltage dc supply •Resistor •Stop clock •Digital voltmeter

4. The smoothing action of a capacitor

A capacitor placed across the output of a rectifier unit will give a smoothing effect to the output. An analogy of this is to use a balloon to smooth the flow of water. Fix a tube to a water tap, and into this fit a T piece with a balloon hanging down from one branch of the T.

As water flows through the tube the balloon will distend. As the flow decreases, the balloon will shrink - maintaining the output flow. If the flow increases the balloon expands, smoothing out the flow, and keeping the flow rate approximately constant. The expansion and contraction of the balloon is analogous to the charging and discharging of the capacitor.

Age range: 15 – 18   Apparatus required: •Tap •Tubing •T piece •Balloon

5. The energy in a charged capacitor

Set up the apparatus shown in the diagram. Charge the 10 mF capacitor to 30 V, and then discharge it through the heating coil. This coil should consist of 2 m of 32 s.w.g constantan wire. The temperature rise produced in the coil should be measured with a copper-constantan thermocouple. The effect on the temperature of a number of charges and discharges on the capacitor energy should be investigated.

Age range: 16-18
Apparatus required: •10 mFcapacitor
•Spot galvanometer •Coil of wire
•0-30V d.c. power supply •Voltmeter
•Switch
•Digital temperature probe or copper-constantan thermocouple •Leads

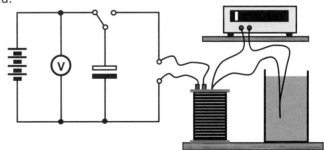

 Large capacitors working at higher voltages should not be used because of the hazard of electric shock that they pose.

ELECTRON PHYSICS

General theory for this section:

All materials consist of atoms. These atoms contain shells of orbiting electrons. In metals some of these electrons become detached from the atoms and "wander" through the material at high speed - they are known as free electrons. There are some 10^{28} of these free electrons per cubic metre in a metal such as copper, but only 10^{22} in a semiconductor at room temperature.

The charge on one electron is -1.6×10^{-19} C.

1. Car parks and energy levels	7. Photoelectric effect
2. Atom model	8. Photoelectric effect - zinc plate
3. Floating in mid air	9. Whales and X ray spectra
4. Energy levels and the escalator	10. Maltese cross
5. Hills and pits in the p.e. effect	11. Thermionic emission
6. Diode and the depletion layer	12. Fish and thermionic emission

1. Car parks and energy levels

The behaviour of electrons and holes in a semiconductor can be shown by considering cars in a multi-storey car park. The cars represent the electrons and the empty parking spaces the positive holes. Cars can move between parking levels in the car park if there are empty spaces, in the same way as electrons move between energy levels if there are empty holes. If the car park is nearly full of cars it is nearly empty as far as the holes are concerned - holes can therefore move freely within it!

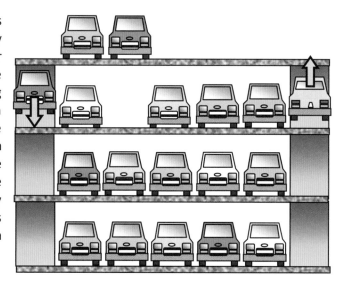

This only really works as an analogy if all the cars are identical – such as a car park full of minis. The inability of the drivers to decide where to park is analogous to the random motion of the electrons!

Age range: 16-18

2. Atom model

A set of polystyrene balls mounted on wires can be used to show the arrangement of electrons in atoms and the transitions between energy levels. Make a rectangular wooden framework, and fix horizontal wires at the correct spacing to represent the energy levels. The polystyrene balls are threaded on vertical wires and can be made to slide along these wires to simulate transitions between one energy level and another.

Age range: 16-18   Apparatus required: •Atom model as described

3. Floating in mid air

The allowed energy states within an atom can be compared with levels on which you could stand in a room. If a person were to be seen apparently floating in mid air you would look for the wires - they would only be stable in that energy state for a fraction of a second. This can be compared with the electron transitions within the atom.

4. Energy levels and the escalator

The top steps of an escalator are rather like the energy levels in a hydrogen atom, they get closer together just as the energy levels get closer together as you get nearer the ionisation level. This means that as you ascend the escalator you make smaller and smaller energy transitions between successive steps. The analogy is really only good if the escalator is stationary.

5. Hills and pits in the photoelectric effect

The fact that free electrons are held within a metal in a sort of energy pit or potential well can be compared to people in a glass sided hole - they cannot get out unless they jump out in one go. They cannot go half way and hang in mid air, waiting for another burst of energy.

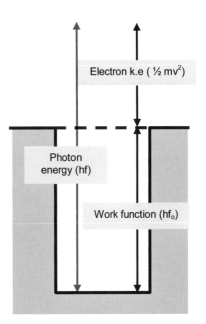

Electron k.e ($\frac{1}{2}mv^2$)

Photon energy (hf)

Work function (hf$_o$)

This is similar to the idea of the quantum of radiation liberating free electrons in photoelectric emission. The electrons have to climb a potential hill to reach a collector, and those with insufficient energy cannot do so. Therefore photoelectrons emitted by radiation with a low frequency will be unable to reach a collector if a negative potential is applied to it while those emitted by radiation of a higher frequency will be able to do so.

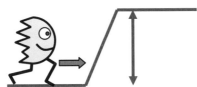

While at London University I took part in a sponsored walk from London to Brighton. Arriving in the outskirts of Brighton, I found that the finish was up a hill into a park. Like the electrons I just about had enough energy left for that final climb.

6. Diode and the depletion layer

I use the idea of a mass of girls and boys in a playground to represent a piece of n type semiconductor joined to a piece of p type - in other words a p-n junction. Initially the children are tightly packed together with all the boys in one half of the playground and all the girls in the other. Interesting things only happen at the join, or close to it. A movement of children will take place - eventually preventing any further movement. Children far from the join are not affected. This is an analogy for the movement of holes and electrons near the join between two pieces of p and n type semiconductor.

7. Photoelectric effect

In the photoelectric effect quanta of light fall on a surface and liberate free electrons from the surface. This liberation is instantaneous if the frequency of the incoming radiation is high enough.

The photoelectric effect, the quantum nature of radiation and the energies of quanta of different types of radiation can all be demonstrated using ping-pong balls, a billiard ball and a coconut shy. Professor Russell Stannard suggested the original version of this experiment on a splendid Open University video. A small boy tries to dislodge a coconut by throwing a ping-pong ball at it. No luck - the ping-pong ball has too little energy! He then tries a whole bowl of ping-pong balls but the coconut still stays put! Along comes the professor with a pistol and fires one bullet at the coconut - it is instantaneously knocked off its support. This simulates the effect of infrared and ultraviolet radiation on a metal surface. The ping-pong balls represent low energy infra-red, while the bullet takes the place of high-energy ultraviolet. I suggest using a billiard ball in the lab these days rather than a bullet.

If you can get hold of a copy of the original video do watch it carefully. They apparently had a lot of trouble setting it up. See if you can spot where their particular simulation breaks down!

8. Photoelectric effect - zinc plate

Fix a cleaned (vital to remove oxide) zinc plate to a gold leaf electroscope. Charge it using an EHT supply by touching the plate briefly with the positive or negative lead to show the effects of the sign of the original charge.

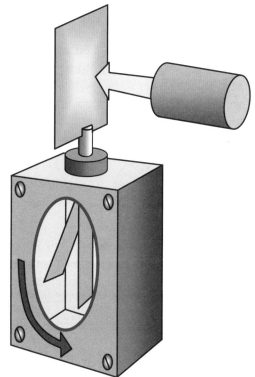

Then try to discharge it with light from a light bulb, a laser (careful) and a u.v. lamp (careful). No discharge occurs if the plate was originally positive - if any electrons are emitted they are immediately attracted back to the surface.

With an initial negative charge only the high-energy ultraviolet quanta will discharge the electroscope, causing the leaf to fall. Refer to the TV camera tube which is sensitive to visible light.

Age range: 16-18
Apparatus required: •Gold leaf electroscope
•TV camera if possible •Zinc plate attachment
•Ultraviolet light
•EHT supply limited to 5 mA or less •Laser •Light bulb

 Avoid viewing the laser and ultraviolet light directly or by reflection.

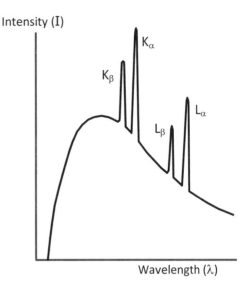

9. Whales and X ray spectra

Have you never thought that the X ray spectrum of a material looks like a multiple spouting whale!?

Maybe it should be thought of as just an aid to your memory of its shape.

10. Maltese cross

An interesting extension of the traditional Maltese cross tube is to demonstrate the tube, but do not connect the cross to the EHT supply. A much fuzzier image of the cross will be formed on the screen. Electrons emitted by the cathode collide with and stick to the cross. This gives the cross a negative charge which repels the electron beam, so giving the shadow of the cross a rather distorted and lumpy appearance. This makes a good demonstration of charge repulsion.

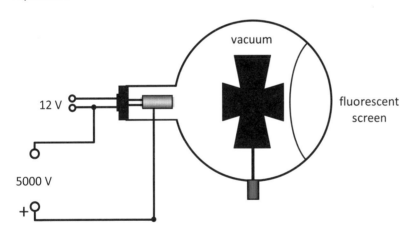

Age range: 14-18
Apparatus required: •Maltese cross tube in holder
•EHT power supply limited to 5 mA or less •Low voltage power supply
•Leads

 The EHT power supply should have its output current limited to 5 mA or less.

11. Thermionic emission

A hot resistance wire held near the cap of a charged electroscope will cause it to discharge, whether it is charged positively or negatively. This is due to the ionisation of the air around it by the electrons emitted from the wire.

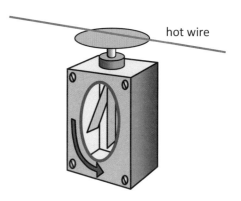

hot wire

Mount a piece of resistance wire horizontally between two clamps so that it passes about a millimetre over the cap of a gold electroscope. Charge the electroscope using a polythene rod.

Now pass a large current (around 4A) through the wire, being careful to tension the wire as you increase the current so that it does not sag on to the electroscope cap. The electroscope will discharge.

 The wire will get hot – don't touch it while the current is flowing.

Age range: 15-18
Apparatus required: •Gold leaf electroscope and means of charging it (•polythene rod and duster) •Length of resistance wire •Low voltage power supply (0-5A) •Two retort stands, bosses and clamps

12. Fish and thermionic emission

Use the idea of a fishpond full of swimming fish as an analogy to explain what is happening inside the cathode of a thermionic valve. Some of the fish will jump out of the water only to fall back - there is a continual jumping out and falling back - a true dynamic equilibrium. This can be compared with the random motion of electrons within a hot metal - some of them gain enough energy to leave the metal surface briefly.

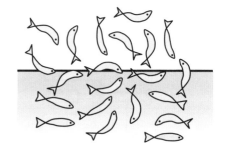

All the fish are the same, so you can't tell which fish is in the water and which in the air. In just the same way free electrons in a metal can give a dynamic equilibrium when the metal is heated - they are continually leaving and re-entering the surface. The attraction of the anode could be represented by a worm lowered in, and the heating of the cathode could be compared with a shark in the water making the fishes swim around more violently!

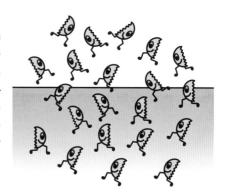

NUCLEAR PHYSICS

General theory for this section
The radius of a nucleus is given by the equation $r = r_0 A^{1/3}$ where A is the nucleon number of the nucleus and r_0 is a constant (1.3×10^{-15} m).

1. Simple atom analogy/model
2. Alpha particle scattering
3. Rutherford scattering (permanent)
4. Rutherford scattering
5. Plum pudding model
6. Mouse traps and chain reactions
7. £20 note and ball - nuclear forces

8. Nuclear fusion analogy
9. Nuclear forces and a boomerang
10. Nuclear collision – watches
11. Accelerator model
12. The bubble chamber
13. The power of the Sun

1. Simple atom analogy/model
A simple way of remembering the relative sizes of the nucleus and the atom of hydrogen is to imagine that if the nucleus is represented by a ball 1 cm in diameter (say a marble) the orbiting electron would be 1 km away.

The ratio of the diameter of the atom to that of the nucleus is about 1 to 100 000.

Theory
The radius of a nucleus is given by the equation:
$r = r_0 A^{1/3}$ where A is the nucleon number of the nucleus and r_0 is a constant (1.3×10^{-15} m)

2. Alpha particle scattering - two alternatives
There are two simple alternatives to the commercially available "tin hat" apparatus to demonstrate alpha particle scattering by a nucleus.

(a) Fix a rubber sucker to a glass sheet placed on an overhead projector. Now roll a ball bearing towards it. The disadvantage of this method is the relatively small size of the sucker.

(b) Use a fixed circular magnet representing the nucleus, and then swing another small magnet towards it to represent the alpha particle (In this version it is important to keep a repulsion between the two magnets by using a suitable method of suspension.)

Age range: 14-18   Apparatus required: •Overhead projector •Ball bearings •Rubber sucker •Magnets

3. Rutherford scattering - a permanent record
A permanent record of the Rutherford scattering experiments can be obtained by using the tin hat simulation of the field but putting it on a piece of white paper resting on carbon paper. Draw a set of lines on the white paper to show the direction of incident ball bearings. Roll the ball bearings down a ramp, and the pressure on the carbon paper will give a permanent record of their tracks after "collision" with the "nucleus". (The ball bearings can be collected by surrounding the apparatus by a magnetic strip or simply just catching them!)

Age range: 14-18
Apparatus required: •Tin hat apparatus •Ball bearings •White paper •Carbon paper •Flexible magnetic strip (optional)

4. Rutherford scattering

Use a row of pins hidden inside a box to represent the nuclei of a set of atoms. Roll ball bearings into the box through a hole in one side, and observe where they come out. Get pupils to predict what sort of obstacles are in the box.

5. Plum pudding model

If we are going to use the special metal tin hat model to simulate the nuclear model of an atom, then we should show the alternative plum pudding simulation. Instead of the "tin hat" I have used a cymbal - the ball bearing will roll across the centre quite easily, showing reduced scattering by this type of atom. There is a deflection, but if the ball bearings are rolled from about half way up the little ramp no ball bearing ever suffers more than a 90° deflection.

Theory

The much lower electric field intensity of the plum pudding model is represented by the lower central height of the cymbal. The potential at the centre is also much smaller resulting in a smaller deflection by the incident alpha particles.

Age range: 16-18   Apparatus required: •Cymbal •Ball bearings

6. Mouse traps and chain reactions

(a) This lovely (although potentially painful) demonstration is a splendid simulation of a nuclear chain reaction. Set up a number of cocked mouse traps side by side in a rectangle (a dozen will work well) to represent uranium nuclei. Put a couple of polystyrene balls representing neutrons on each one.

Throw in another polystyrene ball (neutron) to start the chain reaction. One mouse trap goes off - this sets off others and so on! A simulated chain reaction results.

The balls are shot all over the lab (fast neutrons). Spacing out the mouse traps gives an idea of the shape of fuel rods and the way a chain reaction can fail.

It works best if the mouse traps are placed on the lid of a cardboard box to give a good "linkage" between one "fission" and another.

(b) Alternative methods are to use a set of matches fixed upright in a block of wood - when you light one the others are set alight as the flame spreads through them like a forest fire. You could also knock down a set of dominoes by touching the first one and making it fall so that it collides with another and so on.

 Warn pupils to keep their fingers away from the mouse traps after setting them.

Age range: 16-18

Apparatus required: •Mouse traps •Polystyrene balls •Block of wood with holes   •Matches •Dominoes •Cardboard box

7. £20 note and ball - nuclear forces
These two analogies are designed to explain the forces between sub-nuclear particles
(a) A simulation of long-range electrostatic repulsive forces can be given by two people throwing a ball to each other, each one standing on a skateboard or wheeled trolley. The thrower recoils when they throw the ball, and the catcher recoils when they receive it. There is no limit to the range of the force as long as they throw hard enough.
(b) The short-range strong nuclear force (only effective over distances less than about 10^{-15} m) can be represented by the two people trying to throw a £20 note to each other. For a start there is no possibility of them throwing it to each other unless they are close together because of the large amount of air resistance; it will only work at short distances, but it is certainly attractive!

Theory
Both these experiments are simulations of the exchange of force carriers when a force acts between two objects - a photon in the case of the electromagnetic force and a gluon in the case of the strong nuclear force.

> **Ensure that a clear space is available. Control the ball throwing. Only pupils who know how to use a skate board should take part in experiment (a).**

Age range: 16-18   Apparatus required: •Two heavy balls •Two skateboards •Two notes

8. Nuclear fusion analogy
The problem of the repulsion between two nuclei and the existence of a short-range nuclear force can be explained as follows.

Imagine two people wearing large inflatable suits so that each appears to be standing in the centre of a balloon. The suits are so large that if they stand near each other they cannot hold hands. Only by the people running together at high speed will the suits be sufficiently squashed for them to be able to grasp each other's hand and so "fuse"!

9. Strong nuclear force – attraction and a boomerang
To demonstrate the attractive nature of a force due to the interchange of virtual particles between protons, think of two people standing fairly close together on skateboards but facing away from each other. One throws a boomerang to the other. The boomerang curves round and is caught by the second person, so pushing the two people together.

10. Nuclear collisions - watches
To discover the composition of subatomic particles two particles are fired towards each other at high speed. An example of this is the Large Electron Positron Collider (LEP) at CERN in Geneva where electrons and positrons are made to collide head on in the giant accelerator. In a way this is rather a crude method. It is a bit like trying to find out what is in a watch by throwing two watches together and seeing what bits fly out. The big difference between the analogy and the subatomic particles is that in the nuclear collisions some bits that fly out were not there before the collision; they have been "made" by the conversion of energy to matter in the collision - certainly not true with the watches!

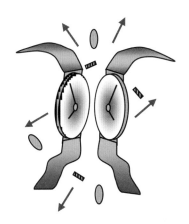

11. Accelerator models

Here are two ideas to simulate the action of a particle accelerator where the particle gets a kick every time it passes between two accelerating electrodes, the first a synchrotron (constant radius) and the second a cyclotron.

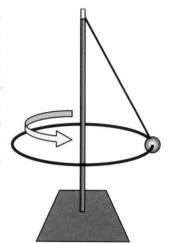

(a) Make a large circular orbit out of plastic curtain rail. Put a marble inside the ring touching the wall to represent the particle, and use an air blower to simulate the kick given by the electric field as the particle orbits the accelerator. If a small section of the track could be made to open, you can simulate the extraction of a charged particle from an accelerator by a magnetic field. A ball fixed to a thread might do as well - no accelerator walls. This simulates the operation of a synchrotron where the orbit radius is fixed and the confining magnetic field is made to increase as the particle's energy increases.

(b) In the second method all you need is a ball suspended by a string from a post (sometimes used to train young children to play tennis) and a bat. Give the ball a push, so that it swings round the post, and every time it passes you give it a hit with the bat. The ball will gain energy on each orbit, move faster and so swing out further from the post.

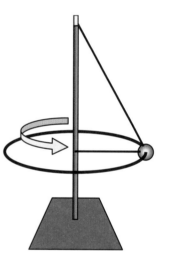

This simulates the operation of a cyclotron where the magnetic field is constant and the orbit radius increases as the particle's energy increases.

Adding a horizontal string, fixed between the ball and the vertical central post, to the swing ball simulates synchrotron operation. As the ball is hit, its velocity increases, but the horizontal string prevents it from changing its orbit radius. However, as its gets faster the centripetal force in the string increases – analogous to the increase in magnetic field in a synchrotron required to keep the particles in a constant orbit as they accelerate.

Age range: 16-18
Apparatus required:
(a) •Length of plastic curtain rail (at least 2m) •Air blower •Polystyrene balls or marbles
(b) •Ball on string tied to the top of a fixed post •Extra string •Bat

12. The bubble chamber

This simple experiment is an excellent demonstration of how a bubble chamber works and can also be used to reinforce the idea of a cloud chamber. Pour out a gassy drink such as lemonade, and allow it to stand for a few minutes until no more bubbles rise. Then drop in a small amount of fine salt (or sand). This gives nuclei for bubbles to form on, and you will see clouds of bubbles begin to rise through the liquid. In a similar manner ions are formed in a bubble chamber when a radioactive particle passes through, and bubbles form on these. Bubble chambers are more effective than cloud chambers, as there are more atoms that can be ionised and hence more "nuclei" on which bubbles can form.

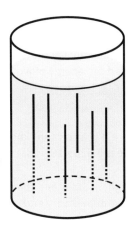

Age range: 16-18
Apparatus required: •Can of fizzy drink •Glass beaker •Salt

13. The power of the Sun

The power of the Sun can be found by measuring the amount of energy falling on a small area of the Earth's surface every second.

Use a blackened tin can containing a known mass of water. Shield the can from the sunlight, measure its temperature, and then put it out in the sun for a known length of time and measure the final temperature. The energy gained by the water can be calculated, and knowing the area exposed to the sunlight enables you to find the energy falling on a square metre of the Earth's surface per second – this is known as the solar constant. From this you can calculate the power of the Sun (see below).

Theory:
Take the solar constant to be 1370 Wm^{-2} at a distance equal to the radius (R) of the Earth's orbit. This means that a total amount of energy equal to $4\pi R^2$ x1370 J is passing out from the Sun every second.

Now the radius of the Earth's orbit is 1.5×10^{11} m and so the energy emitted by the Sun every second is:
$E = 4\pi(1.5 \times 10^{11})^2 \times 1370 = 3.87 \times 10^{26}$ J.

Using Einstein's mass-energy equation ($E = mc^2$) you can calculate the mass of the Sun being converted into energy every second.

Mass converted to energy = E/c^2
$= 3.87 \times 10^{26}/9 \times 10^{16} = 4.3 \times 10^9$ kg
$= 4.3 \times 10^6$ tonnes.

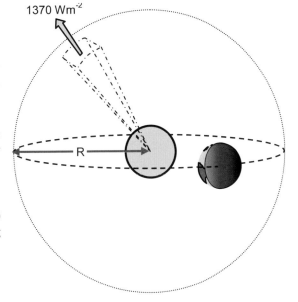

1370 Wm^{-2}

Diagram not to scale

This means that the Sun is converting over four million tonnes of its mass into energy every second!

Age range: 16-18   Apparatus required: •Blackened tin can •Ruler •Thermometer •Stopclock or watch

QUANTUM PHYSICS

General theory for this section

In 1900 Max Planck proposed that radiation was emitted not in a continuous stream of energy but in bundles of energy that he called quanta. In fact we now believe that all energy is quantised. Planck even related the energy of a quantum to its frequency by the formula:

$$\text{Energy (E)} = h \times \text{frequency (f)}$$

where h is a constant known as Planck's constant. This constant can now be measured in school, and its value is 6.626×10^{-34} Js.

1. Flight of stairs and the quantum theory
2. Quantum theory and milk
3. When the quantum theory is effective
4. Gamma radiation and the quantum theory

5. Quantum rainfall
6. Electron waves in atoms
7. Quantum theory of radiation

1. Flight of stairs and the quantum theory

One of the basic results of the quantum theory is that some energy states are not allowed. Because of the very small value of Planck's constant (6.6×10^{-34} Js) we do not usually observe this discontinuity. However we could compare it to a flight of stairs down which a man and an ant are travelling. The steps are effectively classical to the man - he seems to travel down with an uninterrupted energy change - but they are of a quantum nature to the ant. It all depends on your scale of observation.

2. Quantum theory and milk

A man wants exactly a pint of milk. He can get it either by filling a bottle from a tap or by catching a carton as it comes off a conveyor belt. Filling the bottle from the tap represents the classical nature of Physics while using the discrete cartons represents the quantum idea. Notice that with the quantum analogy he may get a quantum (carton) immediately the belt is switched on or have to wait for some time for a carton to arrive. However when it does he will still get the whole carton at once. With the classical theory he gets milk as soon as the tap is turned on, but the rate of flow may be small, and he may not get a pint as quickly as he does by the quantum method!

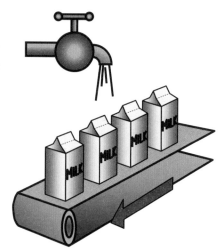

Age range: 16-18

3. When the quantum theory becomes effective

This analogy attempts to show when the quantum theory would be observable in everyday life - a consequence of the value of Planck's constant being very large, i.e. close to one. Imagine a soccer player trying to score a goal through a slot in a defensive wall. In normal life he would expect to be able to hit any part of the goal simply by changing his shooting position. However, if he finds that there are some places the ball cannot get to no matter where he stands, then that's when he has entered the realm of quantum soccer!

4. Gamma radiation and the quantum theory

Revise the work done in earlier years on gamma radiation. Emphasise that it is part of the electromagnetic spectrum and therefore propagated as waves.

To show the quantum nature of this radiation use a gamma source and a Geiger counter connected to a loudspeaker via a ratemeter. Adjust the distance of the Geiger counter from the source so that the incident radiation is of low intensity. The students can hear the individual clicks as each photon arrives at the counter, showing the quantum nature of the radiation.

 | **For details of the use of radioactive sources please see page 259.**

Age range: 16-19
Apparatus required: •Gamma source •Geiger counter •Ratemeter •Loudspeaker •Leads

5. Quantum rainfall

Imagine that you are walking through a shower of rain. At the end of your walk you know that you will be wet. However, you do not get all the water at once! During the walk raindrops fall on you in a chaotic way, and you cannot predict when the next raindrop is going to hit you. The final result is that you are wet, but this is due to many raindrops.

These raindrops are analogous to the quanta in the quantum theory of radiation. The wetness represents the classical theory of radiation.

6. Electron waves in orbits

From Schrodinger's wave equation we can imagine the electron as existing as a wave that fits round an orbit a given number of times.

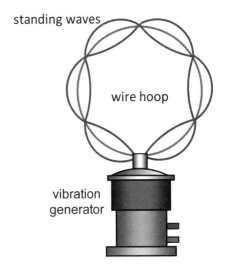

In other words $2\pi r = n\lambda$ where λ is the electron wavelength, n is an integer and r is the radius of the orbit. A simulation of this idea is as follows. A ring of stiff wire should be fitted on top of a vibration generator - I use a loop about 15 - 20 cm in diameter. By adjusting the frequency of oscillation of the vibration generator, standing waves can be produced in the wire ring analogous to electron waves in the orbits of atoms. Multiple rings are impressive.

(b) An extension of this experiment shows the differing wavelengths further out from the nucleus. Two pieces of cord - one light and one heavy - are tied together. One end is fixed to a retort stand, and the other is attached to a vibration generator. When you switch on the generator, standing waves are produced in the cords. The frequency is the same in both, but the wavelength differs since the speed of the waves in the two cords is different.

Age range: 16-18
Apparatus required: •Vibration generator •Loop of stiff wire •Signal generator •Retort stands •Pieces of cord

7. The quantum theory of radiation

Every time an electron falls from one energy level in an atom to another it emits a small 'bundle' of energy called a **photon**. The bigger the energy drop, the higher the frequency of the electromagnetic radiation.

The brightness of the source of light depends on the number of these photons emitted per second. The greater the number of photons, the brighter the light.

Each photon has a tiny energy and a 100 W lamp will emit roughly 100 million million million photons every second! Although they travel at the speed of light (300 000 km/s) they are so tiny that we don't feel them hitting us. However, the radiation pressure from the impact of many millions upon millions of photons does have an effect on the tail of a comet, helping to keep it pointing away from the Sun.

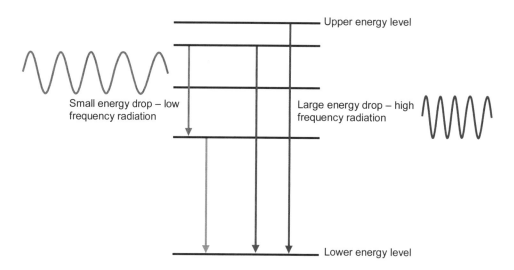

8. Quantum space

Quantum space is the space where quantum effects predominate and can be thought of as a sort of granularity of space. The size of the 'granules' is determined by what is known as the Planck length.

This is the scale at which classical ideas about gravity and space-time cease to be valid, and quantum effects dominate. This is the 'quantum of length', the smallest measurement of length with any meaning. Its value is determined by the equation:

Planck length = $\sqrt{[G \times h/2\pi c^3]}$ It has a value of 1.61×10^{-35} m

(G is the universal constant of gravitation, h Planck's constant and c the speed of light in free space)

It is unlikely that the granularity of space will be observed except by the emission of bursts of high energy gamma radiation passing through from cosmological objects such as quasars.

RADIOACTIVE DECAY

General theory for this section

The decay of a radioactive source is a random process. The half-life of a source is the time taken for the activity of that source to decrease by half. Remember that the half-life of a source is independent of any other physical process such as temperature, pressure, velocity, magnetic and electric fields etc.

1. Simple radioactive decay formula
2. Radioactive decay - Rice grain method
3. Alpha radiation - tissue paper and cling film
4. Half-life of water
5. Half-life - wooden or plastic blocks
6. The radioactive decay series

1. Simple radioactive decay formula

This was suggested by one of my Sixth Form students and seems a simple alternative to the normal decay formula [$N = N_o e^{-\lambda t}$ or $A = A_o e^{-\lambda t}$] [A_o is the original activity of the source, A the activity after a time t and λ the disintegration constant ($\lambda = \ln 2/T$ where T is the half-life)]. For very simple decay problems we use the fact that the activity will decrease by a factor of 2 in one half-life, 4 in two half-lives, 8 in three half-lives and so on. Why does the number of half-lives have to be a whole number? Of course it doesn't - so let's call the number of half-lives that have passed n, where n is any number.

The decay formula suggested is then $A = A_o/2^n$ - it always works!

Age range: 16-18

2. Radioactive decay - Rice grain method

Fix a plastic bottle with the base removed to a vertical glass tube with a clip at the base. Fill the bottle with rice. Mount the bottle and tube in a clamp over a beaker on a top pan balance. Open the tap, and record the mass of rice in the beaker at different times. Plot a graph of mass against time as an analogue of radioactive decay. Will it work with sand?

Age range: 14-18
Apparatus require: •Plastic bottle •Top pan balance •Stopwatch or stop clock •Clamp •Rice

3. Alpha radiation - tissue paper and cling film

The absorption of alpha radiation can best be demonstrated with tissue paper, such as one sheet of a double paper handkerchief. Ordinary paper is rather thick and will stop much of the radiation. It is also worth trying it with very thin aluminium leaf! The alpha particles should go through.

A piece of bacon is the closest thing that we can get to show the absorption of radiation by human flesh.

Another material that can be used to test the penetration of alpha particles is a sample of cling film. The particles will pass through it.

For details of the use of radioactive sources please see page 259.

For details of the use of radioactive sources please see page 259.

Age range: 16-18
Apparatus required:
•Tissue paper •Aluminium leaf •Geiger counter and display •Alpha source in holder •Cling film in holder

4. Half-life of water

The drop in the level of water in a glass tube can be used as an analogy of radioactive decay. In just the same way as the activity of a source decreases as the number of radioactive nuclei decreases so the volume of water coming from the outlet at the bottom of the tube decreases as the height of water in the tube gets less.

Use a vertical glass tube with a short length of capillary tubing fixed to the bottom of it using a length of rubber tubing. Close the rubber tube with a tube clip, and fill the large tube with water. Open the tube clip and allow the water to flow out through the capillary tube. Measure the height of the water against time, and plot a graph of height against time. It gives a very good analogy of radioactive decay!

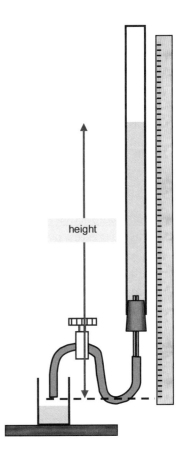

Theory:
$N = N_o e^{-\lambda t}$ or $h = h_o e^{-Ct}$

Age range: 15-18
Apparatus required: •Retort stand •Two bosses and two clamps •Stop watch •Ruler •Glass tube • Rubber tube •Capillary tube •Tube clip

5. Half life - wooden or plastic blocks or dice

This is a classic experiment that gives a very good analogy with radioactive decay. A large number (1000) of small wood (or plastic) blocks (side 1 cm) are given out to the class. Each block has one face coloured or marked with a dot (a set of dice would do but are rather expensive).

Each group records the initial number of blocks and then throws them, taking out any that fall with the coloured side up. They then throw the ones left - i.e. those that fell with a plain side uppermost - and then repeat the process until they have none left. (Usually about 20 throws.)

The data from the whole class is collected and a graph plotted of the number of blocks remaining after each throw. It helps to use a spreadsheet for the collection of results if a computer is available in the lab. The idea of the random way in which the blocks fall should be compared with the random nature of radioactive decay.

I have extended this experiment to my older students. In this extension I use the spreadsheet to process my results and get a print-out of number of blocks (radioactive nuclei) (N) against throw (time). It is worth doing this after just one or two groups have thrown the blocks to show that as more and more blocks are added to the experiment the line becomes smoother.

Then draw tangents to the curve at know values of N and plot the rate of decay (dN/dt) against N - my class obtained a perfect straight line. This makes a very useful point for a discussion of the equation dN/dt = - λN.

The computer works out ln (N) and plots this against t. This will give a graph with a perfect straight line with a negative gradient.

Age range 15-16-18 (with the extra mathematics!)
Apparatus required: •Six sided cubical wood blocks - one side coloured •Computer with spread sheet •Printer

6. The radioactive decay series

Having been concerned by the mathematics of a source producing a daughter product which then decays itself into a stable isotope, I decided to modify the previous two experiments to demonstrate this. We have to adapt experiment six by using six sided dice (or blocks) for the initial radioactive material and then ones with a greater number of faces (say ten) for the daughter product.

If you colour in more than one face it will also represent a different (shorter) half-life – there is more chance of a coloured face falling uppermost.

In the half-life of water experiment, the water from the first tube runs into a second tube with a narrower outlet.

Theory:
For element B $dN_B/dt = \lambda_A N_A - \lambda_B N_B$
$dN_B/dt + \lambda_B N_B = \lambda_A N_0 e^{-[\lambda t]}$
Solving this gives: $N_B = N_0[ae^{-[\lambda t]} - be^{-[\lambda t]}]$ where a = $\lambda_A/(\lambda_B - \lambda_A)$ and b = -a

Age range: 16-18
Apparatus required: •A large number of six sided and ten-sided dice
•Two versions of the apparatus for experiment four with exit tubes of different diameters

RADIOACTIVE SOURCES
The following safety precautions should **ALWAYS** be observed when using radioactive sources.
1. If you are under 16 years of age do not use the sources.
2. Never handle a source directly, always use tongs or tweezers.
3. Keep as far away from a source as possible.
4. Never open a sealed radioactive source.
5. Keep a record of the use of any radioactive source
6. Always return the source to its lead container after use.
7. Keep the sources locked away in a secure cupboard when not in use.
8. Report any accidents immediately.
9. Never point a source towards anyone, including yourself.
10. Wherever radioactive materials are in use the symbol shown above should always be displayed to warn other people, since radioactivity is invisible.

The definitive guide to using radioactive sources is CLEAPPS L93.

ASTRONOMY

1. Volcanoes and heat energy

Although most craters on the Moon and the planets are thought to have been created by meteor impact, some will have been formed by volcanic activity. You can use a saucepan full of custard or porridge being heated to demonstrate the "breakthrough of internal magma"! The air escaping from beneath the surface when they are heated gives a very good simulation of volcanic activity.

Age range: 11-16   Apparatus required: •Porridge or custard •Saucepan •Heater

2. Rotation period of the Moon

This simple demonstration shows why it is that the Moon always presents the same face towards the Earth. Two pupils are needed to demonstrate this. One pupil is used to represent the Earth, the other to represent the Moon. One pupil stands still while the second pupil faces inwards and then moves round the first, making one rotation as they orbit the "Earth" once. You will notice that the "Moon" always faces the "Earth".

3. The Echo of the Big Bang

After the enormous temperatures of the Big Bang the Universe cooled. Fifteen thousand million years later (now) the temperature of the Universe is about 3K. We can detect the radiation produced by this temperature - called the echo of the Big Bang. It has been estimated that about 1% of the background hiss on your television set is due to the after effects of this enormous fireball.

4. When the Universe was dark! 300 000 to one billion years after the Big Bang

As the universe cooled down after the Big Bang a point was reached where the temperature was such that the emitted radiation was in the infra-red - in other words there was no visible light. The Universe became dark.

This was to remain the state until the first stars fused their first hydrogen and this was to happen about one billion years later!

5. Spiral nebula simulation

Get a bowl of tomato soup and stir it gently. Now pour some cream in - the resulting effect is very similar to a spiral galaxy! It will also work with coffee and cream. Make sure that you don't stir too vigorously!

Age range: 11-14   Apparatus required: •Soup and cream

6. Crater experiment

This experiment is a simulation of meteor impact forming craters on a planet. The meteors are replaced by ball bearings or wooden balls, and a tray of sand replaces the planet surface. (I have used icing sugar- both dry and mixed with water - but it is not so good.)

The projectiles are dropped from a known height into the sand and the loss of potential energy is related to the crater size. We measured the diameter, depth, wall height and general shape of the craters and also tried oblique impacts by rolling the ball bearings down a tube. Dampening the sand gives a way of investigating different types of planetary surface.

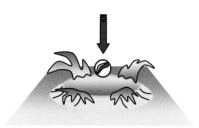

Age range: 14-16
Apparatus required: •Sand •Flour •Ball bearings •Marbles •Wooden balls •Plasticine •Ruler •Balance

7. Model lunar craters

Make a clay model of a lunar crater and use a light bulb to simulate the Sun. A light bulb can be mounted on a retort stand, and the bulb can then be raised and lowered to see the effects of the altitude of the "Sun" on the lengths of shadows on the "lunar" surface.

The photograph shows a model of the crater Clavius made by one of my sixteen-year-old students.

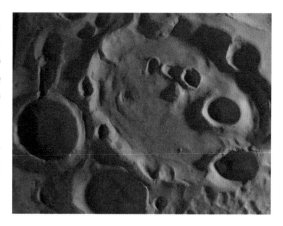

Age range: 11-13
Apparatus required: •Clay •Lamp (probably mains) •Ruler to measure shadow length

8. Expansion of the Universe

Here are three possible analogies of the expansion of the universe.

(a) A balloon with dots marked on it to represent the galaxies. As the balloon is blown up all the "galaxies" recede from each other.

(b) A loaf of bread with currants in it shows a 3D analogy of the recession of the galaxies. The currants represent the galaxies. As the loaf expands when it is cooked, all the "galaxies" recede from each other

(c) Thread three or four large polystyrene balls on to a length of elastic, one end of which is fixed to a hook on the wall or a secure retort stand. Now pull the free end of the elastic - all the balls separate from each other.

The point about all these analogies is that they make their own space as they expand. Similarly, before the universe began to expand there was no space! Actually there was no time either - both space and time were "created" at the start of the universe.

9. Some simple experiments in astronomy

(a) Diameter of the projected image of the Sun to show the varying distance of the Earth from the Sun during a year

(b) A sundial – see page 264

(c) Star trails using a camera and an exposure of an hour or more

(d) Star pictures using a camera with an exposure of five minutes

(e) Sunspots using a projected image of the Sun

(f) Length of a shadow at noon at two points on the Earth's surface lying on a north-south line used to measure the size of the Earth (after Eratosthenes)

(g) Observe the paths of meteors during a meteor shower. The shower dates are: Quarantids January 1 -6, Lyrids April 19 - 25, Eta Aquarids April 24 – May 20, Perseids July 25 - August 20, Orionids October 15 - November 2, Taurids October 15 - November 25, Leonids November 15 - November 20, Geminids December 7 - December 17.

(h) Plot planetary paths

(i) Make a Foucault pendulum to show the rotation of the Earth

(j) Use a telescope and a camera to video the lunar surface - remove both the eyepiece of the telescope and the camera lens.

> **NEVER LOOK DIRECTLY AT THE SUN - ESPECIALLY THROUGH BINOCULARS OR A TELESCOPE.**
>
> **Home-made filters should never be used when observing the Sun with binoculars or a telescope. Commercially produced filters should only be used with great care and I do not recommend their use in schools. It is better to view a projected image of the Sun when studying sunspots or a solar eclipse.**

10. Seasons tubes

Use solid rods of yellow foam rubber to represent the sunlight. Cut off the ends at angles that are equal to that of the Sun at the zenith in mid-winter and mid-summer.

In Taunton in mid-winter the maximum angle that the Sun reaches above the horizon is 16° while in mid-summer it is 61°. The area over which the same 'tube' of sunlight is spread is clearly shown by the angled ends of the foam rubber cylinders.

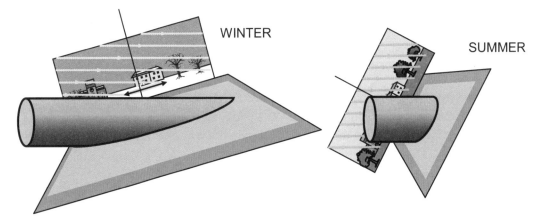

WINTER SUMMER

Age range: 7-14
Apparatus required: •Foam rubber cylinders (used for flotation in swimming pools) •Knife

11. Seasons

The seasons occur because of the different area of the Earth's surface over which the sunlight spreads at different times of the year. Use a projector to represent the Sun, a board that can be rotated representing the surface of the Earth to show this change of area, and an LDR to measure the change in light intensity. As the area on which a certain amount of sunlight falls is larger in winter, it is therefore colder.

Age range: 11-13
Apparatus required: •Projector •Board in clamp that can be tilted •LDR •Method of measuring the angle of tilt

12. The minimum age of the Universe

A minimum age for the Universe can be suggested by considering the elements that exist today. In ordinary stars fusion occurs, building up elements as heavy as iron 56 but no further - they are not hot enough. Heavier elements are formed in the enormous explosions of supernovae, where the temperatures reached are much greater than those in a normal star. Therefore the Universe must be at least old enough for these supernovae to have formed and exploded, in order to give us the abundance of heavy elements necessary for the Universe to be as we know it today!

13. Astronomical distances - simplified

If we represent the distance from the Earth to the Sun as one unit, then the scale of the solar system can be simplified as follows:

Sun to: -

Mercury 1/3	Earth 1	Jupiter 5	Uranus 20	Pluto 40
Venus 2/3	Mars 1.5	Saturn 10	Neptune 30	

The size of the Universe is best considered by expressing distance in terms of the time it would take light to travel that distance at 300 000 km per second: -

Earth - Sun	8 minutes
Across the solar system	11 hours
To the nearest star	4 years
Across the galaxy	100 000 years
From our galaxy to the next	1 million years
To the "edge" of the observable Universe	13 700 million years

N.B these times are approximate.

14. Solar System model

The following data may be used to construct a model of the Solar System with the Sun-Earth distance of 1m.

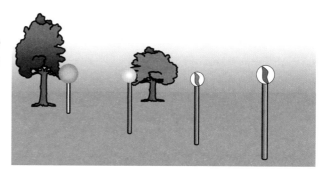

Body	Distance from Sun	Distance (m)	Model ball	Diameter	Model diameter (mm)
Sun		-	Beach ball	1 392 000	464
Mercury	58	0.5	Plastic bead	4840	2
Venus	108	0.7	Plastic bead	12 390	4
Earth	149	1	Plastic bead	12 760	4
Mars	228	1.5	Plastic bead	6800	2
Jupiter	778	5	Polystyrene ball (50)	142 800	48
Saturn	1428	10	Table tennis ball	119 400	40
Uranus	2870	20	Marble	47 600	16
Neptune	4497	30	Marble	48 400	16

Age range: 7-14
Apparatus required: •Dowel rods •Table tennis ball •Marbles •Plastic beads •Polystyrene ball •Beach ball •Measuring tape

15. Sundial

To make a horizontal sundial you need a gnomon (a pointer with an angle equal to your latitude) and a horizontal scale. You will also need a compass to set your gnomon and scale so that the gnomon lines up with the north-south line where you are.

The horizontal scale should look like the one drawn below. The lines show the hours. This one is correct for a person at 51° N. You will have to use the formula in the theory section to draw your own if you live at another latitude.

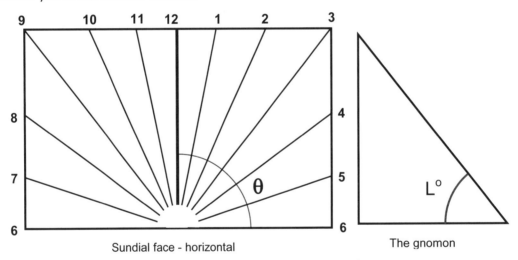

Sundial face - horizontal   The gnomon

You can use these to make a sundial that should be accurate for 51° N. The gnomon goes along the centre line of your dial face, and the thickness of this line should be the same as the width of the gnomon. You can see some more unusual sundials in the photographs on page 265.

Theory:
The angle from the noon line (12:00) is called the hour angle (H). Since the Sun moves through 15° each hour, the hour angle is 15 x the number of hours from noon. You can calculate the angle (θ) from the noon line for various hours using your latitude (L): $\theta = \tan^{-1}[\sin L \times \tan H]$. (The formula does not work for H = 90°.) Don't forget to change the angle of your gnomon to that of your latitude.

Age range: 7-14   Apparatus required: •Stiff cardboard or plywood •Glue •Protractor •Craft knife or saw

16. Movement of the Sun

This experiment can be used to observe and record the movement of the Sun during the day.

> **NEVER LOOK DIRECTLY AT THE SUN - ESPECIALLY THROUGH BINOCULARS OR A TELESCOPE.**
>
> Home-made filters should never be used when observing the Sun with binoculars or a telescope. Commercially produced filters should only be used with great care and I do not recommend their use in schools. It is better to view a projected image of the Sun when studying sunspots or a solar eclipse.

Bang a post into the ground so that it is vertical and firm.
Check that is vertical by using a spirit level.

The altitude of the Sun above the horizon can be found by measuring the height (h) of the top of the post above the ground and the length of the shadow of the stick made by the Sun. (tan A = h/length of shadow)

Record the time of day with a clock.

Measure the angle (B) that the shadow makes with the north-south direction. In the northern hemisphere this will be somewhere north of the east-west line.

Repeat the experiment at different times during the day.

Age range: 7-11
Apparatus required:
•1.5 m long post   •Spirit level •Compass •Sunny day!
•Metre ruler and/or measuring tape graduated in cm

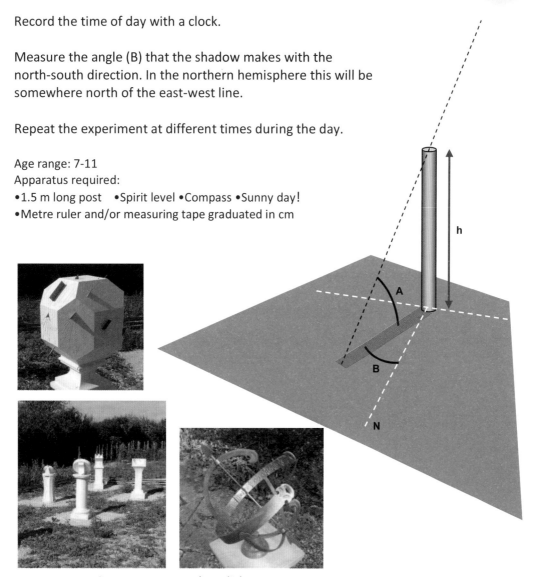

Some more unusual sundials

BIBLIOGRAPHY

There follows a list of some of the books that I have found useful for providing ideas and background information. Some of them may now be out of print but it is worth you trying to obtain second-hand copies.

Hands-on Physics Activities	James Cunningham and Norman Herr	CFAR in Education
The Science Teachers Handbook	Andy Byers et al (VSO)	Heinemann
How things work	Louis Bloomfield	Wiley
Mad about Physics	Chris Jargodski and Franklin Potter	Wiley
Physics on Stage 1-3	Irish Science Team	IOP publishing
Physics demonstrations	Julien Sprott	University of Wisconsin
Fun with Physics	Colin Siddons	Kaye and Ward
Experiments in Physics	Colin Siddons	Basil Blackwell
The Flying Circus of Physics	Jearl Walker	Wiley
Why toast lands jelly-side down	Robert Ehrlich	Princeton
Turning the World inside out	Robert Ehrlich	Princeton
Trickkiste 1	Josef Wittmann	BSV Munich
Trickkiste 2	Josef Wittmann	BSV Munich
Physics experiments at home	T.H.Savory	George Harrap
Toys and Inventions	Herbert McKay	OUP
The book of Experiments	Leonard de Vries	Carousel Books
Physics ideas and experiments	Randel Henly	ASE
Demonstration experiments	Sutton	McGraw Hill
The Resourceful Physics Teacher	Keith Gibbs	IOP

 Safety precautions may not be identified in any of the material mentioned on this page, or they may be out of date. Check with up to date risk assessments and hazard warnings before using material from these sources.

The schoolphysics website and accompanying CD also contain a large amount of useful material including text, animations, problems and answers, lesson plans, physics images, a dictionary, biographies of physicists, historical facts, diagrams and photographs. The Internet material is free.

www.schoolphysics.co.uk

- **Astronomy**
- **Atomic physics**
- **Electricity**
- **Electronics**
- **Heat**
- **General physics**
- **Light**
- **Matter**
- **Mechanics**
- **Nuclear physics**
- **Quantum physics**
- **Relativity**
- **Sound**
- **Waves**

An invaluable resource base for all 11 to 19 year old Physics and Science students and their teachers!

INDEX

References in CAPITALS represent the chapter and/or section headings.